Modern Parasitology

MODERN PARASITOLOGY

A textbook of parasitology

edited by

F.E.G. COX

PhD, DSc
Professor of Zoology
King's College London

BLACKWELL SCIENTIFIC PUBLICATIONS
OXFORD LONDON
EDINBURGH BOSTON MELBOURNE

© 1982 by
Blackwell Scientific Publications
Editorial offices:
Osney Mead, Oxford, OX2 0EL
8 John Street, London, WC1N 2ES
9 Forrest Road, Edinburgh, EH1 2QH
52 Beacon Street, Boston
    Massachusetts 02108, USA
99 Barry Street, Carlton
    Victoria 3053, Australia

First published 1982

Photoset by Enset Ltd,
Midsomer Norton, Bath, Avon
and printed and bound
in Great Britain by
Whitefriars Press
Tonbridge

DISTRIBUTORS

USA
    Blackwell Mosby Book Distributors
    11830 Westline Industrial Drive
    St Louis, Missouri 63141

Canada
    Blackwell Mosby Book Distributors
    120 Melford Drive, Scarborough
    Ontario, M1B 2X4

Australia
    Blackwell Scientific Book Distributors
    214 Berkeley Street, Carlton
    Victoria 3053

British Library
Cataloguing in Publication Data

Modern parasitology
    1. Parasitology
    I. Cox, F.E.G.
    574.5'249   QL757

ISBN 0–632–00612–9

Contents

List of contributors

R.M. Anderson
Reader in Parasite Ecology, Imperial College, University of London, UK

C. Arme
Professor of Zoology, University of Keele, UK

C. Bryant
Reader in Zoology, Australian National University, Canberra, Australia

L.H. Chappell
Senior Lecturer in Zoology, University of Aberdeen, UK

F.E.G. Cox
Professor of Zoology, King's College, University of London, UK

W.E. Gutteridge
Reader in Biochemical Parasitology, University of Kent, Canterbury, UK
Now Head of Biochemical Parasitology, Wellcome Research Foundation, Beckenham, UK

G.A. Schad
Professor of Parasitology, University of Pennsylvania, Philadelphia, USA

P.J. Whitfield
Lecturer in Zoology, King's College, University of London, UK

Preface

Parasites present a continual and unacceptable threat to the well-being of millions of people in the tropics and subtropics and to domesticated animals in all parts of the world and the cost of parasites in terms of human misery and economic loss is incalculable. Parasitology has emerged as a science in its own right from zoology, with its emphasis on what parasites are, and tropical and veterinary medicine, with their emphasis on what parasites do. But parasites are more than interesting animals that happen to live at the expense of others and more than merely the causative organisms of major tropical diseases. They have all evolved ways of existing in the nutritionally abundant, yet paradoxically immunologically hostile, environments of their hosts. It is these adaptations that make them unique and fascinating organisms to study.

It was once thought that when a parasite had been identified as the causative agent of a disease and its life cycle elucidated, its control or eradication would immediately follow with the development of drugs, vaccines or anti-vector measures. Those who thought this seriously underestimated the complete hold a parasite has on its host and the intimacy of the relationship between them. Parasites display combinations of biochemical, physiological and nutritional adaptations unique in the animal world, and at the same time display a range of methods of evading the immune response and its consequences unknown to microorganisms. Their ecology is also turning out to be more complex than that of free living organisms. Parasites, however, are reluctant to yield up their secrets and this has attracted the attention of not only parasitologists but also biochemists, physiologists, immunologists and epidemiologists. The intellectual rewards of their research are matched by the potential practical benefits to be gained.

Parasitology is a rapidly growing science with over twenty major journals devoted solely to it and each year gives rise to a similar number of books or monographs. Most universities in which biology or medicine is taught include parasitology in their curricula and parasitology courses are becoming increasingly popular among students.

It is against this background that this book has been written. Generations of parasitologists have been brought up on classical parasitological textbooks such as that by Chandler and Read (see Chapter 10) and the majority of such books devote much space to individual species of parasites and how each lives. This book is different. It does not set out to duplicate the standard textbooks, in fact serious students will need to use one of these as well, but stresses those aspects of parasitology that are usually either ignored or hidden among information relating to a particular species or group of species.

The first two chapters describe, in a very condensed form, the most important parasites that affect man or his animals and their laboratory counterparts. The next three chapters explain how parasites function and the unique and general aspects of their biochemistry, general physiology and nutrition. The sixth chapter describes what is known of immunity to parasites and the prospects for vaccination. The seventh chapter, which is a large one, deals with the epidemiology of parasites on a comparative basis. This is an area which has only recently been put on a sound mathematical basis and the information given is not easily available elsewhere. The length of the chapter reflects the importance of this subject. The next two chapters deal with control, which is the ultimate objective of all parasitological studies. Chapter 9 is unusual in that most of the information on the drugs used in parasitology is given in the form of tables. This chapter must be regarded mainly as a source of factual information and is the only way in which what is effectively a summary of all our knowledge of the drugs used against parasites could be condensed into the space available. The final chapter is a guide to the literature of parasitology and an invitation to take the information contained in the previous chapters to the limits of our knowledge. More detailed information on the topics covered in the first nine chapters can be obtained by consulting appropriate books or papers listed in the suggested reading at the end of each chapter.

This book is intended mainly for undergraduates who are advised to read the first two chapters and then, selectively, the others in whatever order interests them. For post-graduates, this book is intended to put their particular interests into a more general context and the same applies to more senior workers or technicians from other disciplines who find themselves drawn into the fascinating world of parasitology and wish to orientate themselves within it. Such scientists would be well advised to work their way through the whole book for no area of parasitology is so distinct from any other that it cannot benefit from an understanding of what is being done elsewhere and why it is being done.

Chapter 1
Parasitic protozoa

F.E.G. Cox

1.1 INTRODUCTION

There are living now over 30 000 named species of protozoa of which nearly 10 000 are parasitic in invertebrates and in almost every species of vertebrate. It is, therefore, hardly surprising that man and his domesticated animals should act as hosts to protozoa, but the diseases thus caused are out of all proportion to the number of species involved. The protozoa that infect man range from forms that are never pathogenic to those that cause malaria, sleeping sickness, Chagas' disease and leishmaniasis, now regarded as being among the major diseases of tropical countries which together threaten over one-quarter of the population of the world. As well as these, there are protozoa that cause less serious diseases such as amoebiasis, giardiasis and toxoplasmosis in man, but these diseases are only less serious in comparison with the ravages caused by the better known parasites. In domesticated animals, nagana, babesiosis and theileriosis take a major toll of cattle in Africa and other parts of the world, and coccidiosis, in its various forms, presents a continual threat to poultry and cattle throughout the world, particularly under conditions of intensive rearing. Even fish and invertebrates suffer from a variety of protozoan infections which create major problems for those trying to raise these animals for food.

Protozoa lie between the prokaryotic and higher eukaryotic organisms and share some of the characteristics of each. They are usually small, have short generation times, high rates of reproduction and a tendency to induce immunity to reinfection in those hosts that survive. These are features of infections with microparasites such as bacteria. On the other hand, protozoa are undoubtedly eukaryotic cells with organelles and metabolic pathways akin to those of the host. They have also evolved numerous adaptations to allow them to survive in their hosts and, in particular, to counteract or evade the immune response and, for this reason, infections with parasitic protozoa are not short-lived as with bacteria.

1.2 STRUCTURE AND FUNCTION

Protozoa are unicellular eukaryotic cells mostly measuring 1–150 μm, the parasitic forms tending towards the lower end of this range. Structurally, each protozoan is the equivalent of a single metazoan cell with its plasma membrane,

1

nucleus, nuclear membrane, chromosomes, endoplasmic reticulum, mitochondria, golgi apparatus, ribosomes and various specialized structures adapted to meet particular needs. Among unique structures in the protozoa are the two nuclei characteristic of the Ciliophora and the kinetoplast, a DNA-containing structure found in the kinetoplastid flagellates. Parasitic protozoa are in no way simple or degenerate forms and their particular adaptations frequently include complex life cycles and specialized ways of entering their hosts and maintaining themselves therein. Their nutrition, physiology and biochemistry are largely geared to the parasitic habit and are specialized rather than degenerate. Sexual reproduction also occurs in some protozoa and in the parasitic forms is important only in the Apicomplexa in which it provides for apparently limitless variation and adaptability.

1.3   CLASSIFICATION

The small size of protozoa coupled with the fact that they consist of single cells with few obvious morphological features means that their classification must be based on a wide range of characters including variations in life cycles, details of fine structure and, at the species level, biochemical differences.

Until recently, protozoa have been regarded as a phylum within the kingdom Animalia but are now best considered as a subkingdom. The group is not a natural one and has traditionally been divided into four great classes distinguished by their modes of locomotion: the Mastigophora or flagellates, by means of flagella; the Ciliata, or ciliates, by cilia; the Sarcodina, or amoebae, by pseudopodia; and the Sporozoa, negatively, by the absence of any obvious method of moving. As our knowledge of the life cycles, fine structure, and biochemistry of the protozoa has accumulated, the need for a more sophisticated scheme of classification has arisen and it is now accepted by the majority of protozoologists that the subkingdom consists of seven distinct phyla. The most recent classification is given in Table 1.1 and in this the parasitic groups are classified as far as orders and the remainder in outline only. The more important genera of parasitic protozoa and others mentioned in this book are listed against their appropriate order.

1.4   KINETOPLASTID FLAGELLATES

The kinetoplastid flagellates are characterized by the possession of a unique organelle called the kinetoplast which contains DNA and is an integral part of the mitochondrial system. The kinetoplast is situated near the base of the flagellum and is easily seen in stained preparations. Kinetoplastid flagellates are found in invertebrates and vertebrates, the genera in mammals being *Leishmania*, *Trypanosoma* and *Endotrypanum*, which are transmitted by insects. The typical form is an elongated organism, called a promastigote, with a kinetoplast and a flagellum at

Table 1.1. A classification of the parasitic protozoa based on the scheme adopted by the Society of Protozoologists (from Cox, 1981b).

SUBKINGDOM PROTOZOA (Single-celled eukaryotic organisms)

PHYLUM 1 SARCOMASTIGOPHORA (Locomotion by flagella or pseudopodia or both)

SUBPHYLUM 1 MASTIGOPHORA (Locomotion by flagella)
Class 1 Phytomastigophorea (= Algae. Chloroplasts containing chlorophyll. None parasitic)
Class 2 Zoomastigophorea (Chloroplasts absent) Eight Orders
    Order Kinetoplastida (1 or 2 flagella, kinetoplast present) *Cryptobia, Leishmania, Trypanosoma*
    Order Proteromonadida (1 or 2 pairs of flagella)
    Order Retortamonadida (2 to 4 flagella, one directed posteriorly into cytostome) *Chilomastix, Retortamonas*
    Order Diplomonadida (2 nuclei, organelles duplicated) *Hexamita, Spironucleus, Giardia*
    Order Oxymonadida (4 or more flagella, parasitic in insects)
    Order Trichomonadida (4 to 6 flagella, typically, one running length of body attached to surface) *Dientamoeba, Histomonas, Trichomonas, Tritrichomonas*
    Order Hypermastigida (Many flagella, symbiotic in insects) *Lophomonas, Trichonympha*

SUBPHYLUM 2 OPALINATA (Many short flagella, 2 or more identical nuclei, most parasitic in amphibians)
Class 1 Opalinatea
    Order Opalinida *Opalina*

SUBPHYLUM 3 SARCODINA (Locomotion by pseudopodia, temporary flagellated stage in some forms) Twelve Classes
Superclass 1 Rhizopoda (Pseudopodia other than axopodia) Eight Classes
Class 1 Lobosea (Pseudopodia lobopodia) Five Orders
    Order Amoebida (No flagellated stage in life cycle) *Entamoeba, Acanthamoeba*
    Order Schizopyrenida (Temporary flagellated stage in life cycle) *Naegleria*
Superclass 2 Actinopoda (Pseudopodia axopodia) Four Classes

PHYLUM 2 LABYRINTHOMORPHA (Trophic stage with ectoplasmic network. None parasitic) One Class

PHYLUM 3 APICOMPLEXA (Characteristic apical complex seen with electron microscope, no cilia or flagella except on gametes, life cycles usually involving feeding stages (trophozoites), asexual multiplication (merogony), sexual stages (gametogony) and formation of spores and sporozoites (sporogony). (All parasitic)
Class 1 Perkinsea (Apical complex incomplete)
    Order Perkinsida
Class 2 Sporozoea (Apical complex complete. Infective stages sporozoites resulting from sporogony)
Subclass 1 Gregarinia (Trophozoites and sexual stages large and extracellular. Parasites of body cavity or gut of invertebrates)
    Order Archigregarinida (Life cycles primitive with merogony. Parasites of marine invertebrates)
    Order Eugregarinida (Merogony absent. Common parasites of invertebrates) *Monocytis*
    Order Neogregarinida (Merogony present, acquired secondarily. Parasitic in insects)

continues

Table 1.1. *continued*

Subclass 2 Coccidia (Trophozoites and sexual stages small and intracellular)
   Order Agamococcidiida (No merogony or gametogony)
   Order Protococcidiida (No merogony. Parasites of invertebrates)
   Order Eucoccidiida (Merogony present. Very common parasites of invertebrates and
   vertebrates) *Eimeria, Isospora, Sarcocystis, Toxoplasma, Plasmodium*
Subclass 3 Piroplasmia (Small parasites of vertebrate erythrocytes, transmitted by ticks)
   Order Piroplasmida *Babesia, Theileria*

PHYLUM 4 MICROSPORA (Tough resistant spores containing one sporoplasm and one
polar filament)
Class 1 Rudimicrosporea (Polar filament rudimentary)
   Order Metchnikovellida
Class 2 Microsporea (Polar filament thin coiled tube)
   Order Minisporida
   Order Microsporida *Nosema, Glugea, Pleistophora*

PHYLUM 5 ASCETOSPORA (Spore multicellular, no polar capsules or filaments)
Class 1 Stellatosporea
   Order Occlusosporida
   Order Balanosporida
Class 2 Paramyxea
   Order Paramyxida

PHYLUM 6 MYXOZOA (Spore multicellular, typically 2 polar capsules containing polar
filaments)
Class 1 Myxosporea
   Order Bivalvulida *Myxobolus*
   Order Multivalvulida
Class 2 Actinosporea
   Order Actinomyxida

PHYLUM 7 CILIOPHORA (Locomotion by cilia, two dissimilar nuclei—micronucleus and
macronucleus)
Class 1 Kinetofragminophorea (Body ciliature simple and uniform, oral apparatus
inconspicuous) Fourteen Orders
   Order Prostomatida *Buetschlia*
   Order Trichostomatida *Balantidium, Isotricha, Dasytricha*
   Order Entodiniomorphida *Entodinium, Ophryoscolex*
   Order Cyrtophorida *Chilodonella*
   Order Apostomatida *Foettingeria, Gymnodinoides, Collinia*
Class 2 Oligohymenophorea (Oral apparatus apparent) Four Orders
   Order Hymenostomatida *Tetrahymena, Ichthyophthirius*
   Order Astomatida *Anoplophrya*
   Order Peritrichida *Trichodina*
Class 3 Polymenophorea (Oral apparatus dominant) Four Orders
   Order Heterotrichida *Nyctotherus*

the anterior end. Variations of this form are brought about by the migration of the kinetoplast-flagellum complex within the body of the flagellate and this is associated with changes in the mitochondrial system. The forms in the life cycle of a kineto-plastid flagellate are shown in Fig. 1.1. In some invertebrate parasites, the pro-mastigote form is the only one in the life cycle but the species in vertebrates exhibit two or more forms.

1.4.1   Stercorarian trypanosomes of man

In the stercorarian trypanosomes, the flagellates divide in the hind gut of the insect vector. The most important species is *Trypanosoma cruzi* (Figs 1.2a, 1.3a) which infects 12–24 million people in South and Central America. This trypano-some is infective to about 100–150 species of wild and domesticated mammals. It is not at all certain how many of these act as reservoirs of human infection but the armadillo could be very important as in this host the infections are long-lived. The vectors are 50–60 species of triatomid bugs of which 5–6 are important in the spread of the human disease. When the bug takes up infected blood the trypanosomes multiply in the epimastigote form in the hind gut and infective or metacyclic forms are passed out with the faeces. These infect the human host if they are rubbed into the insect's bite, another wound or the conjunctiva of the eye. Within the human host, the trypanosomes enter various cells, particularly muscle and nerve cells, where they round up and multiply in the amastigote form. The amastigotes develop into trypomastigotes that either enter new cells or are taken up when a vector feeds. The disease is called Chagas' disease and takes various forms depending on where the amastigotes develop, the most serious consequences being cardiac failure due to parasites in the heart muscles or the loss of the nervous control of the alimentary canal due to parasites in the nervous system.

1.4.2   Salivarian trypanosomes of man

In contrast to the stercorarian trypanosomes, the salivarian trypanosomes typically develop in the mid-gut of the vector, which is a fly, and are injected via the salivary glands when the fly feeds. Two subspecies infect man, *T. brucei gambiense* and *T.b. rhodesiense* (Figs 1.3b,c,d) the former in riverine conditions in West and Central Africa, where it causes chronic sleeping sickness, and the latter in the savannah of East Africa where it causes acute sleeping sickness. In actual fact, the distinctions between these two forms of the disease are blurred. Both *T.b. gambiense* and *T.b. rhodesiense* can infect a range of mammalian hosts and some of these are important reservoirs of *T.b. rhodesiense*. Natural reservoirs of *T.b. gambiense* seem to be less important because the infection is essentially a man-to-man one although there is evidence that the pig may be a source of human infection in some places. The

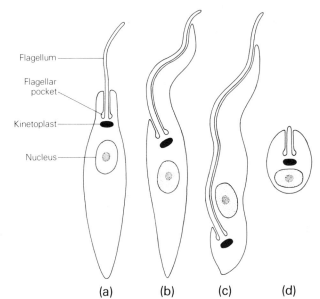

Flagellum

Flagellar pocket

Kinetoplast

Nucleus

Fig. 1.1. Forms in the life cycle of a kinetoplastid flagellate. (a) Promastigote. (b) Epimastigote. (c) Trypomastigote. (d) Amastigote. (After Vickerman, 1976.)

(a)   (b)   (c)   (d)

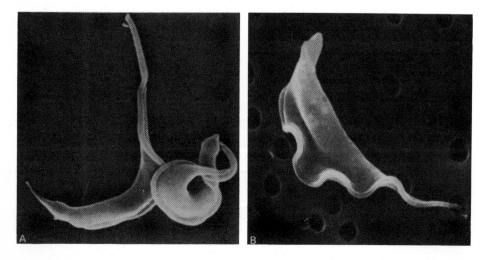

Fig. 1.2. Scanning electronmicrographs of A: *Trypanosoma cruzi* and B: *Trypanosoma brucei*. ×4250. (Photograph A kindly taken by Dr. D. Snary and B by Professor K. Vickerman.)

vector of human sleeping sickness is the tsetse fly, *Glossina*; the wet flies of the *G. palpalis* group transmit *T.b. gambiense* and dry flies of the *G. morsitans* group transmit *T.b. rhodesiense* but, again, these distinctions are not absolute. The life cycles of these parasites are the same as that of *T.b. brucei* which is described in Fig. 1.4. The main cause of sleeping sickness as a disease is the invasion of the nervous system by the trypanosomes.

1.4.3   Salivarian trypanosomes of domesticated animals

Trypanosomiasis is endemic throughout the tsetse belt of Africa, an area of some 10 million square kilometers. The disease, which is commonly known as nagana, embraces a variety of different manifestations—but usually involves fever, anaemia, lack of appetite and wasting—and causative organisms (see Table 1.2) the three most important of which are *T. congolense*, *T. vivax* and *T. brucei* (Fig. 1.3). *T. congolense* is confined to the vascular system and is a particularly important pathogen of cattle although it does also affect other animals. It can be transmitted by most species of *Glossina*. *T. vivax* is also a blood parasite and, like *T. congolense*, is extremely pathogenic in cattle. *T. vivax* can be transmitted mechanically by biting flies and has spread outside the tsetse belt not only in Africa but also to South America where it was imported with cattle from the Old World. The third important trypanosome is *T. brucei brucei* which has been extensively studied particularly as a model for human trypanosomiasis (see Fig. 1.4 for the life cycle). *T.b. brucei* is essentially a tissue parasite, living in subcutaneous and connective tissue but also appearing in the blood (Fig. 1.2b). *T.b. brucei* causes serious disease in horses and camels but not cattle. Among the other trypanosomes of domesticated animals are *T. uniforme*, which resembles *T. vivax* but generally causes mild infections, *T. simiae*

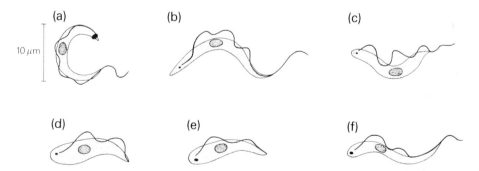

Fig. 1.3. Trypanosomes from the blood of mammals. (a) *Trypanosoma cruzi*. (b) *T. brucei rhodesiense* slender form. (c) *T.b. rhodesiense* intermediate form. (d) *T.b. rhodesiense* stumpy form. (e) *T. congolense*. (f) *T. vivax*. (All drawn from stained slides from the blood of experimentally infected mice.)

Table 1.2. Trypanosomes of man and domesticated animals.

Subgenus	Species	Main hosts	Main reservoirs	Vectors	Disease	Main distribution
Stercoraria						
Megatrypanum	theileri	Cattle		Tabanid flies	None	Cosmopolitan
	melophagium	Sheep		Sheep keds	None	Temperate areas
Herpetosoma	rangeli	Man, cats, dogs		Triatomid bugs	None	Central & S. America
Schizotrypanum	cruzi	Man	150 species of mammals	Triatomid bugs	Chagas' disease	Central & S. America
Salivaria						
Duttonella	vivax	Cattle, sheep, goats, etc.	Various wild mammals	Tsetse flies	Nagana	Africa
	vivax viennei	Cattle	?	Tabanid flies	?	S. America
	uniforme	Cattle, sheep, goats	Wild ruminants	Tsetse flies	None or mild	Central & E. Africa
Nannomonas	congolense	Cattle, sheep, goats, etc.	Wild ruminants	Tsetse flies	Nagana	Africa
Pycnomonas	simiae	Pigs	Warthogs	Tsetse flies	Acute in pigs	Central & E. Africa
	suis	Pigs	Wild pigs	Tsetse flies	Acute in young	Central & E. Africa
Trypanosoma	brucei brucei	Equines, sheep, goats, etc.	Wild game	Tsetse flies	Nagana	Africa
	brucei rhodesiense	Man	Wild game	Tsetse flies	Sleeping sickness	E. Africa
	brucei gambiense	Man	Pigs	Tsetse flies	Sleeping sickness	W. Africa
	evansi	Horses, camels, etc.	Wild mammals	Tabanid flies	Surra	N. Africa, Asia, Middle East
	evansi equinum	Equines, cattle, etc.	Vampire bats capybara	Tabanid flies, vampire bats	Mal de caderas	Central & S. America
	equiperdum	Equines	—	Venereal contact	Dourine	Africa, Middle East

which resembles *T. congolense* in pigs, and *T. suis* also in pigs but a rather rare parasite.

The *T.b. brucei* group of trypanosomes provide an interesting example of evolution in action. Not only has the basic form given rise to the human forms *T.b. gambiense* and *T.b. rhodesiense*, it has also given rise to *T. evansi* which is no longer cyclically transmitted but passed from animal to animal on the mouthparts of biting

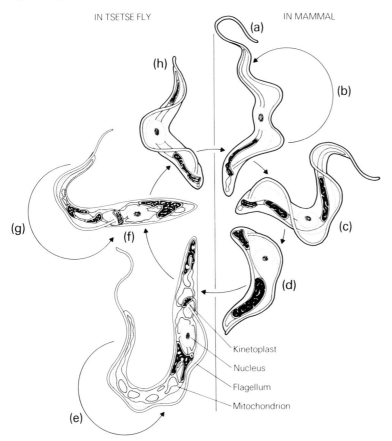

Fig. 1.4. The life cycle of *Trypanosoma brucei*. The infection begins when trypanosomes are injected into the blood of a mammal by a tsetse fly when it feeds (a). The slender forms multiply by binary fission (b) until large numbers build up in the blood and the trypanosomes transform first into intermediate (c) and then stumpy (d) forms that are infective to a tsetse fly. In the slender forms, the mitochondrion is inactive but begins to become active in the stumpy forms. In the midgut of the tsetse fly, the trypanosomes undergo division (e) and then enter the proventriculus and salivary glands where they assume the epimastigote form (f) and undergo further division (g). The forms in the salivary glands infective to the mammal are known as metacyclic forms (h). In the tsetse fly, the mitochondrion is fully active. The blood stream forms are surrounded by a glycoprotein coat which is lost in the midgut of the tsetse fly and is reformed in the salivary glands. (After Vickerman, 1979.)

flies and even vampire bats in South and Central America. The vampire bat can also be infected with *T. evansi* and thus acts as both host and vector. The parasite formerly called *T. equinum* in South America is now regarded as a synonym of *T. evansi*. *T. equiperdum* has dispensed with a vector altogether and is transmitted between horses as a venereal disease. The success of this method of transmission can be seen from the fact that *T. equiperdum* has spread as a disease of horses, donkeys and mules to south and north west Africa, Syria, Turkey and parts of Asia and has been eradicated from Europe, America, India and most of Asia. All these three parasites, like the parent form, *T.b. brucei*, are essentially parasites of equines.

1.4.4   Other trypanosomes of mammals

As well as the trypanosomes described above there are a number of nonpathogenic species that are commonly found in mammals. These all belong to the Stercoraria and include *T. theileri* in cattle, which is transmitted by horse flies, and *T. melophagium* in sheep and sheep keds. *T. rangeli* occurs in a number of mammals including man, primates, cats and dogs in Central and South America. It is transmitted by bugs and although the parasite is quite different from *T. cruzi* the two are occasionally confused. *T. rangeli* is harmless in its vertebrate host but may be harmful in the bug. Rodents are frequently infected with trypanosomes. These also belong to the Stercoraria and are transmitted by fleas. Two species, *T. lewisi* in rats and *T. musculi* in mice, are widely used in laboratory studies.

1.4.5   *Leishmania*

The leishmanial parasites possess only two forms in their life cycles; amastigotes (Fig. 1.5a) in the cells of the lymphoid macrophage system of a mammal or lizard and promastigotes in the gut of the vector which is a sandfly (Diptera, Phlebotomidae). *Leishmania* species cause serious diseases in man. The typical infection is cutaneous but in many species, and in particular individuals, the parasites may invade subcutaneous or deeper tissues causing hideous and permanent disfiguration. The most serious disease, kala azar, involves the macrophages of organs such as the liver. Leishmaniasis in man is now known to be caused by a complex of 6 species and 15–16 subspecies. As the morphology of all these parasites is similar, the identification of species and subspecies tends to be based on isoenzyme and buoyant density techniques. The classification of these parasites is still in a state of flux and the present situation is summarized in Table 1.3. In the Old World the main species causing cutaneous leishmaniasis is *L. tropica* and the species causing visceral leishmaniasis is *L. donovani*. In the New World *L. donovani* introduced from the Old World causes visceral leishmaniasis but cutaneous and mucocutaneous leishmaniasis are caused by *L. braziliensis*, *L. mexicana* (Fig. 1.5a) and *L. peruviana*. A number of species of *Leishmania* have been isolated from hosts other than man and *L. enriettii*, which was found unexpectedly in a guinea pig in Brazil, is widely used in laboratory studies although its relationship with other species is not clear.

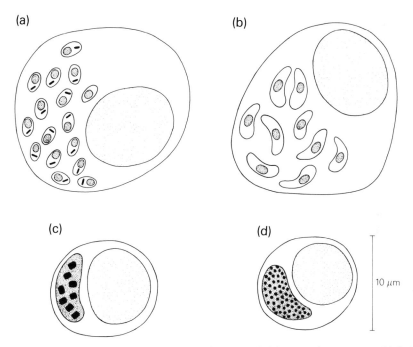

Fig. 1.5. Parasitic protozoa in the cells of the lymphoid macrophage system. (a) *Leishmania mexicana* amastigote stages in a macrophage of an experimentally infected hamster. (b) *Toxoplasma gondii* zoites in a macrophage of an experimentally infected mouse. (c) *Theileria parva* macroschizont in a lymphocyte of an ox. (d) *Theileria parva* microschizont in a lymphocyte of an ox. (All drawn from Giemsa stained slides. The large stippled object in each cell is the host cell nucleus.)

1.5   INTESTINAL AND RELATED FLAGELLATES

Seven of the ten orders in the class Zoomastigophorea contain parasites. The trypanosomes and related forms that, in vertebrates, mostly live in the blood and tissues, and are transmitted by various vectors, belong to the Kinetoplastida. The remaining flagellates are mostly intestinal, where they live anaerobically dividing by binary fission, and are transmitted as cysts or other resistant stages which typically contaminate water or food. Members of the Hypermastigida are very specialized and live as symbionts in the guts of termites, and some other insects, between which they are transmitted directly from adult to young.

Table 1.3. Species of *Leishmania* that cause human disease.

Species	Disease	Distribution	Reservoir	Vector
L. tropica tropica	Dry cutaneous; urban	Europe, Asia, N. Africa	Dogs	*Phlebotomus*
L. tropica major	Wet cutaneous; rural	Asia, Africa	Rodents	*Phlebotomus*
L. aethiopica	Dry cutaneous; diffuse	Ethiopia, Kenya	Hyrax	*Phlebotomus*
L. donovani donovani	Visceral (Kala azar)	Africa, Asia		*Phlebotomus*
L. donovani archibaldi	Visceral	Kenya, Sudan	Rodents	*Phlebotomus*
L. donovani infantum	Infantile visceral	Mediterranean	Dogs, foxes	*Phlebotomus*
L. mexicana mexicana	Cutaneous	Central America	Rodents	*Lutzomyia*
L. mexicana amazonensis	Cutaneous	Brazil	Rodents, etc.	*Lutzomyia*
L. mexicana pifanoi	Cutaneous	Venezuela	Rodents	*Lutzomyia*
L. braziliensis braziliensis	Mucocutaneous	Brazil	Rodents	*Lutzomyia*
L. braziliensis guyanensis	Cutaneous	S. America	?	*Lutzomyia*
L. braziliensis panamensis	Cutaneous	Panama	Sloths etc.	*Lutzomyia*
L. peruviana	Cutaneous	S. America	Dogs	*Lutzomyia*
L. donovani chagasi	Visceral	S. America	Foxes	*Lutzomyia*

1.5.1   Intestinal flagellates and related forms in man

A number of flagellates are ubiquitous and common parasites of man. Few do any real harm but some occasionally give rise to unpleasant symptoms which can fortunately be easily treated.

(a)   Chilomastix mesnili

A cosmopolitan parasite of the caecum and colon of pigs, primates and man, in which its prevalence is 1–10%. Transmission is by cysts usually in drinking water. This flagellate is a mild pathogen often associated with diarrhoea.

(b)   Retortamonas intestinalis

A rare and harmless parasite of the caecum and large intestine of primates and man in Africa, America and Asia. In man the prevalence may reach 2%. Transmission is by cysts.

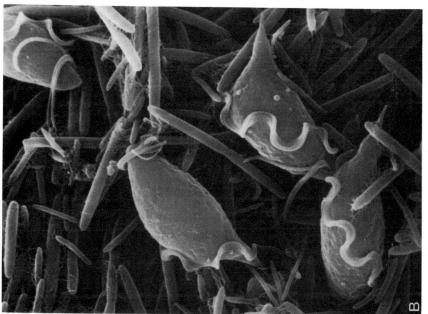

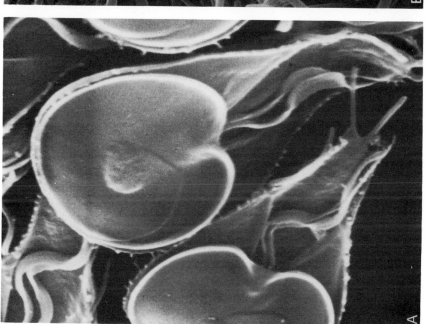

Fig. 1.6. Scanning electronmicrographs of (a) *Giardia intestinalis* and (b) *Trichomonas muris*. The sucking disc of *G. intestinalis* and the undulating membrane of *T. muris* are characteristic features. The photograph of *T. muris* also shows some of the flora of the gut. (a) × 3000. (b) × 7000. (Both photographs kindly given by Professor K. Vickerman.)

(c)   Enteromonas hominis

A cosmopolitan and harmless parasite of the caecum of man, monkeys, rats and hamsters. In man the prevalence ranges from 0.2 to 0.7% but in hamsters it is about 1%. Transmission is by cysts.

(d)   Giardia intestinalis (Fig. 1.6a)

This parasite is known by a variety of names: *G. intestinalis* in Europe, *G. lamblia* in America and *Lamblia intestinalis* in eastern Europe. It is common in the duodenum, jejunum and ileum of man, baboons and monkeys throughout the world. Infections are usually symptomless but large infestations may cause diarrhoea, vomiting, pain and loss of weight especially in children. The prevalence in man is 1–30% and sometimes as high as 70% with occasional epidemics especially in institutions. Transmission is by cysts.

(e)   Dientamoeba fragilis

Parasitic in the caecum and large intestine of man in which it may cause diarrhoea. Transmission may be through the eggs of the pinworm *Enterobius vermicularis*.

(f)   Trichomonas *spp.* (Fig. 1.6b)

Three species of *Trichomonas* are common in humans in all parts of the world: *T. hominis* in the caecum and large intestine; *T. tenax* in the mouth; and *T. vaginalis* in the vagina and urethra of women and in the urethra, seminal vesicles and prostate of men. *T. hominis* and *T. tenax* are harmless. *T. vaginalis* is usually harmless but may cause inflammation and discharge and is an increasingly important venereal disease infecting an estimated 180 million people worldwide. These species do not form cysts. *T. hominis* forms rounded resistant stages while *T. tenax* and *T. vaginalis* are transmitted by direct contact.

1.5.2   Intestinal flagellates and related forms in domesticated animals

The flagellates of domesticated animals are in general more serious pathogens than those of man.

(a)   Histomonas meleagridis

This is parasitic in an amoeboid form in the cells of the small intestine and liver and in a flagellated form in the caecum of chickens and turkeys throughout the world. In turkeys, it causes a serious disease, blackhead, which may kill 50–100% of young birds. Transmission occurs when the parasite enters the eggs of the caecal nematode *Heterakis gallinarum*.

(b)   Tritrichomonas foetus

This parasite is sometimes called *Trichomonas foetus*. It is parasitic in the genital organs of cattle throughout the world. Although frequently mild, the most serious effect is early abortion and in herds in Europe and the USA up to 30% of calves may be lost. Transmission is by direct contact and bulls harbour the infection for life. There is no reliable treatment.

(c)   Trichomonas gallinae

This parasite occurs in the upper digestive tract of birds, particularly pigeons, in all parts of the world. Most strains are harmless but parasites from the digestive tract may invade other parts of the body, including the brain, and cause serious disease.

(d)   Tetratrichomonas gallinarum

This parasite is also known as *Trichomonas gallinarum* or *T. pullorum*. It is found in the caecum and liver of chickens, turkeys and other gallinaceous birds throughout the world.

(e)   Spironucleus meleagridis

This cosmopolitan parasite of the duodenum and small intestine causes catarrhal enteritis in young turkeys.

1.5.3   Other flagellates

A variety of flagellates commonly occur in wild, domesticated and laboratory animals throughout the world. Mice, for example, harbour species of *Giardia*, *Spironucleus* (*Hexamita*) and *Trichomonas* (Fig. 1.6b). The first two may be pathogenic in laboratory colonies. *Opalina* is a multinucleate flagellate common in amphibians and *Trichonympha* and other genera are symbionts in the guts of termites where they break down the wood that the termites feed on but cannot digest.

1.6   PARASITIC AMOEBAE

Six species of amoebae are common in man in most parts of the world but only one, *Entamoeba histolytica*, is an important pathogen.

1.6.1   *Entamoeba histolytica* (Fig. 1.7a)

This parasite occurs throughout the world in man, apes, monkeys, dogs, cats and rats. The trophozoite, or feeding stage, inhabits the lower small intestine and colon where it multiplies by binary fission and forms characteristic 4-nucleated cysts which are passed out and subsequently ingested in contaminated food or water. Sometimes the amoebae invade the mucosa and submucosa and may be carried via the portal vein to the liver and other parts of the body. Considerable damage may be caused in the wall of the bowel or in the liver. In most people, there is no tissue invasion and the parasite causes no harm. The symptoms following the invasion of the tissues are variable but usually include diarrhoea or dysentery with the loss of blood (amoebic dysentery). In Europe and the USA the prevalence of *E. histolytica* is less than 5% and overt symptoms are rare. In many parts of the tropics and subtropics, however, the prevalence is more than 50% and dysentery and liver involvement may be common.

1.6.2   Other intestinal amoebae of man

There are four other amoebae commonly found all over the world. *E. hartmanni,* once regarded as a small race of *E. histolytica*, resembles the pathogenic

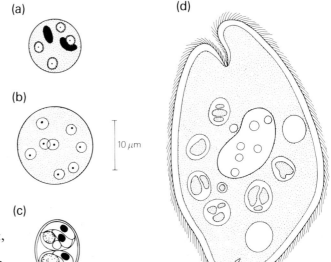

(a)

(b)

10 μm

(c)

(d)

Fig. 1.7. Protozoa from the human gut. (a) *Entamoeba histolytica* cyst, (b) *Entamoeba coli* cyst, (c) *Toxoplasma gondii* oocyst, (d) *Balantidium coli* trophozoite. (All drawn from stained slides.)

form but has smaller cysts. *Entamoeba coli* (Fig. 1.7b) is the most common amoeba of man and has cysts with 8 nuclei. *Endolimax nana* inhabits the upper part of the colon and has 4-nucleate cysts. *Iodamoeba buetschlii* has cysts with a single nucleus. None of these four parasites is pathogenic.

1.6.3   Facultative amoebae of man

There have been occasional records of free-living amoebae infecting man sometimes with fatal results. *Naegleria fowleri* produces primary amoebic meningoencephalitis if the trophozoite form is inhaled. The infection is acute and may be fatal within a few days. Over 100 cases have been recorded. Several species of *Acanthamoeba* cause a variety of symptoms from meningoencephalitis to vaginitis.

1.7   COCCIDIA

The coccidia are very common parasites mainly of the intestinal tracts of vertebrates. Some are major pathogens of domesticated animals and losses attributed to them run into millions of pounds each year. The life cycle usually involves one host and is shown in Fig. 1.8. There are a number of minor variations on this basic pattern mainly relating to the site of the infection and the number of schizogonic generations. The genera are identified on the morphology of the infective stage or oocyst. Each oocyst contains a number of sporocysts each containing sporozoites. In the two most important genera, the oocysts of *Eimeria* contain four sporocysts while those of *Isospora* contain two. Certain parasites with isosporan features have two hosts in their life cycles and these will be discussed in section 1.7.2.

1.7.1   Coccidiosis in domesticated animals

Coccidia are extremely common in domesticated animals and some cause very serious diseases. Coccidia normally have self-limiting infections followed by the acquisition of immunity to reinfection. Under natural conditions, animals become infected with small numbers of oocysts and are only mildly affected by the infection. Under crowded conditions, such as exist in batteries, large numbers of oocysts may be ingested causing severe or fatal infections, particularly in young animals. The actual pathological effects produced depend to a large extent on the number of oocysts ingested. It is therefore difficult to attribute pathogenicity to particular species and, as the species are extremely difficult to identify, there is considerable controversy about the number of species that exist in any given host and exactly how important one particular species may be. A list of the more important and widely accepted species of *Eimeria* is given in Table 1.4.

The species listed in Table 1.4 represent only some of the species actually described. Among the unlisted species in chickens, *Eimeria mivati* and *E. mitis* have long been regarded by some workers as synonymous with *E. acervulina* but there is no longer any doubt that certainly the former and probably the latter are true species. There are 5–6 species in turkeys, 13 or more in cattle and 15 or so in sheep and goats.

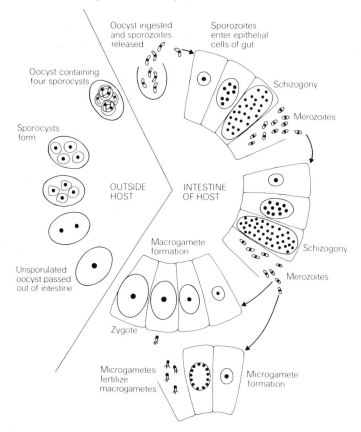

Fig. 1.8. The life cycle of *Eimeria* spp. The infection begins when oocysts are swallowed and sporozoites released in the gut. The sporozoites enter gut cells and undergo a phase of multiplication (schizogony) resulting in the formation of uninucleate merozoites. These merozoites invade other cells and the cycle is repeated two or three times. Eventually merozoites enter other cells where they develop into male and female gametocytes. The nucleus of the male or microgametocyte divides and produces flagellated microgametes which fertilize the female or macrogamete to produce a zygote. A cyst wall or oocyst forms round the zygote within which the nucleus divides twice to produce four uninucleate bodies. Another cyst wall or sporocyst forms round each of these and one further cell division occurs to produce two sporozoites in each. The oocyst containing four sporocysts each with two sporozoites is the infective stage.

There are a number of variations on this life cycle pattern, the main ones being in the number and sites of the schizogonic cycles.

At one time it was thought that *E. ahsata* was the only species in sheep and *E. arloingi* the only one in goats. It is now clear that there are several species in sheep and several different ones in goats. This kind of situation, the existence of several species exhibiting different pathogenicities, is true for coccidiosis in most domesticated animals. The species in rodents, *E. nieschulzi* and *E. falciformis*, are widely used in experimental investigations.

Table 1.4. Important *Eimeria* species.

Species	Host	Pathogenicity	Distribution
E. acervulina	Chickens	+	C
E. necatrix	Chickens	++++	C
E. maxima	Chickens	+++	C
E. brunetti	Chickens	+++	C
E. tenella	Chickens	++++	C
E. meleagrimitis	Turkeys	+++	C
E. danailova	Ducks	+++	Europe
E. anseris	Geese	++	Europe
E. alabamensis	Cattle	+	C
E. bovis	Cattle	+++	C
E. zuernii	Cattle	+++	C
E. ahsata	Sheep	++	C
E. arloingi	Goats	+	C
E. debliecki	Pigs	++	C
E. stiedai	Rabbits	+++	C
E. magna	Rabbits	+++	C
E. nieschulzi	Rats		
E. falciformis	Mice		

++++ Most pathogenic. + Least pathogenic. C Cosmopolitan.

1.7.2   Toxoplasma and related coccidia

Until 1970 all coccidians with two sporocysts in the oocyst were classified as *Isospora* species and it was assumed that all had simple life cycles in a single host like that of *Eimeria*. Since 1970, it has become clear that many of these isosporans

Table 1.5. Isosporan coccidia of man and domesticated animals.*

Definitive host	Intermediate hosts						
	None	Man	Cattle	Sheep	Horses	Pigs	Rodents
Cats		T. gondii	S. hirsuta (S. fusiformis) (S. bovifelis) B. besnoiti	T. gondii S. gigantea		S. porcifelis	T. gondii H. hammondi S. muris B. wallacei C. felis C. rivolta
Dogs			S. cruzi (S. bovicanis) H. heydorni	S. tenella	S. bertrami S. fayeri	S. miescheriana (S. suicanis)	C. canis C. ohioensis H. pardalis
Man	I. belli		S. hominis (S. bovihominis)			S. suihominis	
Unknown					B. bennetti		B. jellisoni

*This list is not complete and the nomenclature of the group is still being clarified. Some alternative names are given in brackets.

develop in an intermediate host which may or may not be obligatory. In such life cycles, the oocysts are passed out from the definitive host and are ingested by an intermediate host within which multiplication in various organs occurs and eventually cysts are formed which, when ingested by the definitive host, initiate the typical coccidian life cycle once again. The problem has been that the parasites in the intermediate hosts were all well-known and had been given valid names. The various parts of each life cycle have now been put together and it is possible to identify each parasite from the stages in either the definitive or the intermediate host. The most important species are given in Table 1.5.

This group now includes some seven genera, the characteristics of each of which are summarized below. *Isospora* is classified on the stages in the definitive host while all the others are classified on the stages in the intermediate host.

●*Isospora*. Direct life cycle.

●*Toxoplasma*. Intermediate host not essential. Development in the lymphoid macrophage system. Cysts thin walled containing many organisms.

●*Hammondia*. Similar to *Toxoplasma* but intermediate host essential.

●*Cystoisospora*. Intermediate host not essential. Similar to *Toxoplasma* but thin walled cyst contains only one infective organism.

●*Sarcocystis*. Septate cysts in muscle of intermediate host.

●*Besnoitia*. Thick walled cysts in connective tissue of intermediate host.

●*Frenkelia*. Cysts in brain of intermediate host.

As a result of these discoveries, the species of *Isospora* in man, cats, and dogs have to be redefined. The two species originally described from man were *I. belli* and *I. hominis*. *I. belli* remains unchanged while *I. hominis* becomes *S. hominis* and *S. suihominis*. In the dog, *I. canis* becomes *C. canis*; *I. rivolta* becomes *C. ohioensis*; and *I. bigemina* becomes *S. tenella*, *S. cruzi* and *H. heydorni*. In the cat, *I. felis* becomes *C. felis*; *I. rivolta* becomes *C. rivolta* and *I. bigemina* could apply to so many species that it is impossible to identify the original descriptions with any certainty.

The majority of this group of parasites cause little harm to their hosts, the most important exception being *Toxoplasma gondii* (Figs 1.5b, 1.7c). *T. gondii* is a parasite of felids with a very wide range of intermediate hosts, including man. In cats, and other felids, the life cycle is a normal eimerian one (Fig. 1.9). If, however, the oocysts are ingested by other warm blooded animals, multiplication by a form of internal budding, called endodyogeny, occurs in various cells of the body and eventually cysts are formed. If the intermediate host is eaten by a definitive host the parasite enters the cells of the gut and reverts to a normal eimerian life cycle. If, on the other hand, the intermediate host is eaten by another potential intermediate host disseminated infections occur as before. The infection may cause no symptoms or it may kill the intermediate host. Most humans acquire their infections from meat or from cats and develop antibodies against the parasite. Infections are normally symptomless but in the unborn foetus or immunosuppressed patients they may be

Fig. 1.9. The life cycle of *Toxoplasma*. The life cycle begins when oocysts are swallowed by a cat and the sporozoites are released in the gut. A typical eimerian life cycle with schizogony and the formation of gametocytes occurs and eventually oocysts are formed and the cycle is repeated if these are swallowed by cats. If the oocysts are swallowed by mice, schizogony occurs in various parts of the body but no oocysts are formed. Instead cysts are produced that lie dormant until the host is eaten. If eaten by a cat the normal eimerian life cycle follows. If eaten by another host an infection similar to that in mice occurs. This may occur in a variety of mammals including herbivores. Man becomes infected either by oocysts from cats or by eating infected meat. Congenital transmission in this alternative cycle also occurs.

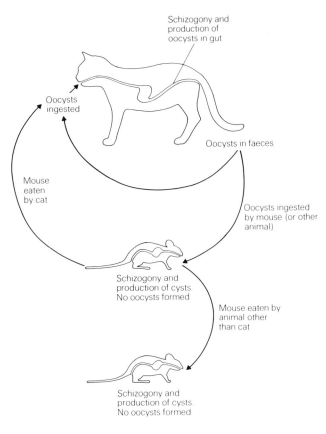

very serious and occasionally in healthy individuals they may cause ocular damage. The infection may also be serious in lambs and puppies.

1.8   MALARIA PARASITES

The malaria parasites belong to the same order as the coccidians, the Eucoccidiida, but to a different suborder, the Haemosporina, all the members of which are parasitic in the blood of vertebrates and have dipteran insects as their vectors. There are four genera in the group, *Leucocytozoon*, *Hepatocystis*, *Haemoproteus* and *Plasmodium*. The life cycle of *Plasmodium* is shown in Fig. 1.10. The life cycles of the other parasites are similar but do not have a cycle of multiplication in the blood. The malaria parasites, proper, belong to the genus *Plasmodium* which, for convenience, has been divided up into subgenera. The primate malarias belong to the subgenera *Plasmodium* and *Laverania*, the rodent forms to *Vinckeia* and the avian forms to *Haemamoeba, Huffia, Giovannolaia* and *Novyella*. The mammalian species are transmitted by mosquitoes of the genus *Anopheles* while the avian forms may be transmitted by culicine mosquitoes. There are also malaria parasites in reptiles.

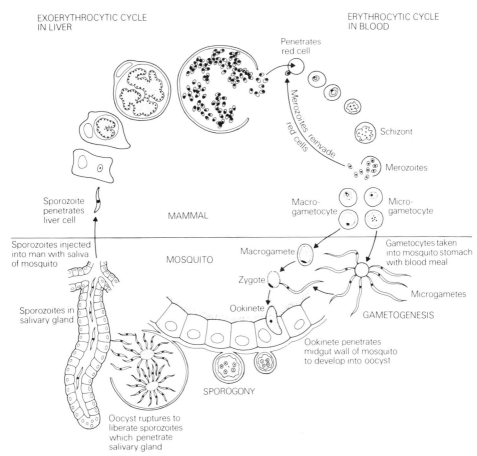

Fig. 1.10. The life cycle of *Plasmodium* spp. in mammals. The infection begins when sporozoites are injected directly into the bloodstream from the salivary glands of a mosquito. The sporozoites enter liver cells where they begin a phase of multiplication called 'exoerythrocytic schizogony', during which thousands of uninucleate merozoites are formed. These enter red blood cells in which they undergo a second phase of multiplication or erythrocytic schizogony, during which fewer than 24 merozoites are formed. These merozoites invade new red blood cells and the cycle may be repeated many times. Some of the merozoites are capable of developing into sexual stages or gametocytes. These are taken up by a mosquito. In the gut of the mosquito microgametes are produced and these fertilize the macrogametes and the resulting zygote or ookinete bores through the gut wall to come to lie on the outer surface where it forms an oocyst. Within the oocyst a third stage of multiplication occurs resulting in the formation of sporozoites that enter the salivary glands of the mosquito. (After Vickerman K. and Cox F.E.G., 1967.)

1.8.1   Malaria parasites of man

Human malaria is one of the most important diseases in the world with over 500 million people at risk in tropical and subtropical parts of the world , especially in Africa. Malaria is caused by four species of *Plasmodium: P. falciparum, P. vivax, P. ovale* and *P. malariae* (Table 1.6). The disease is characterized by periodic fevers coinciding with the liberation of merozoites during the erythrocytic phase of the infection; these fevers occur every 72 hours in the case of *P. malariae* and every 48 hours in the other species. In all species, there is a single phase of exoerythrocytic schizogony and in *P. falciparum* and *P. malariae* this phase lasts for 5–15 days. After this, the only parasites in the body are those in the blood and subsequent bouts of fever are caused by recrudescences of these blood forms. In *P. vivax* and *P. ovale* some of the parasites in the liver lie dormant for several years and subsequent infections due to the maturation of these forms are called relapses.

Table 1.6. Malaria parasites of man.

Species	Disease	Periodicity (hours)	Distribution
P. vivax	Benign tertian	48	Cosmopolitan, between summer isotherms 16°N & 20°S
P. ovale	Ovale tertian	48	Worldwide, patchy, mainly W. tropical Africa
P. falciparum	Malignant tertian	48	Cosmopolitan, mainly tropics and subtropics
P. malariae	Quartan	72	Cosmopolitan but patchy

P. falciparum (Fig. 1.11a) causes malignant tertian malaria and is the most common and serious of all the forms of malaria. The infection is acute and the parasites tend to stick to endothelial cells causing blockage and cerebral and intestinal damage, often resulting in death. *P. vivax* causes benign tertian malaria and is the second most serious infection. *P. ovale* causes ovale tertian malaria and is concentrated in West Africa. *P. malariae* causes quartan malaria and infections may last 30 years or more. Infections with these last three parasites, although debilitating, are seldom fatal in themselves.

1.8.2   Other malaria parasites

The parasites of man, with the exception of *P. malariae*, are not naturally transmissible to other animals so the malaria parasites of primates and rodents have received considerable attention both in their own rights and as models for the human

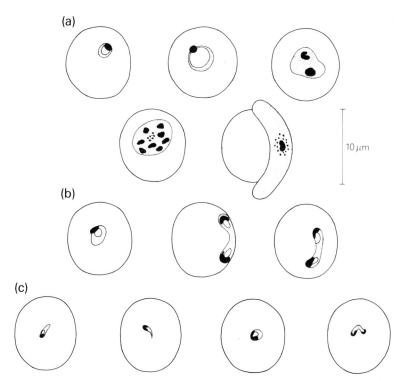

Fig. 1.11. Sporozoans in the blood of mammals. (a) *Plasmodium falciparum* from the blood of man. These stages are a young ring, mature ring, early schizont, mature schizont and macrogametocyte. Schizonts rarely occur in the peripheral blood. (b) *Babesia divergens* in the blood of a cow. (c) *Theileria parva* in the blood of a cow. (All drawn from stained slides.)

infections. There are about 20 species of *Plasmodium* in non-human primates of which *P. cynomolgi* and *P. simium* resemble *P. vivax* in both morphology and periodicity. *P. simiovale* and *P. fieldi* resemble *P. ovale*; *P. fragile* and *P. coatneyi* resemble *P. falciparum*; and *P. brasilianum* and *P. inui* resemble *P. malariae*. Of these, *P. cynomolgi*, *P. simiovale* and *P. fieldi* are known to exhibit relapses of the *P. vivax* type. *P. cynomolgi* has been the most studied of these parasites but another species from macaques, *P. knowlesi*, is now the most widely used primate malaria parasite in laboratory studies despite the fact that it has a 24 hour periodicity and does not closely resemble any of the human species. *P. cynomolgi*, *P. brasilianum*, *P. inui* and *P. knowlesi* infect man under experimental (or accidental) conditions.

The malaria parasites of rodents have been much more extensively studied than any others. These fall into two major groups, *P. berghei* and *P. yoelii* and their subspecies and *P. vinckei* and *P. chabaudi* and their subspecies. The *berghei* group typically invade immature erythrocytes and the *vinckei* group invade mature cells. They all have 24 hour periodicities and only distantly resemble the human forms but, nevertheless, have provided a wealth of information on the biology of malaria parasites which would have been otherwise unobtainable.

1.9   PIROPLASMS

The piroplasms are parasites of the erythrocytes of vertebrates in which, if they multiply, they divide by simple binary fission. The parasites in the blood do not contain pigment and this, together with the absence of schizogony, distinguishes them from the malaria parasites. The vectors are ticks.

1.9.1   *Babesia*

Babesia species live in the blood of vertebrates and are transmitted by ticks. The life cycle is shown in Fig. 1.12. The form in the vertebrate is the trophozoite that lives in red blood cells in which it divides by binary fission to produce two merozoites each of which invades a new cell (Fig. 1.11b). These blood stages cause serious diseases in domesticated animals (see Table 1.7) and the general name given to these is babesiosis. The symptoms of babesiosis are fever, anaemia, jaundice and haemoglobinuria, and the infections are often fatal. The species are identified on the stages in the blood but as there are few morphological characters this is not altogether satisfactory. The main division is into 'large' and 'small' forms and in the past a number of genera have been created on this characteristic alone, but at present only one genus, *Babesia*, is generally accepted. The distinction between 'large' and 'small' is a convenient starting point for the identification of any *Babesia* in a particular host (see Table 1.7).

There are a number of *Babesia* species in wild animals including *B. bovis* in deer, *B. caballi* in zebra and *B. gibsoni* in wild carnivores, but whether or not these play any significant part in the transmission of these parasites to domesticated animals is not known. There are also two important species in rodents, *B. rodhaini* and *B. microti*, that have been widely used in laboratory studies. *B. microti* occasionally infects man in America. In Europe splenectomized humans are sometimes infected with *B. bovis* and the infection frequently proves fatal. The *B. microti* infections are not fatal and infect intact individuals.

1.9.2   *Theileria*

Theileria species are parasites of cattle, sheep and goats in which the majority of the life cycle occurs in the lymphoid tissues (Fig. 1.5c,d) and the stages infective to ticks occur in the red blood cells (Fig. 1.11c). The life cycle is shown in Fig. 1.13 and the various parasites that cause disease are listed in Table 1.7. The most serious diseases caused by *Theileria* occur in cattle in which four valid species are recognized. *T. parva*, causing African theileriosis or East Coast Fever, is often lethal, *T. annulata* is sometimes lethal but as the infected cattle remain carriers for long periods this infection is probably more important on a world scale than

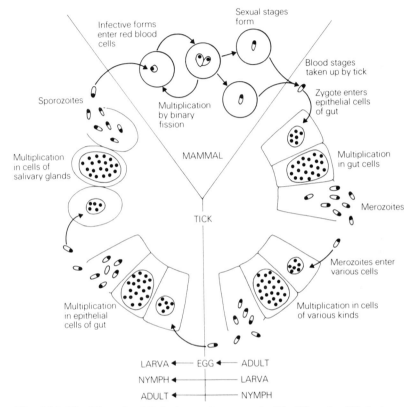

Fig. 1.12. The life cycle of *Babesia* spp. in mammals. The life cycle of *Babesia* spp. is complicated by the facts that any one of three stages in the life cycle of the tick vector may become infected and that ticks may have one, two or three hosts during their life cycles. These variations have marked effects on the life cycle of various *Babesia* species and the cycle described is a generalized one. The cycle in the mammal begins when infective forms are injected into the blood by a tick and the parasites enter red blood cells where they multiply by binary fission. Blood forms, probably gametocytes, are taken up by a tick when it feeds. These become gametes that fuse to form zygotes which enter epithelial cells of the gut where multiplication takes place. The resulting products are comparable with the merozoites in coccidian life cycles. These enter various cells in the body of the tick where further phases of multiplication occur. If the tick is a female, the merozoites may enter and multiply in the egg. When the larva hatches from the egg it is already infected and the parasites multiply once again in the epithelial cells of the gut. The uninucleate forms produced invade other tissues including the salivary glands from which small rounded infective bodies (sporozoites) are injected into the mammalian host. In some species, the nymph and not the larva harbours the infective parasites. The stage of the tick infected is never infective and usually the infection goes from larva to nymph, nymph to adult or adult to larva via the egg.

Table 1.7. Piroplasms causing disease in domesticated animals.

Species	Size	Main hosts	Main vectors	Pathogenicity	Main distribution
B. bigemina	L	Cattle, deer	Boophilus, Rhipicephalus	+++	Worldwide, tropics and subtropics
B. bovis	S	Cattle, deer	Boophilus, Ixodes, Rhipicephalus	++(+)	Worldwide, mainly temperate
B. divergens	S	Cattle, reindeer	Ixodes, Haemaphysalis	++	Europe
B. major	L	Cattle	Ixodes	+	Africa, Europe, S. America, Israel
B. caballi	L	Horses	Dermacentor, Hyalomma, Rhipicephalus	++	Africa, America, Europe, USSR
B. equi	S	Horses, zebra	Dermacentor, Hyalomma, Rhipicephalus	+++	Africa, Europe, USSR
B. motasi	L	Sheep, goats	Dermacentor, Haemaphysalis, Rhipicephalus	+	Europe, USSR
B. ovis	S	Sheep, goats	Ixodes, Rhipicephalus	+	USSR
B. trautmanni	L	Pigs	Rhipicephalus	+	Africa, USSR
B. canis	L	Dogs	Dermacentor, Hyalomma, Rhipicephalus	+++	Worldwide
B. gibsoni	S	Dogs	Hyalomma, Rhipicephalus	+++	India, China
B. felis	S	Cats	Haemaphysalis	+	Africa, India
T. annulata		Cattle	Hyalomma	+++	N. Africa, Asia, Europe
T. mutans		Cattle	Amblyomma, Haemaphysalis, Rhipicephalus	+	Africa, Asia, Australasia, Europe
T. parva		Cattle	Rhipicephalus	+++	Africa
T. sergenti		Cattle	Haemaphysalis	++	Asia
T. hirci		Sheep, goats	Hyalomma	+++	N. Africa, Asia
T. ovis		Sheep, goats	Rhipicephalus	+	Africa, Asia, Europe
H. veliferus		Cattle	Amblyomma		Africa

+ + + Most pathogenic. + Least pathogenic. L large. S small.

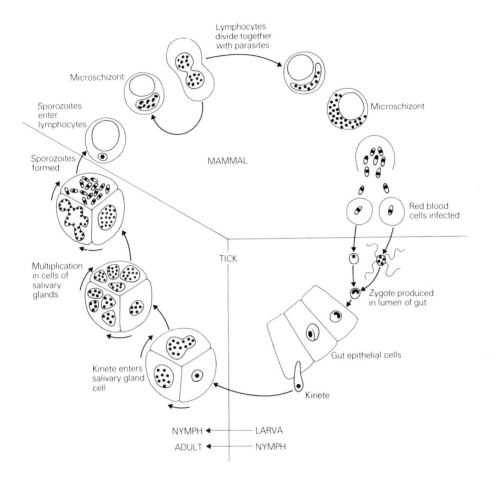

Fig. 1.13. The life cycle of *Theileria* spp. The cycle in the mammal begins when infective stages are injected by a tick. These enter lymphocytes in which a phase of multiplication occurs producing multi-nucleate bodies or macroschizonts. The parasites cause the lymphocytes to divide and are themselves divided between the two daughter host cells, and a massive infection is built up. After a predetermined number of divisions, nuclear division (which is not accompanied by cell division) occurs, and microschizonts are produced, the products of which invade red blood cells. These blood stages are taken up by ticks and within the lumen of the gut of the tick sexual stages are found. Fertilization occurs and the zygotes enter the epithelial cells of the gut where they become large club-shaped kinetes which migrate through the haemocoel to the salivary glands. Here several phases of multiplication occur with the nuclei becoming progressively smaller until eventually sporozoites are produced. These are injected into the vertebrate host when the tick feeds. The stage in the life cycle of the tick that is infected is never infective and there is no transovarian transmission; thus if the nymph is infected multiplication and sporozoite formation occur in the salivary glands of the adult.

T. parva. T. mutans is not very pathogenic and *T. sergenti* is probably a synonym of *T. mutans*. In *T. parva* and *T. annulata* infections, the damage is done during the phase of schizogony in the lymphoid tissues and the symptoms include hypertrophy of the lymphoid tissues, fever and loss of weight. In *T. mutans* (and *T. sergenti*) there may be anaemia and jaundice. In sheep and goats, *T. hirci* is very pathogenic when newly introduced into an area but *T. ovis*, which is morphologically indistinguishable from *T. hirci*, is hardly pathogenic at all. An unusual parasite, *Haematoxenus veliferus*, which has a veil-like appearance, is sometimes found in cattle and resembles *T. mutans*.

1.10   MICROSPORA

The Microspora were formerly classified with the Myxospora as the Cnidospora on superficial similarities, but, although there is still some uncertainty about the actual classification within the group, there is now no doubt that this is a distinct phylum. There are some 700 species of microsporidians and these are found in nearly all groups of vertebrates and invertebrates, particularly fish and arthropods. Microsporidians are characterized by the possession of a thick-walled spore containing an infective body or sporoplasm surrounded by a coiled hollow tube, the polar filament, through which the sporoplasm is injected into its host. The infection begins when a spore is ingested and the sporoplasm enters a cell of the gut. The actual details of what follows vary from species to species, but multiplication by binary fission and the spread of the infection to other tissues occurs, and eventually spores are formed and released when the host dies or is eaten.

Encephalitozoon cuniculi occurs in rodents, rabbits, carnivores and primates and there are a few records from man. This is a parasite of peritoneal macrophages but may also spread to other parts of the body including the brain where spores can be found. In fish, *Pleistophora hyphessobryconis* occurs in the skeletal muscle of many freshwater species in aquaria. *Glugea anomala* occurs in the connective tissues of three-spined sticklebacks, in which it causes gross deformities, and *Pleistophora salmonae* contaminates trout farms. *Nosema bombycis* causes silkworm disease, or pebrine, and *N. apis* causes a similar disease in bees.

1.11   MYXOSPORA

In the Myxospora, the spore usually consists of two or more valves and contains an infective amoeboid body and polar filaments, which are used to anchor the spores, enclosed in capsules. The majority of species occur in the coelom or various tissues of freshwater fish. Infection begins when a spore is ingested, and the infective amoeboid form is released to make its way to a suitable site for development where nuclear division occurs and eventually large multinucleate forms are produced. These become surrounded by host tissue to form cysts, either in the tissues or in the coelom, and eventually numerous spores are formed and released when the host dies. There are few species of fish that are unaffected by myxosporidians and, in general, the histozoic forms are more harmful than the coelozoic ones. *Myxobolus cerebralis* infects members of the Salmonidae and erodes the cartilage supporting the central nervous system, causing whirling disease—a serious problem in hatcheries and fish farms.

1.12   CILIOPHORA

The Ciliophora is a distinct phylum, even considered by some to be a subkingdom, containing 4700 free-living and 2500 parasitic species. Parasitic ciliates occur in most groups of vertebrates and invertebrates and those in amphibians and earthworms are frequently encountered in elementary biology classes. Few of the parasitic ciliates are of any economic importance.

1.12.1   *Balantidium coli*

Balantidium coli (Fig. 1.7d) is a common parasite of pigs in all parts of the world and has also been recorded in rats, dogs, monkeys, apes and man. It is difficult to know how many human cases there have been but about 1000 have been recorded, mainly in the tropics. The ciliate lives in the lumen of the large intestine and may invade the gut wall where it produces ulcers resembling those caused by *Entamoeba histolytica* although the majority of cases are asymptomatic. Transmission is by cysts and epidemiological evidence suggests that most human infections are acquired from pigs.

1.12.2   Rumen ciliates

Cattle, sheep, goats, camels and other ruminants harbour massive numbers of flagellates and ciliates. The ciliates are the most important constituent of the fauna of the rumen and up to 1×10^{11} individual ciliates, occupying one-tenth of the volume of the rumen, have been recorded. Many species of ciliates may be present, ranging from 'primitive' forms such as *Buetschlia*, *Isotricha* and *Dasytricha* to 'advanced' forms like *Entodinium*, *Ophryoscolex* and *Diplodinium*, in the order Entodiniomorphida, that are highly adapted to life in the anaerobic conditions in the rumen. Exactly what role these ciliates play is unclear. They cannot be true symbionts because defaunated ruminants thrive as well as untreated ones, but they can provide up to one-fifth of the total daily protein requirements of an ox and also fermentation products that help to break down cellulose. Similar ciliates live as commensals in the caecum and colon of horses and other equines.

REFERENCES AND FURTHER READING

Ackers J.P. (1980) Giardiasis: Basic parasitology. *Trans. R. Soc. trop. Med. Hyg.* **74**, 427–9.

Adam K.M.G., Paul, J. & Zaman V. (1979) *Medical and Veterinary Protozoology: An Illustrated Guide*, 2nd ed. Edinburgh, Churchill Livingstone.

Albach R.A. & Booden T. (1978) Amoebae. In J.P. Kreier (ed.) *Parasitic Protozoa*, vol.II, pp. 455–506. New York, Academic Press.

Baker J.R. (1982) *The Biology of Parasitic Protozoa*, London, Edward Arnold.

Barnett S.F. (1977) *Theileria*. In J.P. Kreier (ed.) *Parasitic Protozoa*, vol.IV, pp. 77–113. New York, Academic Press.

Bruce-Chwatt L.J. (1980) *Essential Malariology*, London, Heinemann Medical Books.

Canning E.U. (1977) Microsporidia. In J.P. Kreier (ed.) *Parasitic Protozoa*, vol.IV, pp. 155–96. New York, Academic Press.

Carter R. & Diggs C.L. (1977) Plasmodia of rodents. In J.P. Kreier (ed.) *Parasitic Protozoa*, vol.III, pp. 359–465. New York, Academic Press.

CIBA Foundation (1974) *Trypanosomiasis and Leishmaniasis*. CIBA Foundation Symposium No. 20. Amsterdam, Elsevier–Excerpta Medica–North Holland.

Coleman, G.S. (1980) Rumen ciliate protozoa. In W.H.R. Lumsden, R. Muller & J.R. Baker (eds.) *Advances in Parasitology*, vol.18, pp. 121–73. London, Academic Press.

Corliss J.O. (1979) *The Ciliated Protozoa: Characterization, Classification, and Guide to the Literature*. 2nd ed. Oxford, Pergamon Press.

Cox F.E.G. (1981a) The malaria parasites: *Plasmodium* spp. *Biologist* **28**, 9–17.

Cox, F.E.G (1981b) A new classification of the parasitic protozoa. *Protozoological Abstracts* **5**, 9–14.

Dubey J.P. (1977) *Toxoplasma, Hammondia, Besnoitia, Sarcocystis*, and other tissue cyst forming coccidia of man and animals. In J.P. Kreier (ed.) *Parasitic Protozoa*, vol.III, pp. 101–237. New York, Academic Press.

Fife E.H. (1977) *Trypanosoma (Schizotrypanum) cruzi*. In J.P. Kreier (ed.) *Parasitic Protozoa*, vol.I, pp. 135–173. New York, Academic Press.

Friedman M.J. & Trager W. (1981) The biochemistry of resistance to malaria. *Scient. Am.* **244** (3), 112–20.

Garnham P.C.C. (1966) *Malaria Parasites and other Haemosporidia*, Oxford, Blackwell Scientific Publications.

Hammond D.M. & Long P.L. (eds.) (1973) *The Coccidia*, Baltimore, University Park Press.

Hoare C.A. (1972) *The Trypanosomes of Mammals*, Oxford, Blackwell Scientific Publications.

Honigberg B.M. (1978) Trichomonads of importance in human medicine. In J.P. Kreier (ed.) *Parasitic Protozoa*, vol. II, p. 275–454. New York, Academic Press.

Joyner L.P. & Donnelly J. (1979) The epidemiology of babesial infections. In W.H.R. Lumsden, R. Muller & J.R. Baker (eds.) *Advances in Parasitology* vol.17, pp. 115–40. London, Academic Press.

Killick-Kendrick R. & Peters W. (eds.) (1978) *Rodent Malaria*, London, Academic Press.

Kreier J.P. (ed.) (1977–8) *Parasitic Protozoa*, vol.I, 1977; vol.II, 1978; vol.III, 1977; vol.IV, 1977. New York, Academic Press.

Kreier J.P. (ed.) (1980) *Malaria*, vols.1,2,3. New York, Academic Press.

Kulda J. & Nohýnková E (1978) Flagellates of the human intestine and of intestines of other species. In J.P. Kreier (ed.) *Parasitic Protozoa*, vol.III, pp. 1–138. New York, Academic Press.

Levine N. (1973) *Protozoan Parasites of Domestic Animals and of Man*, Minneapolis, Burgess Publishing Company.

Lumsden W.H.R. & Evans D.A. (eds.) (1976) *Biology of the Kinetoplastida*, vol.I. London, Academic Press.

Lumsden W.H.R. & Evans D.A. (eds.) (1979) *Biology of the Kinetoplastida*, vol.II. London, Academic Press.

Mahoney D.F. (1977) Babesia of domestic animals. In J.P. Kreier (ed.) *Parasitic Protozoa*, vol.IV, pp. 1–52. New York, Academic Press.

Mansfield J.M. (1977) Nonpathogenic trypanosomes of mammals. In J.P. Kreier (ed.) *Parasitic Protozoa*, vol.I, pp. 297–327. New York, Academic Press.

Melhorn H. & Heydorn A.O. (1978) The Sarcosporidia (Protozoa, Sporozoa): Life cycle and fine structure. In W.H.R. Lumsden, R. Muller & J.R. Baker (eds.), *Advances in Parasitology*, vol.16, pp. 43–91. London, Academic Press.

Meyer E.A. & Radulescu S. (1979) Giardia and giardiasis. In W.H.R. Lumsden, R. Muller & J.R. Baker (eds.) *Advances in Parasitology*, vol.17, pp. 1–47. London, Academic Press.

Mitchell L.G. (1977) Myxosporidia. In J.P. Kreier (ed.) *Parasitic Protozoa*, vol.IV, pp. 115–54. New York, Academic Press.

New York Academy of Medicine (1981) *Symposium on Amebiasis. Bull. N.Y. Acad. Med.* **57**, 173–242.

de Raadt P. & Seed J.R. (1977) Trypanosomes causing disease in man in Africa. In J.P. Kreier (ed.) *Parasitic Protozoa*, vol.I, pp. 175–237. New York, Academic Press.

Rieckmann K.H. & Silverman P.H. (1977) Plasmodia of Man. In J.P. Kreier (ed.) *Parasitic Protozoa*, vol.III, pp. 493–527. New York, Academic Press.

Ristic M. & Lewis G.E. (1977) Babesia in man and wild laboratory-adapted mammals. In J.P. Kreier (ed.) *Parasitic Protozoa*, vol. IV, pp. 53–76. New York, Academic Press.

Royal Society of Tropical Medicine and Hygiene (1980) Symposium on Giardiasis. *Trans. R. Soc. trop. Med. Hyg.* **74**, 427–48.

Ruff M.D. & Reid W.M. (1977) Avian Coccidia. In J.P. Kreier (ed.) *Parasitic Protozoa*, vol. III, pp. 33–69. New York, Academic Press.

Soltys M.A. & Woo P.T.K. (1977) Trypanosomes producing disease in livestock in Africa. In J.P. Kreier (ed.) *Parasitic Protozoa*, vol.I, pp. 239–68. New York, Academic Press.

Todd K.S. & Ernst J.V. (1977) Coccidia of mammals except man. In J.P. Kreier (ed.) *Parasitic Protozoa*, vol.III, pp. 71–99. New York, Academic Press.

Vickerman K. (1970) Morphological and physiological considerations of extracellular blood protozoa. In A.M. Fallis (ed.) *Ecology and Physiology of Parasites*, pp. 58–89. Toronto, University of Toronto Press.

Vickerman K. (1976) The diversity of the kinetoplastid flagellates. In W.H.R. Lumsden & D.A. Evans (eds.) *Biology of the Kinetoplastida*, vol.I, pp. 1–34. London, Academic Press.

Vickerman K. & Cox F.E.G. (1967) *The Protozoa*, London, John Murray.

Woo P.T.K. (1977) Salivarian trypanosomes producing disease in livestock outside of sub-Saharan Africa. In J.P. Kreier (ed.) *Parasitic Protozoa*, vol.I, pp. 269–96. New York, Academic Press.

Zaman V. (1979) *Atlas of Medical Parasitology*, Lancaster, MTP Press.

Zuckerman T. & Lainson R. (1977) *Leishmania*. In J.P. Kreier (ed.) *Parasitic Protozoa*, vol.I, pp. 57–133. New York, Academic Press.

Chapter 2
Parasitic helminths

P.J. Whitfield

2.1 INTRODUCTION

The vast majority of metazoan parasites living in or on vertebrate hosts are representatives of three particular phyla—the Platyhelminthes, Nematoda and Acanthocephala. 'Helminth' is a practically useful but imprecisely defined term which includes all the parasitic members of these three phyla. It is as the causative agents of a terrible list of debilitating, deforming and killing diseases of man and his domesticated animals, that helminths are principally studied.

Some helminth infections are numbered among the major diseases of mankind. Schistosomiasis (bilharzia), caused by digeneans of the genus *Schistosoma* which inhabit blood vessels, is a most important cause of morbidity with over 200 million infected persons in Africa, South America and the Far East. The complex of diseases called filariasis, caused by highly pathogenic filarial nematodes of man such as *Wuchereria bancrofti, Brugia malayi, Loa loa* and *Onchocerca volvulus,* are similarly widespread, with a probable total of over 250 million cases of bancroftian filariasis in the world at present and an estimated 122 million cases in India alone in 1969. Although the vector-transmitted filarial nematodes provoke the most dramatic forms of pathology such as elephantiasis and blindness, a wide range of other nematodes with direct life cycles can also be very harmful, especially when present as multiple-species infections in poorly nourished patients. Pre-eminent in this context are ascariasis caused by *Ascaris lumbricoides*; hookworm disease which is the result of infections with *Ancylostoma duodenale* and *Necator americanus*; trichuriasis caused by *Trichuris trichiura*; and strongyloidiasis, the causative agent of which is *Strongyloides stercoralis.* Human cestode disease is a relatively nonpathogenic affliction although two types of larval cestodiasis—hydatid disease produced by the hydatid cysts of *Echinococcus granulosus* and cysticercosis caused by the cysticercus stage larvae of *Taenia solium* (the pork tapeworm)—can both be highly injurious.

2.2 STRUCTURE AND FUNCTION

Helminths are very diverse in their body structures, life cycle organizations, respiratory and nutritional physiology and behaviour. Part of this diversity is a result of the phylogenetic complexity of the group, containing as it does two dramatically different animal types, the acoelomate flatworms and the pseudocoelomate nematodes and acanthocephalans. Another part consists of the

34

multiple specific adaptations of helminths for their one- , two- or three-host life cycles.

All the adult helminths considered in this text range in size from a few hundred μm to about 10 m in length. Most adult digeneans measure 0.1–3 cm, adult nematodes 0.3–80 cm and cestodes from a few millimetres to more than 10 m. Larval stages, some of which have a brief free-living existence, are usually less than 1 mm long.

Monogenean, digenean and cestode platyhelminths all share a solid triploblastic acoelomate body plan, with complex reproductive organs embedded in mesenchymal tissue, and a gut, when it is present, which possesses only a single, oral opening. The reproductive system is almost always of a hermaphroditic type. All the parasitic flat-worms possess a living syncytial body wall whose outer surface is differently modified in the three groups.

Nematodes and acanthocephalans both possess a pseudocoelomic body cavity, unlined by a mesodermal epithelium. The pseudocoelomic fluid within this cavity plays an important hydrostatic skeletal role in locomotion. Most nematodes and acanthocephalans are dioecious, with the male and female reproductive tracts located in the pseudocoelomes of the separate sexes. Nematodes have a body wall consisting of an outer syncytial hypodermis surmounted by an apparently non-living, mainly collagenous cuticle, and underlain by groups of longitudinal muscles. Almost all species possess a functional gut with a mouth and anus. Acanthocephalans possess a syncytial body wall whose outermost region is bounded by a plasma membrane modified for nutrient uptake by the presence of high densities of tegumentary pore canals. Both longitudinal and circular muscles are found beneath the body wall. No acanthocephalans possess a gut of any sort.

Within the helminths, many life cycle modes are utilized and some, such as *Strongyloides stercoralis* and *Hymenolepis nana*, can use more than one mode. Direct life cycle strategies, with only a single host species involved, are used by all monogeneans, many nematodes and the cestode *Hymenolepis nana* in one of its life cycle modes. Indirect life cycles are those in which more than one host is used to complete the life cycle. In such cycles, the final or definitive host, that is the host in which parasitic sexual reproduction takes place, is almost always a vertebrate. The intermediate hosts, those in which development, growth, encystment or asexual reproduction occurs, can be invertebrates or vertebrates. Indirect life cycles with two or three hosts are the rule among digeneans, acanthocephalans and the vast majority of cestodes. Among the nematodes, filarial worms and *Dracunculus medinensis* (the guinea worm) utilize two-host indirect cycles. In the dioecious nematodes, acanthocephalans and schistosome digeneans, sperm transfer between the sexes is obligatory, often preceeded by complex copulatory behaviour. In the hermaphroditic digeneans and cestodes self-fertilization is sometimes possible but unidirectional or reciprocal cross-insemination is nearly always favoured.

Actual transmission of helminth infections from host to host in indirect or direct life cycles is achieved by eggs or larvae. Eggs are usually directly ingested by a host. Larvae may be ingested in this way or they may be consumed while attached to a plant or located within an intermediate host, when the intermediate host acts as a prey item for the next host in the life cycle. Free living mobile, larval forms such as monogenean oncomiracidia, digenean miracidia and cercariae and L_3 larval nematodes are often able to find, recognize, and then invade new hosts. They usually possess impressive sensory and locomotory abilities which enable them to carry out these functions.

2.3   CLASSIFICATION

It must be admitted from the outset that the classification of helminths is a difficult task for student and research worker alike. Firstly, a number of unresolved problems exist at high taxonomic levels. There is no real consensus, for instance, on the interrelationships and hierarchical status of the main pseudocoelomate taxa or on the relationships between parasitic platyhelminth classes. Specifically, the much used term 'Trematoda', including at least the digeneans and monogeneans, is believed by some to be an artificial grouping. Secondly, particularly among the nematodes, there are difficulties in making the taxonomic systems used for free-living and parasitic forms fully compatible. Lastly, and probably most importantly, there are a number of intrinsic weaknesses in the data base on which helminth

Table 2.1. An outline classification of helminths parasitic in vertebrates.

PHYLUM: PLATYHELMINTHES
Class 1 Monogenea
Class 2 Cestoda (*Diphyllobothrium, Taenia, Echinococcus*)*
Class 3 Aspidogastrea
Class 4 Digenea (*Schistosoma, Fasciolopsis, Fasciola, Paragonimus*)

PHYLUM: ACANTHOCEPHALA
Class 1 Palaeacanthocephala
Class 2 Archiacanthocephala (*Moniliformis, Macracanthorhynchus*)
Class 3 Eoacanthocephala

PHYLUM: NEMATODA
  Order 1 Rhabditida (*Strongyloides*)
  Order 2 Strongylida (*Necator, Ancylostoma*, etc.)
  Order 3 Ascaridida (*Ascaris, Toxocara*, etc.)
  Order 4 Oxyurida (*Enterobius*)
  Order 5 Spirurida (*Dracunculus, Wuchereria, Brugia, Loa, Onchocerca*)
  Order 6 Enoplida (*Trichinella, Trichuris*)

---

*Important genera which infect man are listed after the appropriate taxa.

taxonomy is founded. The parasites themselves are small soft-bodied invertebrates usually without extensive hard skeletal structures and possessing multiple, highly varied, life-cycle stages. Most of these attributes cause taxonomic problems when identification is based solely on gross and microscopical morphology. Body and organ sizes and shapes are easily altered by fixation methods, and by the specific identity and status of the host in which it developed. This variability has lead to many species being erected on invalid morphological criteria. Equally, many helminths are known only as a single life-cycle stage, and many links between otherwise isolated descriptions of adults and larval types remain to be made.

Increasingly, though, a wider range of character types is being utilized in specific descriptions which offsets some of the problems described above. Particularly important in this respect is the use of isoenzyme characters assessed by a range of electrophoretic and isoelectric focusing techniques.

Table 2.1 provides a working outline classification for the helminth groups described in this book. More detailed classification systems will be provided for each of the major helminth groups as they are considered in turn.

2.4   PLATYHELMINTH PARASITES OF VERTEBRATES

Of the four classes of entirely parasitic platyhelminths only two, the Cestoda and Digenea, cause important diseases in man or his domesticated animals, although monogeneans of fish can cause serious losses in stocks kept under high-density fish farming conditions. Table 2.2 outlines the main characteristics of the Monogenea and Aspidogastrea, the two classes that do not have significant medical or economic importance, while Fig. 2.1 illustrates the adult structure of a typical monogenean and aspidogastrean.

Table 2.2. Biological characteristics of monogeneans and aspidogastrans.

Characteristic	Monogeneans	Aspidogastreans
Life cycle mode	Always direct	Direct (possibly occasionally indirect)
Hosts	Fish, amphibians, reptiles, cetaceans and cephalopods	Molluscs, elasmobranchs, teleosts, turtles, decapod crustaceans
Location on or in host	Typically ectoparasitic on skin or gills, some forms endoparasitic in cloaca, bladder, etc.	Typically endoparasitic
Attachment organs	Posterior sucking opisthaptor with hooks and hooklets or clamps	Huge ventral adhesive organ divided into alveoli

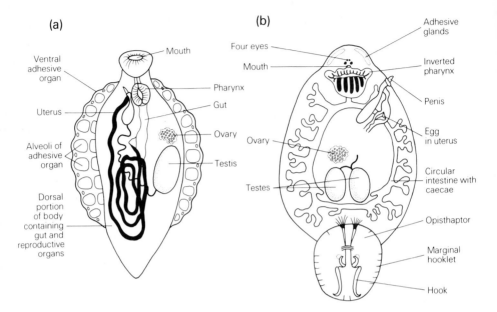

Fig. 2.1. (a) Diagrammatic dorsal view of a typical aspidogastrean demonstrating the division of the body into a large ventral sucker and a dorsal body portion containing gut and reproductive organs (based on *Aspidogaster*). (b) Diagrammatic view of a typical skin-dwelling monogean of fish (*Entobdella*) demonstrating the posterior opisthaptor with hooks and hooklets for attachment to host.

2.4.1   Cestode parasites

Cestodes are a unique and in many ways aberrant group of platyhelminth parasites. They certainly represent the most extreme specializations of the basic flatworm body plan for an endoparasitic existence. With very few exceptions they all share two remarkable attributes: firstly they possess no gut, and secondly they have a very elongated body often hundreds of times longer than it is broad. One small subclass, the Cestodaria, have nonsegmented compact bodies (Fig. 2.2), but members of the principle subclass, the Eucestoda, have a characteristically segmented adult body made up of a string of proglottids each of which contains in time a complete set of reproductive organs (Fig. 2.3). A mature adult eucestode may consist of several thousand such proglottids behind an anterior attachment organ—the scolex—which is equipped with muscular grooves, hooks or suckers (Fig. 2.4). The serial multiplication of reproductive organ sets which the segmented body represents, is a unique modification for enhanced reproductive capacity among helminths and individual adults can sustain daily egg outputs of thousands or even millions of eggs.

The body wall of a cestode consists of a living syncytial tegument, the outer plasma membrane of which is thrown into a regular array of specialized microvilli termed 'microtriches', each surmounted by a posteriorly directed electron-dense spine (see Figs. 5.7, 5.8). The tegumentary plasma membrane is covered with a polyanionic glycocalyx. Microtriches on the tegumental surface produce a large amplification of surface area which operates in a digestive/absorptive manner in respect of external nutrients. Low molecular-weight organic molecules are absorbed by diffusion and active transport mechanisms across the plasma membrane. This also bears intrinsic phosphohydrolases which probably play a role in nutrient acquisition. There is increasing evidence that the tegument can also absorb macromolecules such as proteins, by an endocytosis mechanism. This repertoire of nutrient uptake techniques appears to restrict adult eucestodes to nutrient-rich internal locations within their vertebrate hosts. The vast majority are found in the lumen of the small intestine atached to its mucosa by their scolices.

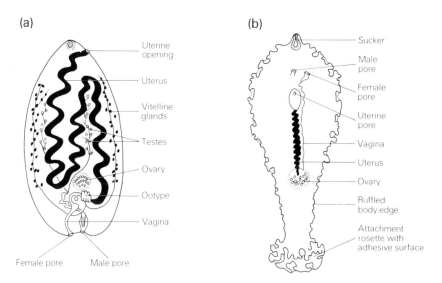

(a)

Uterine opening

Uterus

Vitelline glands

Testes

Ovary

Ootype

Vagina

Female pore   Male pore

(b)

Sucker

Male pore

Female pore

Uterine pore

Vagina

Uterus

Ovary

Ruffled body edge

Attachment rosette with adhesive surface

Fig. 2.2. Diagrammatic views of cestodarians. (a) *Amphilina* sp. from the body cavity of a sturgeon. (b) *Gyrocotyle* sp. from the intestinal lumen of a rat fish. Both have unsegmented bodies containing only a single set of hermaphroditic reproductive organs.

Except for *Hymenolepis nana* in one of its life-cycle modes, all eucestodes have an indirect life cycle with larval development and/or asexual reproduction occurring in one or two intermediate hosts. Fig. 2.5 illustrates a selection of cestode larval forms from these hosts.

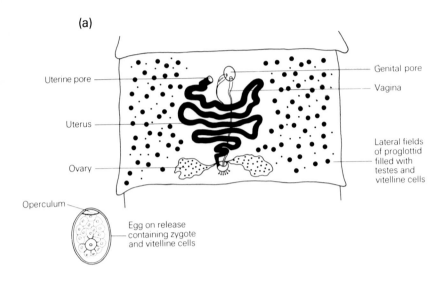

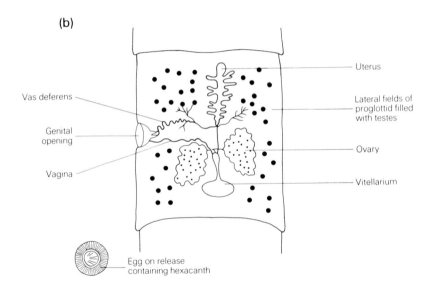

Fig. 2.3. Proglottids and eggs of pseudophyllidean and cyclophyllidean cestodes.
(a) Proglottid of *Diphyllobothrium latum*, a pseudophyllidean, demonstrating extensive areas of vitelline cells, genital openings on the ventral proglottid surface, and a uterine pore through which the gravid uterus can communicate with the outside world. The egg of *D. latum* when released is unembryonated. (b) Mature proglottid of *Taenia saginata* or *T. solium*, demonstrating a lateral genital opening and a uterus which does not directly communicate with the outside world. The egg of *T. saginata* or *T. solium* when released in human faeces contains a fully formed hexacanth larva.

Fig. 2.4. Typical cyclophyllidean and pseudophyllidean cestode scolices. (a) The scolex of the cyclophyllidean *Echinococcus granulosus* from the dog gut, with four muscular suckers and an apical rostellum surmounted with recurved rostellar hooks. (b) The unhooked scolex of the pseudophyllidean, *Diphyllobothrium latum*, with two muscular grooves or bothria.

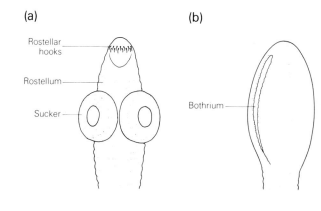

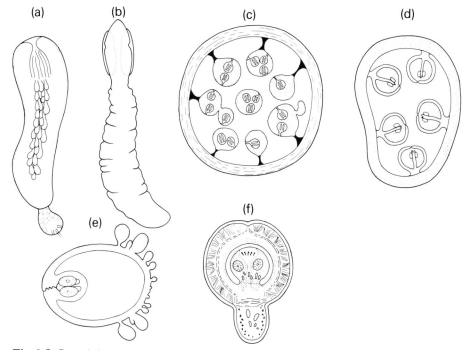

Fig. 2.5. Cestode larval stages. (a) Proceroid larva of *Diphyllobothrium latum* with a central core of gland cells and retained hooks from the hexacanth stage. (b) Plerocercoid larva of *Diphyllobothrium latum* with anterior bothria present. (c) Hydatid cyst of *Echinococcus granulosus* with an outer laminated layer and proliferative brood capsules within it containing infective protoscolices. (d) Coenurus larva of *Multiceps multiceps* with infective protoscolices budding directly from a germinal membrane. (e) Cysticercus larva of *Taenia crassiceps* with scolex invaginated into wall of bladder. The posterior portions of the external bladder wall produce new cysticerci by exogenous budding. Such budding does not occur from the otherwise similar cysticerci of *T. saginata* and *T. solium*. (f) Cysticercoid larva of *Hymenolepis nana* with the uninvaginated scolex housed within an anterior vesicle.

2.4.2   Human cestodiasis

Within the Eucestoda there is considerable uncertainty about the appropriate subdivision into orders. Conveniently, however, the species that cause disease in man all fall within two well-recognized and reasonably homogeneous orders, the Pseudophyllidea and the Cyclophyllidea. Table 2.3 sets out an outline classification of the two orders with emphasis on the groups that cause disease in man.

Tapeworm-generated disease or cestodiasis can conveniently be considered under two headings, namely adult cestodiasis where the pathology is due to adult

Table 2.3. An outline classification of pseudophyllidean and cyclophyllidean cestodes.

Class: Cestoda
Subclass: Eucestoda

Order 1: Pseudophyllidea. Scolex with two long superficial bothria. Mainly gut-dwelling parasites of non-elasmobranch fish, fish-eating mammals including man and birds. Proglottids dorso—ventrally flattened, usually bearing the uterine pore and genital apertures medially on the ventral surface. Each egg hatches in water to release a ciliated coracidium larva containing a hexacanth. Indirect life cycles including procercoid and plerocercoid larvae. e.g. *Spirometra, Diphyllobothrium.*

Order 2: Cyclophyllidea. Scolex typically with four large suckers surmounted with a muscular rostellum normally armed with hooks. Gut-dwelling parasites of amphibians, reptiles, birds and mammals including man. Eggs contain non-ciliated hexacanth larvae. Genital apertures marginal on proglottids. Posterior gravid proglottids often shed containing eggs. Indirect life cycles include a variety of nonproliferative and proliferative larval forms in vertebrate and invertebrate intermediate hosts.

Family (i) Taeniidae. Adults in the gut of mammals and birds. Scolex with permanently everted rostellum typically bearing two whorls of hooks. Larval form in vertebrate intermediate host a nonproliferative cysticercus or a proliferative coenurus or hydatid cyst. e.g. *Taenia, Echinococcus.*

Family (ii) Hymenolepidae. Adults in the gut of mammals and birds. Scolex with retractible rostellum normally bearing hooks. Larval forms (usually a cysticercoid) in invertebrates (typically insects). e.g. *Hymenolepis.*

Family (iii) Anoplocephalidae. Adults in the gut of mammals, birds and reptiles. Scolex with no rostellum. Eggs usually possess a pair of crossed horn-like projections (pyriform apparatus) on one egg envelope. Oribatid mites are the typical intermediate hosts, containing a cysticercoid. e.g. *Bertiella, Moniezia.*

Family (iv) Dilepidiidae. Adults in the gut of mammals, birds and reptiles. Scolex large with one to eight rows of thorn-shaped hooks. Larval stage a cysticercoid in an insect. e.g. *Dipylidium.*

Family (v) Davaineidae. Adults in the gut of mammals or birds. Scolex with minute spines on both rostellum and sucker margins. Larval stage a cysticercoid in insects or molluscs. e.g. *Raillietina, Davainea.*

Family (vi) Mesocestoididae. Adults in the gut of mammals or birds. Scolex with no rostellum. 3-host life cycles common. e.g. *Mesocestoides.*

Table 2.4. Human cestodiasis.

Parasite[*]	Disease	Adult (A) or larval (L)	Location of worms in man	Geographical distribution	Typical pathology
Pseudophyllideans *Diphyllobothrium latum*	Diphyllobothriasis	A	Lumen of small intestine	Finland, Central Europe, Italy, France, Ireland, Japan, Siberia, Argentina, Great Lakes area of USA and Canada	Very rarely pernicious megaloblastic anaemia
Spirometra spp.	Sparganosis	L	A variety of deep tissues	Tropical and subtropical regions of Africa, N. and S. America, Europe, Far East and Australasia	Mild, various
Cyclophyllideans *Taenia saginata*	Beef tapeworm infection	A	Lumen of small intestine	Cosmopolitan	Very infrequently gut obstruction or perforation
Taenia solium	Pork tapeworm infection	A	Lumen of small intestine	Cosmopolitan	Very infrequently gut obstruction or perforation; risk of cysticercosis
Taenia solium	Cysticercosis	L	A variety of deep tissues including the brain	Cosmopolitan, but particularly in S. and Central America, USSR, India and S. and E. Africa	A range of brain pathologies are produced by larvae in the CNS, including epilepsiform attacks
Hymenolepis nana	Dwarf tapeworm infection	A	Lumen of small intestine	Cosmopolitan especially in children	Usually none; diarrhoea and abdominal pain in heavy infections
Echinococcus granulosus	Echinococcosis: hydatid disease	L	A variety of deep tissue sites with liver and lungs predominating	Most sheep and cattle farming areas of the world	Various; depending on the sites of the hydatid cysts

[*]A number of other cestodes occasionally infect man, namely *Bertiella studeri*, *Dipylidium caninum* and *Hymenolepis diminuta* (adult cestodiasis); *Echinococcus multilocularis*, *Mesocestoides* spp. and *Multiceps* spp. (larval cestodiasis).

worms in the alimentary tract of man, and larval cestodiasis in which larval cestodes in a variety of tissue sites are the origin of disease symptoms. Table 2.4 lists the well- recognized examples of human cestodiasis and Fig. 2.6 describes the life cycle organization of *Diphyllobothrium latum* and *Taenia saginata*.

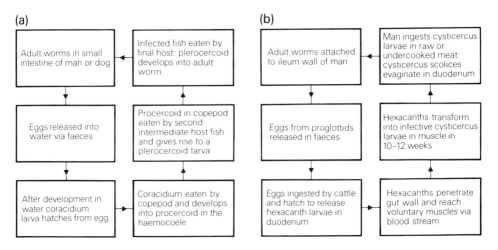

Fig. 2.6. Outline life cycles of cestodes. (a) A pseudophyllidean, *Diphyllobothrium latum*. (b) A cyclophyllidean, *Taenia saginata*.

(a)   *Larval cestodiasis in man*

There are three main types of larval cestodiasis in man: sparganosis caused by pleroceroids of diphyllobothriid cestodes in the genus *Spirometra*, cysticercosis caused by cysticercus stage larvae of *Taenia solium*, and hydatid disease caused by the proliferative hydatid cyst larvae of *Echinococcus granulosus*. In none of these examples is man an extensively used intermediate host, and his infection can contribute little or nothing to the reproductive success of the parasites as he is so very rarely consumed by the relevant final hosts in the life cycles.

A variety of carnivores are the normal final hosts for sparganosis-producing *Spirometra* species. Eggs in the faeces of these hosts hatch to produce coracidia which develop into procercoids within copepods in small bodies of fresh water. The crustaceans are eaten by a variety of amphibians, reptiles and mammals, in which plerocercoids develop. Spargana are wandering plerocercoids in human tissues. Persons become infected either by ingesting copepods containing pro-cercoids inadvertently or by the utilization of a folk remedy in Thailand and Vietnam used for ulcers and sores, in which uncooked frog flesh is applied to the troubled area: if the frog contains plerocercoids they can migrate into the patient's tissues through the pre-existing lesion. The spargana wander in deep tissues and are eventually encased in a fibrous capsule.

Adult worms of the pork tapeworm *Taenia solium* inhabit the human intestine while the larval stages normally develop in pig muscles. Human cysticercosis occurs when man ingests the eggs of this tapeworm and cysticercus larvae, each about 10 mm long, subsequently become lodged in a variety of tissues. Symptoms are particularly severe if the larvae are present and then die in the human central nervous system. The most common mode of human infection is likely to be the human faecal contamination of food, but it is possible that direct autoinfection can occur in patients harbouring adult worms, if segments which contain mature eggs are regurgitated from the small intestine into the stomach so that egg activation can commence.

Echinococcosis or hydatid disease is rarely highly prevalent in human populations. Nonetheless, it must be considered as one of the most damaging cestodiases because neither surgery nor chemotherapy can produce an effective cure in many cases. It is a complex disease from the point of view of parasite taxonomy. Most human infections with the endogenously budding hydatid larvae are due to one of several strains of *Echinococcus granulosus* with its discrete spherical cysts. Man can act as an accidental intermediate host for *E. granulosus* in its domestic cycle— where it is transmitted between dogs as final hosts and sheep or cattle as normal intermediate hosts—and can become infected by contact with the feral cycle of this species between wild carnivores and herbivores. Less frequently, man becomes infected by strains of *E. multilocularis* whose irregularly expanding cysts are intensely pathogenic. *E. multilocularis* is always feral, with foxes acting as final hosts and rodents as intermediate hosts. In all instances human infection occurs because of contact with faecally contaminated material from infected canine hosts, be they dogs or foxes. The highest community prevalences of hydatid disease around the world are always in cattle or sheep herding populations with high levels of contact between dogs and man.

(b)   Adult cestodiasis in man

The common adult cestodiases of man are far less potentially pathogenic than either cysticercosis or hydatid disease. Adult cestodes at low densities in the human gut often cause no symptoms. Only rarely when parasite densities are high do problems due to gut wall damage or intestinal obstruction occur. The only other serious consequences of adult cestodiasis, in otherwise healthy persons, are the increased personal risk of cysticercosis in carriers of adult *T. solium* (25% of patients with proven cysticercosis are likely to have adult worms in their small intestine), and the geographically restricted risk of pernicious anaemia in some carriers of *Diphyllobothrium latum*.

Only four adult cestodiases are at all common in man, namely those caused by *D. latum*, *Taenia saginata*, *T. solium* and *Hymenolepis nana*.

Diphyllobothrium latum (Figs. 2.3, 2.4 and 2.6) is the only adult pseudo-phyllidean tapeworm which commonly infects man. Transmission is due to human consumption of raw, undercooked or lightly smoked fish containing viable plerocercoids. These fish may be second intermediate hosts, such as perch, which have acquired an infection by ingesting infected copepods, or they may be larger carnivorous fish further up the food chain such as pike. These accumulate plero-cercoids from their predation of smaller fish. Plerocercoids in the ingested fish are activated in the pike gut, can penetrate it and persist in the peritoneal cavity or other tissues. Dogs can act as final hosts as well as man.

The pernicious megaloblastic anaemia caused by *D. latum* infections appears to be confined to a proportion of patients in Finland or of Finnish ancestry. It is caused by the avid competitive uptake of vitamin B_{12} by the worms which restricts the amount of dietary B_{12} available for the human host.

Taenia saginata (Figs. 2.3, 2.4 and 2.6), the beef tapeworm of man, can some-times reach 20 m in length but 5 m is more common. It has a cosmopolitan distri-bution generated by the practice of eating raw or undercooked beef. In this way cysticercus larvae (about 8 mm in length) in the voluntary muscles of an infected cow are ingested in a viable condition: the unhooked scolex of the larvae everts in the duodenum and attachment and subsequent growth occurs in the ileum. It is possible that over 60 million cases exist worldwide and there is no doubt that beef tapeworm infections in man are much more common than those caused by the closely related pork tapeworm *T. solium*.

Taenia solium is very similar in morphology and life-cycle characteristics to *T. saginata*. It differs mainly in having a hooked rather than an unarmed adult scolex and fewer lateral branches in the gravid proglottid uterus. Human consumption of undercooked or raw pork is the route of infection. Thorough cooking or prolonged deep freeze storage at $-10°C$ or below kills the cysticercus larvae. Infections with adult worms of *T. solium* cause remarkably few pathological abnormalities and most cases only become apparent when shed proglottids are seen in the patients' faeces. The serious objective risk of a human adult *T. solium* infection is the enhanced likelihood of cysticercosis.

Hymenolepis nana is the smallest adult cestode to infect man, being only 15–40 mm in length. It can occur at high densities in an infected person's small intestine, however, with populations of several thousand worms being regularly noted. Children and young adults are particularly at risk especially those in institutions. Low density infections induce few or no symptoms, but at higher parasite levels of more than 2000 worms, vomiting, diarrhoea, loss of appetite and abdominal pain, have been recorded. Transmission of the parasite is mainly by a method which is extremely unusual among cestodes, that is ingestion of eggs which complete larval then adult development in the same human host. This is the direct life-cycle mode of *H. nana*. Ingested eggs hatch in the small intestine to release hexacanth larvae, which invade gut villi. In this internal location they develop into tailless cysticercoid larvae in 90 hours, and subsequently re-enter the ileal lumen to produce adult worms that are releasing eggs 30 days after the ingestion of the infective eggs. A very small proportion of human infections probably stem from the alternative, more orthodox life-cycle mode of *H. nana*. In this, eggs are eaten by insects in which the hexacanths develop into cysticercoids. Infected insects, if consumed accidentally by man or in a predatory manner by small mammals, can initiate an adult cestode infection.

2.4.3   Other cestodes

A number of other eucestode species can be considered of importance despite the fact that they are not normally parasites of man. Their significance stems either from their use as laboratory models for studies on tapeworm physiology, development, biochemistry or chemotherapy, or from the parasites' utilization of domesticated animals as hosts. The main characteristics of some of these species are outlined in Table 2.5.

2.4.4   Digenean parasites

Adult digeneans are flattened or cylindrical, ovoid-to-elongate helminths, that in man and his domesticated animals always inhabit endoparasitic locations. The vast majority of species live in the gut or its developmental offshoots such as the bile duct or lungs. Externally, the adult worm is characterized by an oral sucker around the anterior mouth and often an additional ventral sucker or acetabulum. The former sucker is important in feeding activity and both are involved in attachment to host surfaces and locomotion. The outer surface is a living syncytial tegument, the distal cytoplasm of which often contains spines. The internal organization of a typical hermaphroditic digenean (only schistosomes are dioecious) is described in Fig. 2.7. A basic taxonomy of digeneans is outlined in Table 2.6, with special emphasis on those groups that contain species infecting man.

The life cycle of the great majority of digeneans displays a remarkable and highly characteristic alternation of asexual and sexual reproductive phases, in molluscan and vertebrate hosts respectively. The basic life-cycle patterns employed by digeneans and examples of their larval stages are displayed diagrammatically in Fig. 2.8. Hermaphroditic adults which normally cross-inseminate utilize sexual reproduction in the final host, and tanned eggs are produced. These leave the host in faeces, urine or sputum, and the zygote within the egg develops or has already developed by this stage into a ciliated larva—the miracidium. In all life cycles utilizing man or domesticated animals the miracidium then infects a gastropod

Table 2.5. Other cestodes.

Name	Final hosts	Intermediate hosts	Comments
Pseudophyllidea			
Diphyllobothrium dendriticum	Gulls (rat in laboratory)	Copepod then teleost	Useful laboratory model for *D. latum*
Schistocephalus solidus	Fish-eating birds and mammals (rat and hamster in laboratory)	Copepod then *Gasterosteus*	Progenetic plerocercoids in sticklebacks. Useful laboratory model
Ligula intestinalis	Fish-eating birds	Copepod then cyprinid fish	Progenetic plerocercoid in cyprinids. Useful laboratory model
Cyclophyllidea (a) Taeniidae			
Taenia crassiceps	Fox	Small mammals	Exogenously budding metacestode larvae in the peritoneal cavity and other tissue spaces of intermediate hosts. Can be maintained by syringe passage of larvae in mice and rats in the laboratory
T. taeniaeformis	Cat, stoat, lynx, fox	Mice, rats, etc.	Larval form in the intermediate host is a strobilocercus in the liver. Useful laboratory model
T. pisiformis	Dog, etc.	Rabbits	Larval forms in the intermediate host are liver-, then peritoneal cavity-inhabiting cysticerci. Useful laboratory model
T. ovis	Dog	Sheep	Larvae develop in sheep muscles. Economic importance in the meat industry

Multiceps multiceps	Dog, coyote, fox, jackel	Sheep, goats, cattle, horses, (occasionally man)	Larval form a budding coenurus developing in brain and spinal cord of sheep causing a disease called gid or staggers. Very dangerous larval cestodiasis in man
(b) Hymenolepidae *Hymenolepis diminuta*	Rats, mice hamsters (occasionally man)	Many insects including fleas and beetles (*Tenebrio* and *Tribolium* in laboratory)	The most commonly used laboratory model cestode. Life cycle easily maintained experimentally
(c) Dilepididae *Dipylidium caninum*	Dogs, cats (occasionally man)	Fleas	Causes an uncommon and nonpathogenic human adult cestodiasis especially in children. Infections caused by ingesting infected fleas from pets
(d) Anoplocephalidae *Moniezia expansa* and *M. benedini*	Sheep, cattle	Soil inhabiting mites	Causes a common adult cestodiasis of low pathogenicity in sheep
(e) Davaineidae *Raillietina cesticillus*	Chickens	Many arthropod species, especially beetles	Causes a common adult cestodiasis in chickens
Davainea proglottina	Chickens	Slugs	Causes a reasonably pathogenic adult cestodiasis in chickens

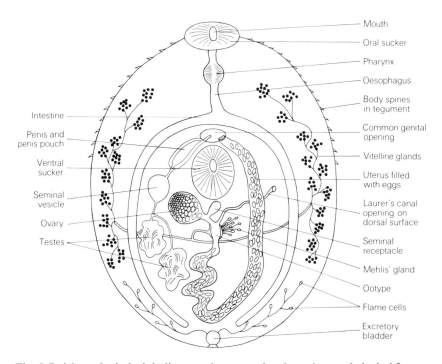

Fig. 2.7. A hypothetical adult digenean demonstrating the main morphological features.

mollusc (in other cycles lamellibranchs or scaphopods are occasionally utilized). Infection is either by direct penetration of the snail by a free-swimming, hatched miracidium or the ingestion of the digenean egg by a snail. In the latter case the miracidium hatches in the alimentary tract of the mollusc and penetrates its tissues internally. Within the snail the miracidium transforms into a sporocyst which is a tegument-covered, gutless germinal sac, containing germinal cells. The latter can develop (in different species) into either a second generation of sporocysts or a new larval type with a rhabdocoele-like gut—the rediae. These larvae then migrate to the snail's digestive gland. Here they carry out further asexual reproduction by the multiplication of the germinal cells within them. Rediae can often produce further generations of rediae but eventually rediae or daughter sporocysts begin, again asexually, to produce cercariae, which are the larval stages that can leave the molluscan host. A cercaria is a tailed larval form, the head of which will develop into an adult worm and often possesses partially developed reproductive organs. Cercariae leave the snail intermediate host, often with a marked circadian rhythm, and they, or metacercariae which develop from them, infect the final host.

The sequence of asexually reproducing larval digeneans in the mollusc often produces extremely high overall reproductive rates. Ultimately many tens or

Table 2.6. An outline classification of digeneans (several families excluded).

Class: Digenea

Superorder 1: Anepitheliocystida. In the cercaria the bladder wall of the excretory system is the retained wall of the primitive bladder formed from the fusion of the two main lateral excretory canals.

Order 1: Strigeatida. Cercariae fork-tailed.

Family (i) Bucephalidae (e.g. *Bucephalus*)

Family (ii) Strigeidae (e.g. *Alaria*, *Cotylurus*)

Family (iii) Schistosomatidae. The schistosomes: adults parasitic in the blood vessels of birds and mammals. Dioecious with males and females occurring in *in-copulo* pairs with the female held in the gynaecophoric canal of the male (e.g. *Schistosoma*).

Order 2: Echinostomida. Cercariae with cyst-producing gland cells. Encystation of cercariae occurs on vegetation or in molluscs.

Family (i) Echinostomatidae. The echinostomes: adults parasitic in the intestine, bile ducts or ureters of reptiles, birds and mammals. Elongate forms with a raised collar behind the oral sucker carrying large backwards pointing spines. (e.g. *Echinostoma*).

Family (ii) Fasciolidae. Large, flattened, spinose leaf-shaped worms of mammals (commonly herbivores). (e.g. *Fasciola*, *Fasciolopsis*).

Family (iii) Paramphistomatidae. The amphistomes: gut parasites of mammals (commonly herbivores). Large, thick-bodied digeneans with an anterior oral sucker and a ventral sucker at the extreme posterior end of the worms. (e.g. *Paramphistomum*, *Gastrodiscoides*).

Superorder 2: Epitheliocystida. In the cercaria the bladder wall of the excretory system has a thick epithelial organization with mesodermal origins which replaces the original primitive bladder.

Order 1: Plagiorchiida. Operculate eggs. Oral stylet usually present in oral sucker of cercaria.

Family (i) Plagiorchiidae. Small flukes, mainly parasites of amphibians and birds, occasionally of fish, reptiles and mammals. Genital opening between well spaced oral and ventral suckers, tandem testes behind ovary. Y-shaped excretory bladder. Cercariae encyst in arthropods and possess oral stylet. (e.g. *Plagiorchis*).

Family (ii) Dicrocoeliidae. Small flukes found in the intestine, liver, gall bladder and pancreas of most vertebrate groups. Oral sucker subterminal, vitelline glands do not extend in front of ventral sucker. Cercariae encyst in arthropods and possess oral stylet. (e.g. *Dicrocoelium*).

Family (iii) Troglotrematidae. Flukes of birds and mammals, often in lungs or intestine but also in nasal cavities, frontal sinuses and subcutaneous tissues. Vitelline glands compact. Cercariae encyst in arthropods and possess oral stylet. (e.g. *Paragonimus*).

Order 2: Opisthorchiida. Operculate eggs. Cercariae have no oral stylet.

Family (i) Opisthorchiidae. Medium-sized flukes of the gall bladder and bile duct in mammals, birds and reptiles. Weakly developed suckers. (e.g. *Opisthorchis*).

Family (ii) Heterophyidae. Small or minute flukes found in a variety of sites in mammals and birds. Genital sucker, closely associated with the ventral sucker (gonotyl) often present. (e.g. *Heterophyes*, *Metagonimus*).

(a)

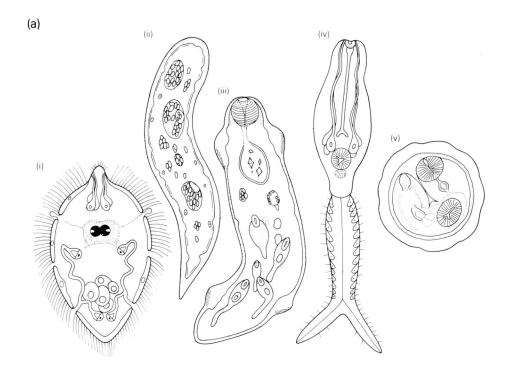

(b)

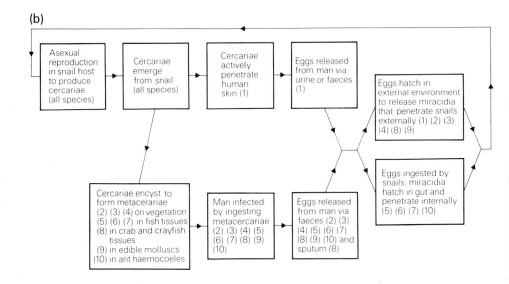

hundreds of thousands of cercariae may develop from a single miracidium. The nutritional cost to the snail host of this intense parasitic reproductive rate can be high. Infected molluscs usually grow more slowly, have a higher death rate and lower reproductive rate, than uninfected snails of the same species. Digeneans typically demonstrate a greater host specificity with respect to their first intermediate hosts than they do to any subsequent hosts in the life cycle.

The majority of digenean life cycles involve metacercariae. These are cercariae that have shed their propulsive tails and have encysted either on external objects like snail shells or vegetation, or within second intermediate host species—vertebrate or invertebrate. Within these cysts, produced by cystogenous glands in the cercarial head, the cercaria carries out a partial development towards somatic and reproductive maturity. The remainder of this development is completed when the cyst is consumed by a final host. Only in a few digeneans is the free-swimming cercaria directly infective to the final host, by an active penetrative process that eliminates the need for a metacercarial phase. This process has, however, great epidemiological significance as it is that employed by schistosomes.

Of the 6000 or so known species of digeneans only about a dozen are regular and important parasites of man. Many more species, however, are spasmodically diagnosed as accidental human infections. The main non-schistosome digeneans of man are listed in Table 2.7 along with some of their basic biological characterstics. Schistosomes, however, must be considered the most important human digeneans with a global total of over 200 million cases, a significant proportion of which will demonstrate moderate-to-severe levels of morbidity.

Fig. 2.8. (a) Diagrammatic representation of digenean larval stages. The larvae illustrated are completely schematic and do not represent an actual developmental sequence. (i) Miracidium: with tiers of epithelial ciliated cells, anterior gland cells, central 'eye spot' consisting of two pigment cup ocelli overlying a nervous cerebral ganglion, flame cells and posteriorly positioned germinal cells. (ii) Sporocyst: a sac shaped larval stage with no gut and a central cavity containing clusters of dividing germinal cells. (iii) Redia: with a large oral sucker and a simple gut, muscular processes in the body wall and a central cavity containing developing larval stages. (iv) Cercaria: a larva with a muscular propulsive tail and a head with gut, oral and ventral suckers and often penetration glands and cystogeneous glands. (v) Metacercaria: a transformed cercarial head surrounded by a secreted cyst wall. The cercarial head usually shows some development of somatic and reproductive characteristics towards the adult state.

(b) Diagrammatic flow-chart of the basic organization of the life cycles of medically important digeneans that infect man. Species identities: 1: *Schistosoma*; 2: *Fasciolopsis*; 3: *Fasciola*; 4: *Gastrodiscoides*; 5: *Opisthorchis*; 6: *Heterophyes*; 7: *Metagonimus*; 8: *Paragonimus*; 9: *Echinostoma*; 10: *Dicrocoelium*.

Table 2.7. Some features of non-schistosome digenean diseases of man.

Name*	Site of adult worms in man	Route of egg emergence	Snail (first intermediate) host and mode of snail infection	Mode of human infection	Geographical distribution
Fasciolopsis buski	Small intestinal mucosa, rarely in stomach or colon	Faeces	*Segmentina* (external miracidial invasion)	Metacercarial cysts on water plants, such as water caltrop and water chestnut: eaten	China, Taiwan, India, Thailand, Laos, Kampuchea and Bangladesh
Heterophyes heterophyes	In crypts of jejunum and upper ileum	Faeces	*Pirenella* and *Cerithidia* (egg ingestion)	Metacercarial cysts in fish, such as mullet and *Tilapia*: eaten	Egypt, Israel, Romania, Greece, Japan, China, Taiwan, Philippines
Metagonimus yokogawaii	Muscosal folds of jejunum	Faeces	*Semisulcospira* (egg ingestion)	Matacercarial cysts in fish, such as carp and trout: eaten	Japan, Korea, China, Taiwan, Siberia
Gastrodiscoides hominis	Mucosal lining of caecum and ascending colon	Faeces	*Helicorbis* (external miracidial invasion)	Probably by ingestion of metacercarial cysts on water plants such as water caltrop	India, Bangladesh, Vietnam, Philippines
Opisthorchis sinensis	Bile duct	Faeces	*Bulinus, Parafossarulus, Alocima* (egg ingestion)	Metacercarial cysts in fresh water fish: eaten. Juvenile flukes migrate directly up bile duct from gut	China, Taiwan, Korea, Japan, Vietnam
Fasciola hepatica	Bile duct	Faeces	*Lymnaea* (external miracidial invasion)	Metacercarial cysts on watercress or lettuce: eaten. Juvenile flukes penetrate gut wall then liver from the perivisceral cavity	Central and S. America, Cuba, France, UK, North Africa
Paragonimus westermani	In cysts in lungs, rarely in a variety of extra-pulmonary sites	Sputum and faeces	*Semisulcospira, Thiara* and *Oncomelania* (external miracidial invasion)	Metacercarial cysts in fresh water crabs and crayfish: eaten	China, Taiwan, Korea, Japan, Philippines, India, Malaysia, Indonesia

*Several additional species of *Opisthorchis* and *Paragonimus* as well as a number of echinostome species have also been recorded from man.

2.4.5   Human schistosomiasis

Schistosomes are bizarre digeneans. Many aspects of their morphology, physiology and life-cycle tactics are unorthodox or unique in the context of the other members of the taxon. Adult worms live in the lumina of blood vessels and feed directly on the cellular and plasma fractions of the blood. As an adaptation for this unusual microhabitat the worms are threadlike in shape, 10–30 mm in length but only 0.2–1.0 mm in width. The worms are dioecious and display considerable sexual dimorphism (Fig. 2.9). Cylindrical, elongate females live permanently held in an extensive ventral groove, the gynaecophoric canal, of the shorter but more massive males. In most schistosomes, although males can produce motile sperm in unisexual infections, female sexual maturity only follows pairing with a male worm. In unisexual female infections the vitelline glands and ovary do not usually mature or become functional.

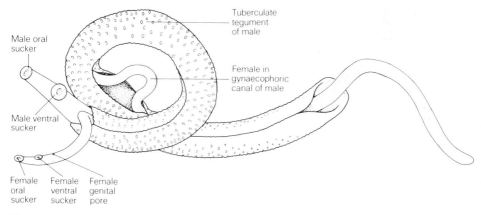

Fig. 2.9. *In copulo* pair of adult schistosomes (based on *S. mansoni*).

Living as they do in a host location in which immunological defences might be expected to be both rapidly engendered and effective, adult schistosomes possess their own adaptations which enable them partially to counter these defences (see section 6.7). Adult schistosomes are thus able to live and reproduce for many years in a host which is relatively resistant to new infections.

Pairs of adult worms produce eggs which are laid into the lumina of the venules in which they live. There is obviously no direct, nonpathological route by which these eggs can escape from this location in the host to continue the parasitic life cycle. In fact, most schistosome eggs possess a single sharp spine which helps to provide a means of escape. Eggs are laid so that the spines tend to lodge in the intima of the venule and impede the process of egg removal by blood flow. Some small blood vessels packed with such eggs rupture, providing the eggs with a pathologically generated route into connective tissue. A proportion of these eggs eventually reach the outside world via the lumen of the gut or bladder. This necessarily unusual exit route for schistosome eggs is at the heart of their considerable pathogenicity. Very many eggs remain lodged in the tissues all over the body during their difficult translocation to the exterior. In these locations, at first living, and later moribund and dead, eggs become immobilized in spherical granulomatous lesions which lead to a generalized fibrosis. It is these progressively accumulating lesions in many different organs which give rise to most chronic schistosome-induced pathology.

All human digenean infections other than schistosomiasis are initiated when man eats metacercarial cysts. Schistosome transmission to man is quite different. Furcocercariae emerging from aquatic and amphibious snails survive on average for about a day at 20°C, swimming tail first through the water. During this brief, free-living and non-feeding existence fuelled by endogenous glycogen reserves, they are directly infective to people entering the water in which they are swimming. Aided by small backward-pointing anterior spines and cytolytic secretions the cercaria rapidly

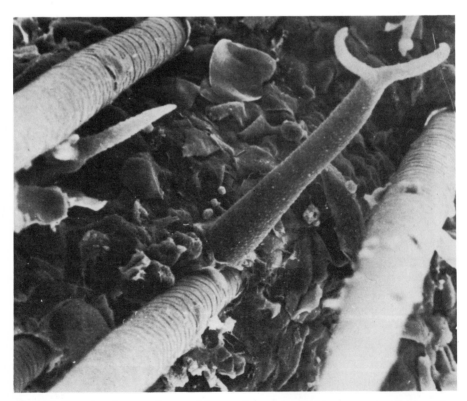

Fig. 2.10. Scanning electronmicrograph image of a cercaria of *Schistosoma mansoni* penetrating the skin of a mouse down the side of a hair shaft. The head of the cercaria has already disappeared beneath the keratinized skin epithelial cells, leaving only the forked tail visible. (Supplied by Dr. H.D. Blankespoor, Museum of Zoology, University of Michigan, USA).

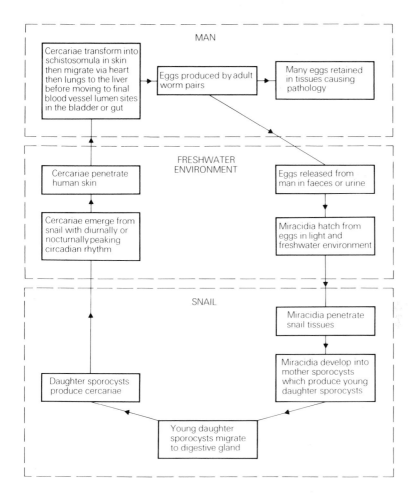

Fig. 2.11. Diagrammatic flow-chart of the main features of the life cycles of human schistosomes.

penetrates human skin, often down the side of a hair shaft and sheds its tail in the process (Fig. 2.10). The remaining cercarial head can now be considered as an immature schistosome or schistosomulum. It quickly transforms its tegument from a glycocalyx-covered cercarial conformation to a multilaminate adult one. Simultaneously it alters physiologically from a low osmotic pressure-tolerant state to a condition in which it can tolerate mammalian body-fluid osmotic pressures.

Schistosomula enter the peripheral lymphatic vessels or venules and are carried eventually to the lungs, usually within a week of initial penetration. From the lungs the larvae migrate to the liver where they mature and pair up. Pairs of worms then move to their final egg-producing sites. The life cycle of a generalized human schistosome including the molluscan stages is illustrated in Fig. 2.11.

Table 2.8. Some features of human schistosomes.

Name	Site in man	Route of egg emergence	Morphology of mature egg
Schistosoma mansoni	Mesenteric veins	Faeces	
Schistosoma haematobium	Vesical veins of the bladder	Urine	
Schistosoma japonicum	Mesenteric veins	Faeces	
Schistosoma intercalatum	Mesenteric veins	Faeces	

Intermediate hosts	Geographical distribution	Reservoir hosts
Biomphalaria spp.	Egypt, Middle East, W., Central and S.E. Africa, Malagasy, Brazil, Venezuela and some Caribbean islands	Probably not important except in S. America where some rodents are infected
Bulinus spp.	Africa, Malagasy and Middle East	No important reservoir hosts
Oncomelania spp.	China, Philippines, Japan, Vietnam, Thailand, Laos and Kampuchea	Important throughout range: dogs, rats, pigs, cattle, etc.
Bulinus spp.	Limited distribution in Zaire, Central African Republic, Cameroon and Gabon	No important reservoir hosts

Four species of the genus *Schistosoma* are important parasites of man around the world. Of these *S. mansoni*, *S. haematobium* and *S. japonicum* have widespread distribution, whereas *S. intercalatum* is restricted to rather specific foci of infection in parts of Africa. Some basic facts concerning these species are assembled in Table 2.8.

(a)   Schistosoma mansoni

This is the classic mesenteric vein-inhabiting human schistosome with lateral spined eggs (see Table 2.8) which leave an infected person via the faeces. It has proved the most adaptable human schistosome in terms of its spread from a presumed entirely African initial distribution to its present much more extensive one. *S. mansoni* infections are now present in much of the Middle East, Egypt, Libya, and large tracts of West, Central and South Eastern Africa, including Malagasy. In the New World the disease is found in Brazil, Surinam, Venezuela and some Caribbean islands.

The pathological effects of *S. mansoni* schistosomiasis are slowly progressive and complex with, ultimately, several separate organ systems being involved. During the cercarial invasive stage there may be a transient dermatitis or 'swimmers' itch'. Thereafter most pathology is the direct or indirect result of the host's immunological responses to schistosome eggs (see section 6.8). In light infections egg-induced damage may be subclinical in extent. In heavier infections, however, eggs lodged in the mucosa and submucosa of the gut cause granulomatous reactions which can extend into the gut lumen as pseudopapillomas, with or without egg calcification. Low order changes of this sort produce few problems but when more extensive they can cause colonic obstruction and blood loss. Many eggs are carried by blood flow from the hepatic portal system to the liver. Eggs which become trapped there set up a complex series of cellular responses around them. General damage to the liver induced in this way produces liver enlargement (hepatomegaly) and following portal hypertension, splenomegaly also occurs. Damage to the portal circulation causes collateral circulatory shunts to be set up and these enable circulating eggs to bypass the filtering function of the liver. Consequently, eggs begin to lodge in the lungs in large numbers resulting in degenerative pulmonary blood vessel changes, which in turn bring about cardiac pathology.

Different snail hosts in the genus *Biomphalaria* are utilized by the parasite in different parts of its global distribution. Almost all of them, however, are fully aquatic snails which usually live in slowly running freshwater such as is found in streams, ditches, irrigation canals and some lakes. There is a circadian rhythm of cercarial emergence from the snails, most being released in the middle of the day.

S. mansoni schistosomiasis is, like the other types, a rural disease. Contact with infective mud or water comes about by children playing in water, water gathering or washing in water systems, or, very importantly, in the course of work. Agricultural practices which involve contact with irrigation water are especially hazardous as are some fishing methods. One reason for the increasing prevalence of all rural schistosomiases is the increasing construction of dams for hydroelectric or irrigation purposes in many developing countries. Such schemes inevitably produce new water bodies for snail colonization.

(b)   Schistosoma intercalatum

Utilizing bulinid host snails, *S. intercalatum* is a schistosome with terminal spined eggs (see Table 2.8) that has a very restricted distribution in some parts of Central and West Africa. *Bulinus forskalii*, the host used in Cameroon and *B. africanus* utilized in Zaire are typically inhabitants of the non-moving waters of pools and lakes and these are the usual infection sites for man. As a mesenteric vein-inhabiting schistosome, *S. intercalatum* is associated with a pattern of pathology similar to that caused by *S. mansoni*, but less severe.

(c)   Schistosoma japonicum

The third mesenteric vein-inhabiting schistosome species in man, *S. japonicum*, has a distribution which is allopatric with respect to those of *S. mansoni* and *S. intercalatum*. It is restricted to the Far East. Eggs of this parasite are effectively unspined (see Table 2.8) and are considerably smaller than those of other human schistosomes. The symptomatology of *S. japonicum* schistosomiasis is similar to that of the other two gut-associated species except that colonic pathology generated by the presence of calcified eggs is often more severe.

An important manner in which *S. japonicum* schistosomiasis differs from all other human schistosome diseases is in its zoonotic aspects, being mainly adapted for transmission to a range of nocturnally active small mammals. Over much of its range a number of wild and domesticated animals function as important reservoir hosts for this human disease. Rats, dogs, buffaloes, pigs, goats and cattle may be infected and this makes control of this disease an even more complex task than it is for the other schistosomiases.

The amphibious habits of the snail hosts of this schistosome mean that the transmission sites for *S. japonicum* are different from the aquatic risk areas for the other schistosomes. *S. japonicum* cercariae are active in the water film above, and the water pockets in, the mud of rice paddies and the edges of water courses.

Schistosoma mekongi is a recently recognized species, the eggs of which resemble *S. mansoni*. It occurs in the mesenteric veins of man and eggs are passed in the faeces. The distribution is limited to the Mekong River. The snail host is *Tricula (Lithoglyphopsis) aperta* and the reservoir host is the dog.

(d)   Schistosoma haematobium

This schistosome infects man over much of Africa, Malagasy and parts of the Middle East. The *Bulinus africanus* group snails are the important hosts in Southern and Eastern Africa while the *truncatus* group are utilized in Egypt and Iran. The disease symptoms differ from those associated with other schistosomes mainly because of the location of the adult worms in the vesical veins of the bladder. Eggs are deposited in the walls of the bladder and ureters. Granulatomous reactions, and later fibrosis and calcification, induce a wide range of pathological manifestations including haematuria and dysuria, hyperplasia of the bladder lining, partial ureteric blockage, and secondary damage to the kidneys.

2.4.6   Other human digeneans

The non-schistosome digenean infections of man enumerated in Table 2.7 constitute a morphologically varied assemblage of helminths with very different distribution patterns around the world. In other ways, however, this group of human parasites is remarkably homogeneous. All seven major species are transmitted to man when eaten as metacercarial cysts either attached to plants *(Fasciolopsis buski, Gastrodiscoides hominis* and *Fasciola hepatica)*, within fish *(Heterophyes heterophyes, Metagonimus yokogawaii* and *Opisthorchis sinensis)* or in freshwater crustaceans *(Paragonimus westermani)*. In all cases, eggs produced by the adult worms leave the human host in the faeces. Those of *P. westermani* are also found in the sputum as the worms live in the lungs. Adults of the remaining six species inhabit locations in or closely associated with the human gut.

Only in rare cases of high worm densities in individual patients is severe pathology present. Infections with *Opisthorchis* and *Paragonimus* are those most likely to cause serious problems of this sort. At more usual levels of infection symptoms are often unpleasant but rarely life-threatening.

2.4.7   Other digeneans

Fasciola hepatica, the liver fluke, is primarily a parasite of sheep and cattle but it can also infect man. There is, of course, a wide range of digenean infections of domesticated animals that never, or only extremely rarely, cause human disease.

Among the liver and bile duct inhabiting forms are *Fasciola gigantica*, living in a variety of domesticated and feral ruminants in Africa and the Far East; *Fascioloides magna* that infects deer, horses, cattle and sheep in North America; and *Dicrocoelium dendriticum*, infecting sheep and other herbivores particularly in Europe and Asia. In the first two species metacercarial cysts on vegetation are responsible for transmission. *D. dendriticum*, in contrast, utilizes ants as second intermediate hosts and the ruminants become infected by consuming infected ants along with vegetation. Other important digenean parasites of domesticated ruminants include the paramphistomes usually in the genus *Paramiphistomum* which can cause considerable loss of condition in cattle.

Other schistosomes also warrant some attention. *Schistosomatium douthitti,* a schistosome of rodents, has been extensively utilized as an easily maintained laboratory analogue of the human schistosomes. Many animal schistosomes have been proved to be the sources of schistosome cercariae that cause 'swimmers' itch' when they penetrate human skin. These may be bird schistosomes such as *Trichobilharzia* spp. from ducks or *Gigantobilharzia* spp. in a variety of passerine birds, or mammal infecting genera such as *Schistosomatium* and *Schistosoma* itself.

In many of the warmer parts of the world cattle and sheep are severely damaged by a large number of schistosome species in the genus *Schistosoma*. *S. bovis* in Southern Europe, Africa and Asia, *S. mattheei* in Southern Africa and *S. spindale* in India and Africa all cause serious losses.

2.5   ACANTHOCEPHALAN PARASITES

Acanthocephalans, or spiny-headed worms, constitute a homogeneous phylum of highly specialized pseudocoelomates with some convergent similarities to cestodes. As dioecious adults all species inhabit the small intestines of vertebrates, attached to the gut lining by an eversible hooked proboscis (the hook patterns of which have considerable taxonomic significance). Nutrients from the lumen of the host gut are absorbed across the syncytial body wall of the parasites, the surface area of which is enormously expanded by an extensive array of tegumentary pore canals. After insemination by male worms, females produce large numbers of shelled eggs by the activities of many hundreds or thousands of separate ovaries (ovarian balls) which float either free in the pseudocoelome (in the palaeacanthocephalans) or in large chambers termed ligament sacs (in archiacanthocephalans).

Eggs pass out in the faeces and are ingested by the intermediate host which is almost invariably an insect or a crustacean. In the gut of this host a hooked acanthor larva hatches from the egg and penetrates the gut wall to enter the haemocoele. Here it transforms via an intermediate acanthella stage into a cystacanth, a resistant infective form which can reinfect the final host when the intermediate host is consumed as a prey item.

Only infrequent accidental infections of man with acanthocephalans have been recorded and the vast majority of instances involve one of two archiacanthocephalans (Fig. 2.12). The first, *Moniliformis dubius* (= *Moniliformis moniliformis?*) is a common acanthocephalan parasite of rats and other rodents. Cystacanths are found in cockroaches and a variety of beetles. The rare human infections in such locations as Russia, Italy, Sudan, Iran and the USA probably arise from human ingestion of infected grain beetles. The second species is a common pig acantho-cephalan, *Macracanthorhynchus hirudinaceus*, with a world wide distribution. The intermediate hosts in this case are soil-dwelling beetle larvae.

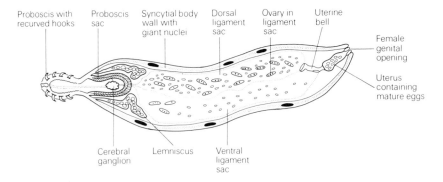

Fig. 2.12. Basic morphology of a hypothetical female archiacanthocephalan.

2.6   NEMATODE PARASITES

The nematodes are unquestionably the most successful group to have been produced by the evolutionary experiments that have taken place among the pseudocoelomic, eutelic Aschelminthes. The relative lack of interspecific morpho-logical variation among nematodes belies their ecological diversity and success. They are almost all unsegmented, spindle-shaped roundworms with bilateral symmetry (Fig. 2.13). Both free-living and parasitic species take this form and the vast majority have a highly conservative life cycle developmental sequence (Fig. 2.14). This begins when dioecious adults produce eggs that hatch to release L_1 larvae, which, with intervening cuticular moults and size increases, develop through three more larval phases (L_2, L_3 and L_4) before attaining full sexual maturity after a final post-L_4 moult.

The cuticle, which is repeatedly moulted and rearranged during this ontogenetic sequence is a central element in the structural organization of all nematodes. It is a multilayered secreted structure consisting of collagen and a number of other com-ponents such as hyaluronic acid, chondroitin sulphate and mucopolysaccharides, and covers the nematode body externally. A number of surface invaginations of the nematode body wall are also cuticle-lined. Hence, cuticle covers the inner surfaces of the buccal cavity, pharynx, excretory pore, vulva, chemosensory pits called amphids and phasmids, rectum, cloaca and spicule pouches. Stylets, teeth and cutting blades in the buccal cavity, and the copulatory spicules, are essentially cuticular structures. The cuticle of the general body surface often contains layers of aligned fibrous

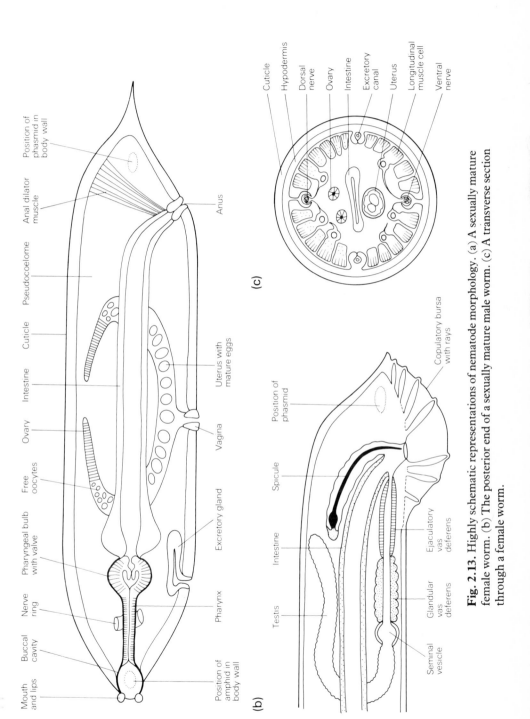

Fig. 2.13. Highly schematic representations of nematode morphology. (a) A sexually mature female worm. (b) The posterior end of a sexually mature male worm. (c) A transverse section through a female worm.

elements at angles to one other. These fibre systems interacting with the hydrostatic skeletal properties of the pseudocoelomic fluid allow locomotion by sinusoidal wave propagation and changes in body conformation in nematodes which all possess only longitudinal body musculature.

The body plan and behavioural repertoire of nematodes appear to have provided a considerable degree of preadaptation for endoparasitic modes of existence within this group. The chemically and physically resistant cuticle presumably enabled originally free-living nematodes to exist in the damaging conditions within vertebrate guts into which they could be accidentally transferred by host feeding activity. Similarly the substrate burrowing abilities of many nematodes coupled with their spindle-like shape must have meant that the penetration of host integuments and internal tissues was a distinct possibility.

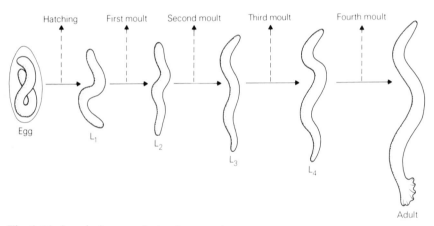

Fig. 2.14. A typical nematode developmental sequence.

Table 2.9 outlines a classification of nematodes that are parasitic in vertebrates. It will be noted that such is the intensity of speciation among parasitic nematodes, that *Homo sapiens* is host to at least one example (and often more than one) from each of the orders of vertebrate parasitic nematodes. This means that an anthropocentric consideration of nematodes provides a comprehensive introduction to the range of diversity within this parasitic taxon.

The horrifyingly long inventory of human nematode diseases can be split epidemiologically into two naturally homogeneous principal subsets and a single less natural one (Table 2.10). Direct life cycle intestinal nematodes form one natural grouping, insect-vector transmitted filarial nematodes the second. The remaining species consist of a heterogeneous mixture of larval and adult infections that are neither insect transmitted nor have simple direct life cycles with free-living eggs or larvae as infective stages.

Table 2.9. Outline classification of the nematode parasites of vertebrates with particular emphasis on orders and superfamilies containing important human parasites.

PHYLUM: NEMATODA

Subclass 1: Secernentea (Posterior phasmid chemoreceptive organs present)
  Order 1: Rhabditida. Parasitic female adults parthenogenetic, pharynx often possesses prominent posterior muscular bulb. (e.g. *Strongyloides*).
  Order 2: Strongylida. Adult males possess copulatory bursa with supporting rays. L_1 and L_2 larvae often free living.
    Superfamily 1: Ancylostomatoidea. Prominent buccal capsule often with cuticular teeth or cutting plates—'hookworms'. (e.g. *Ancylostoma, Necator*).
    Superfamily 2: Strongyloidea
    Superfamily 3: Trichostrongyloidea
    Superfamily 4: Metastrongyloidea
  Order 3: Ascaridida. Large intestinal nematodes; 3-lipped mouth; simple pharynx. (e.g. *Ascaris, Toxocara*).
  Order 4: Oxyurida. Pharynx possesses posterior bulb with valves. Adult female has long pointed post-anal tail. (e.g. *Enterobius*).
  Order 5: Spirurida. Pharynx divided into two sections, a shorter anterior muscular portion and a longer glandular posterior one.
    Superfamily 1: Filarioidea. Very elongate adults; usually viviparous; intermediate hosts blood sucking arthropods—'filarial worms' (e.g. *Wuchereria, Brugia, Loa, Onchocerca, Dipetalonema, Mansonella*).
    Superfamily 2: Dracunculoidea. Very elongate adults with extreme sexual dimorphism—females much longer than males. Mature female vulva nonfunctional; viviparous; intermediate hosts copepods (e.g. *Dracunculus*).
    Superfamily 3: Gnathostomatoidea
    Superfamily 4: Thelazoidea
    Superfamily 5: Habronematoidea
    Superfamily 6: Physalopteroidea
Subclass 2: Adenophorea (Phasmids absent; pharynx usually forms a stichosome).
  Order 1: Enoplida
    Superfamily 1: Trichuroidea. Adult body divided into slim anterior region and broader posterior section. Female possesses only a single ovary and uterus; males have single or absent spicule. (e.g. *Trichinella, Trichuris*).
    Superfamily 2: Dioctophymatoidea

2.6.1   Intestinal nematodes of man

These are the most important intestinal helminth parasites of man in terms of both their overall prevalences and their potential for causing serious clinical harm. All the six important species (Table 2.10) in this category can occur at high prevalence levels. They all have direct life cycles and apart from *Enterobius vermicularis* they all are soil-transmitted in the sense that the eggs or larvae responsible for transmission normally become infective after a period of development

Table 2.10. Nematode species causing important disease in man.

Name	Adult size (mm)		Geographical distribution
Intestinal parasites			
Strongyloides stercoralis	Female:	2	Worldwide in tropical zone
Ancylostoma duodenale	Female:	12	Worldwide in tropics and subtropics
	Male:	9	plus Mediterranean fringes
Necator americanus	Female:	10	Worldwide in tropics and subtropics
	Male:	7	including S.E. states of USA
Enterobius vermicularis	Female:	11	Cosmopolitan
	Male:	3	
Ascaris lumbricoides	Female:	300	Cosmopolitan
	Male:	200	
Trichuris trichiura	Female:	30–50	Cosmopolitan
	Male:	30–45	
Filarial parasites			
Wuchereria bancrofti	Female:	90	Asia, Africa, S. America,
	Male:	40	Pacific Islands
Brugia malayi	Female:	90	S.E. Asia
	Male:	40	
Onchocerca volvulus	Female:	400	Yemen, Africa, S. and Central
	Male:	30	America
Loa loa	Female:	70	W. and Central Africa
	Male:	30	
Dipetalonema perstans	Female:	75	Africa, S. America
	Male:	40	
Dipetalonema streptocerca	Female:	?	W. and Central Africa
	Male:	?	
Mansonella ozzardi	Female:	75	S. America, Caribbean
	Male:	?	
Other nematodes			
Toxocara spp.	Various		Cosmopolitan
(only larvae in man)			
Dracunculus medinensis	Female:	500–800	Africa, Middle East, Pakistan,
	Male:	15–40?	India
Trichinella spiralis	Female:	3	Cosmopolitan
(adults intestinal)	Male:	1	

in the soil. The similarity in transmission mode, and the extensive and overlapping geographical distributions of these helminths, together ensure that many individuals suffer from concurrent infections with two or more species of these intestinal parasites. Such multiple infections are often particularly harmful.

(a)   Ascaris lumbricoides (Fig. 2.15)

A. lumbricoides is the largest of the intestinal nematodes of man and probably one of the most prevalent, with around 700 million persons infected globally. The majority of cases occur in the Far East and tropical Africa although *Ascaris* is a truely cosmopolitan parasite with sporadic cases occurring almost anywhere in the world. Transmission potential is largely determined by human faecal disposal practices. It is highest where soil around dwellings is heavily contaminated with human faeces or where human faecal slurry (night soil) is used as an agricultural fertilizer. The very long-lived eggs (maximum survival around seven years) are typically ingested on uncooked, unwashed vegetables or in contaminated water.

ASCARIS LUMBRICOIDES

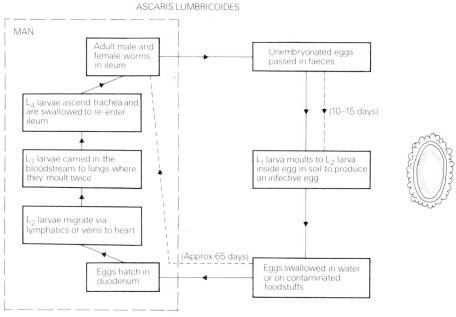

Fig. 2.15. The life cycle and egg of *Ascaris lumbricoides*.

Migrating larvae cause pneumonitis or pneumonia while in the lungs (see Fig. 2.15). Transient itching and an urticarial rash may occur during this phase. Adult parasites in the gut are associated with a symptomatology related to worm density. At low densities little may be suffered apart from some intestinal colic. At higher densities massed worms in the small intestine can cause intestinal obstruction and pain, possibly followed by gut perforation or volvulus. In such infections worms may migrate into unusual sites such as the bile and pancreatic ducts as well as the liver itself and the stomach. The pathology caused by heavy infections of adult worms in malnourished children in the tropics is particularly severe.

(b)   Trichuris trichiura (= Trichocephalus trichiurus) (Fig. 2.16)

This worm, the causative agent of trichuriasis or whipworm infection, is an unusually shaped nematode about 4 cm long with an extremely long, thin, pharyngeal region and a wider posterior section containing the rest of the gut and the reproductive organs. The buccal cavity contains a small stylet with which the worms

(a)

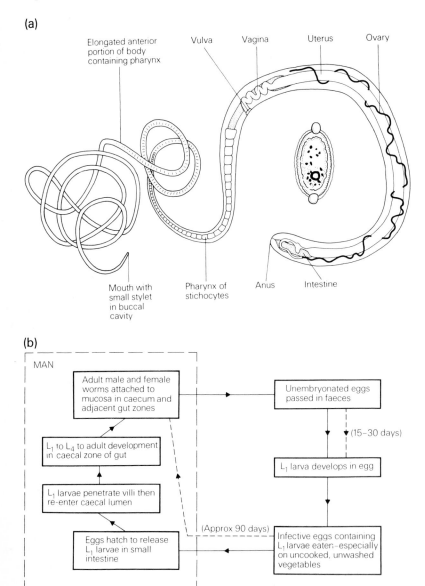

(b)

Fig. 2.16. (a) An adult female worm and egg of *Trichuris trichiura*. (b) the life cycle.

disrupt the caecal mucosa. The thin anterior region of the body lies embedded shallowly in the surface of the mucosa, with the rear portion free in the gut lumen.

Like *Ascaris*, this is a cosmopolitan infection but one that is most common in humid tropical countries. Global infections probably total around 700 million. Conditions predisposing to efficient transmission of the disease are broadly similar to those for *Ascaris* and these two worms often occur together.

Mild *Trichuris* infections can be without symptoms or may present with indefinite abdominal pains. Higher density infections, however, especially in undernourished children, can be highly pathogenic and result in chronic bloody diarrhoea, anaemia and rectal prolapse.

(c)   Ancylostoma duodenale *and* Necator americanus (Fig. 2.17)

These two morphologically and developmentally similar blood-feeding nematodes cause hookworm disease (ancylostomiasis) in man. Although in the past the global distributions of the two species were rather different, in recent decades both types have become extensively distributed in the tropical and subtropical zones of the world. As a consequence of this and the similarities between the patterns of disease caused by the two species, it is both convenient and rational to consider them together.

Hookworms are transmitted to man by a skin-penetrating L_3 larva that arises subsequent to L_1 and L_2 development in the soil. The first two larval stages feed on soil bacteria but the infective L_3 forms are non-feeding. Adult worms develop after a larval migration via the heart and lungs. Adult males and females of both species attach themselves to gut villi with their subterminal, dorsally opening buccal capsules. They abrade the surface of the gut with cutting plates and teeth in the buccal capsules and feed on blood. *Ancylostoma* infections can cause blood losses of about 0.15 ml per worm per day and anaemia is a prominent symptom in many cases of hookworm disease. It occurs so commonly that ancylostomiasis should probably be considered as a diagnosis in all patients with unexplained anaemia in or returning from hookworm-endemic areas. The degree of anaemia induced in an individual patient is a complex resultant of the species of hookworm present, the changing worm burden with time caused by the balance of new infections and worm mortality, the nutritional status of the host, and the level of the patient's iron reserves. A typical picture of developing anaemia in a hookworm sufferer is of a hypochromic, microcytic anaemia of gradual onset. Especially in children, the hypoalbuminaemia caused by serum loss causes a generalized oedema with a puffy face and swollen abdomen.

Invading L_3 larvae cause 'ground itch' at the sites of skin entry, this affliction consisting of tracks of itchy, vesicular lesions. Lung pathology can be provoked by migrating larvae and in Japan it is recognized as a distinct clinical entity—'Wanaka disease'. L_3 larvae of a number of non-human hookworm species can penetrate human skin and cause irritating 'cutaneous larval migrans' as they move laterally in the skin. Such larvae never develop to adulthood so the infections are self-limiting.

(a)

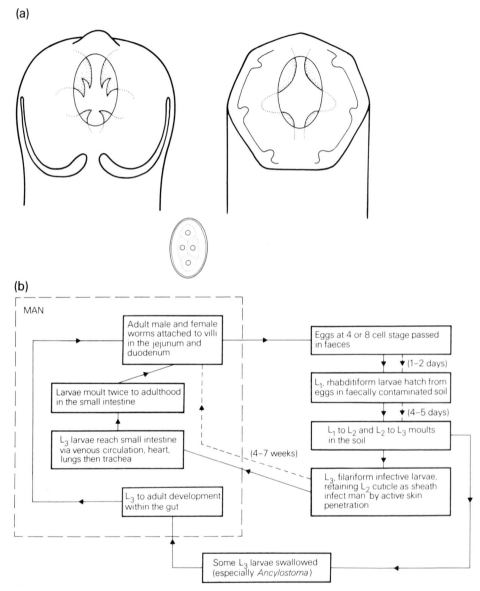

(b)

Fig. 2.17. Human hookworms. (a) The head regions of *Ancylostoma duodenale* (left) and *Necator americanus* (right) showing cutting teeth in the buccal cavity of the former and cutting plates in the latter. The recently released egg has developed to the 4-cell stage. (b) The life cycle of human hookworms.

(d)   Enteriobius vermicularis (Fig. 2.18)

Arguably the commonest helminth infection in the world, this parasite causes little obvious pathology. Enterobiasis or pinworm disease is more prevalent in temperate than tropical countries and is a group infection especially common among children. The mode of transmission can be considered contaminative as the eggs are infective almost immediately after release onto the anal skin, and it is assumed that most transmission occurs within dwellings. Eggs are found in clothing and bedding and in addition a patient can reinfect himself by transferring eggs from anus to mouth by finger contamination or by larvae hatching on the perianal skin and entering the anus.

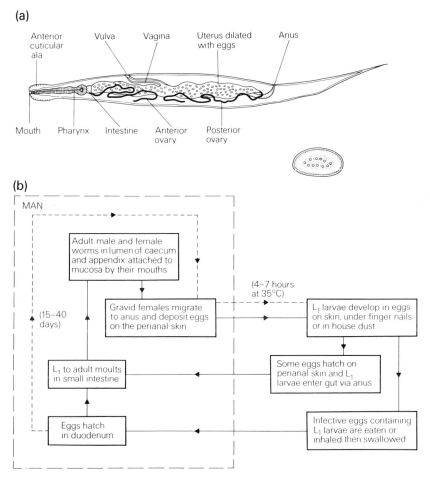

Fig. 2.18. *Enterobius vermicularis.* (a) Gravid female worm and recently released egg. (b) Life cycle.

The vast majority of cases of infection are symptomless. Emerging female worms and their sticky eggs can, however, induce a severe irritation in the perianal area. Female emergence and egg laying occurs at night so a common picture in infected children is of disturbed sleep and irritability. Pruritis ani leads to scratching of the itching anal area by children and this undoubtedly transfers infective eggs to the fingers, aiding self-infection. In some girls migrating female worms move to the vagina and cause vulval irritation.

(e)   Strongyloides stercoralis (Fig. 2.19)

Man becomes infected with *Strongyloides* either when L_3 larvae penetrate his skin from the outside or develop directly within the gut. The life cycle organization of this parasite is further complicated by the existence in some circumstances of an entirely free-living cycle of sexually reproducing adult forms and their larvae in the soil. This alternative cycle can produce L_3 larvae that are also able to infect man.

The pathology associated with this disease can be divided into larval and adult-generated phases. L_3 skin penetration in sensitized individuals can lead to a vesicular rash at the sites of invasion similar to hookworm 'ground itch'. Adults in the gut mucosa often cause few symptoms. In heavy infections, however, considerable mucosal damage is produced and malabsorption can be a feature. Patients who have a reduced ability to mount cell-mediated immune responses because of severe malnutrition, concurrent infections, or immunosuppressive drugs, can exhibit a peculiarly life-threatening infection called disseminated strongyloidosis. In such patients larvae are found in almost all the organs of the body.

2.6.2   Human filariasis

Filarial worms are long-lived nematode parasites of man that all require a period of larval development (L_1 to L_3) in a blood-sucking insect host. These biting vectors can reinfect man. Table 2.10 lists the seven common species that infect man and Fig. 2.20 outlines the basic features of their essentially similar life cycles.

It is relatively easy to order the seven species in terms of their medical importance. *Wuchereria bancrofti* which causes lymphatic filariasis, and *Onchocerca volvulus* which induces river blindness and onchodermatitis, are widespread and extremely damaging infections. *Brugia malayi* and *Loa loa*, although potentially pathogenic, are much more restricted in distribution, while *Dipetalonema perstans*, *D. streptocerca* and *Mansonella ozzardi* cause relatively few pathological abnormalities.

Adult filarial worms are rarely seen diagnostically. Diagnosis depends on symptomatology in endemic areas and the collection and microscopical identification of L_1 larvae termed 'microfilariae' in either the peripheral blood or skin, depending

(a)

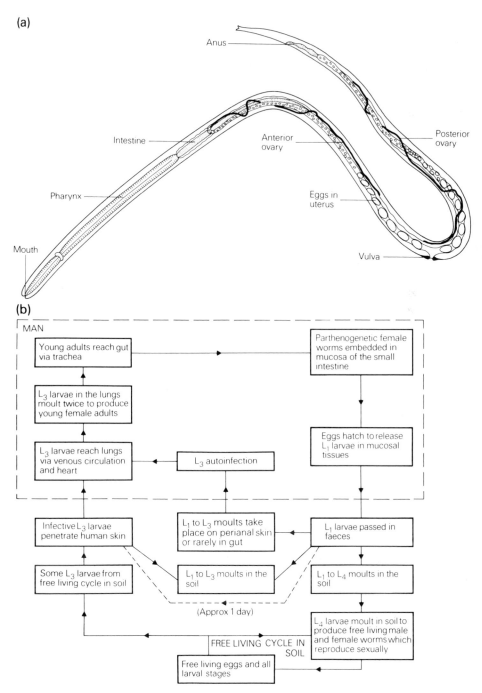

(b)

Fig. 2.19. *Strongyloides stercoralis.* (a) Parthenogenetic adult female from human gut. (b) Life cycle.

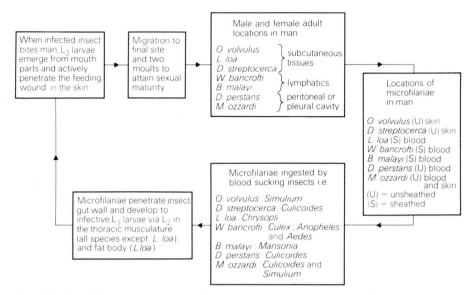

Fig. 2.20. The life cycle organization of the seven most important human filarial parasites.

on the worm species involved. Most, if not all, filarial species are divided into geographical subspecies or strains that may utilize different vectors and be associated with distinctive pathological patterns in man. One aspect of this subspecific variation concerns the phenomenon of microfilarial periodicity. *W. bancrofti* is transmitted over much of its range by night-biting mosquitoes in the genus *Culex*. Correlated with this host utilization *W. bancrofti* microfilariae show periodic population changes in the peripheral blood. At night peripheral microfilaraemias are high; during the day larvae are almost completely absent from surface blood and remain in the blood vessels of the lungs. In some Polynesian Islands, however, a diurnally peaking form of *W. bancrofti* exists. This utilizes day-biting *Aedes* mosquitoes. Similar periodic phenomena characterize infections with other filarial species.

(a)   *Lymphatic filariasis*

Two filarial species *W. bancrofti* and *Brugia malayi*, which are very similar morphologically, live as adults in the afferent lymphatic vessels of man and produce blood-dwelling microfilariae which can attain very high densities. The characteristic pathology associated with these two species, however, is hardly ever related to these larvae but to the male and female adult worms in the lymphatics.

The pathological changes in the lymphatic system are usually slow, progressive, and dependent on a continuous cumulative input of adult worms. Most cases of lymphatic filariasis are effectively symptomless with the only evidence of a positive infection being the presence of microfilariae in the blood. Once a population of adult worms is present, however, the lymph ducts and nodes may become inflamed due to immunological responses to adult filarial antigens. With continual antigenic insult over several years, patterns of more severe lymphatic-centred pathological changes are set up. *W. bancrofti* adults are often found in the lymphatics of the spermatic cord and in such cases scrotal changes including hydrocoele are relatively common. Elephantiasis is the classic terminal manifestation of lymphatic filariasis but is in fact a relatively rare consequence of it. *Brugia malayi* has a much more restricted geographical distribution than *W. bancrofti* but can induce the same type of elephantiasis as the latter species, usually in the lower parts of the legs.

Bancroftian filariasis probably affects over 250 million people in the tropics and subtropics of the world, with the most severely infected populations being found in India, the Far East, Polynesia and East Africa. In view of the increasing rural-to-urban shift in population distributions in many developing countries, the urban transmission mode of *W. bancrofti* assumes increasing importance. It usually involves the utilization of *Culex fatigans* an anthropophilic, night-biting mosquito which breeds in any small polluted pockets of water in slums and shanty towns. It is the important vector in city transmission sites like Calcutta and Singapore. Rural transmission modes use a wide range of different mosquito species.

Brugia, because of its restriction to *Mansonia* mosquito vectors, is almost entirely a rural disease in S.E. Asia. *Mansonia* breeds in forest lakes and swamps with the larvae and pupae attached to the underwater parts of aquatic plants. A subperiodic form of the disease exists which can infect man but is predominantly a parasite of forest mammals such as monkeys. For this form of *Brugia*-induced lymphatic filariasis, animal reservoir hosts play an important part in the epidemiology of the disease. Normal nocturnally periodic *Brugia* infections and bancroftian filariasis have no such zoonotic complications.

Diagnosis of lymphatic filariasis depends on finding and identifying microfilariae in the peripheral blood. This has been done in the past with thick blood smears stained with Giemsa. More recently this technique has been supplemented by the use of 5 ml blood samples filtered through 3 μm pore size Nucleopore filters.

(b)   *Onchocerciasis*

Onchocerca volvulus is the only species of *Onchocerca* to infect man, and it does so causing considerable morbidity across Africa and in relatively minor pockets of infection in Brazil, Colombia, Guatemala, Venezuela, Mexico and Yemen. Across this considerable geographical range about seven reasonably distinct parasite strains exist, each transmitted by particular species of blackfly in the genus *Simulium*, and each associated with its own particular pathological pattern. Most of the blackflies are restricted to sites with well-oxygenated fast-flowing freshwater for breeding purposes, and the detailed spatial distribution of onchocerciasis largely reflects this riverine pattern.

The disease causes two types of severe pathological damage—ocular change including blindness (river blindness); and onchodermatitis, a range of painful and disfiguring skin changes. Both are the result of microfilariae, in contrast to the damage caused by lymphatic filariasis where adult filariae are responsible.

The unsheathed microfilariae of *O. volvulus* are found in the skin rather than the blood system and they arise from groups of copulating worms located in fibrous nodules in the subcutaneous tissues. These nodules, called onchocercomas, which may be several centimetres in diameter, can often be seen externally as rounded elevations of the skin. Other, deeper nodules are, however, invisible externally.

Microfilariae induce a wide range of skin changes in all strains of *O. volvulus*. Early, light, infections may produce an itchy rash. In more chronic infections patchy depigmentation or increased pigmentation can occur, and the skin becomes thickened and coarse while losing its elasticity. This change in the mechanical properties of the integument predisposes patients to hernias, 'hanging groins' or hanging pouches under the eyes. Microfilariae moving through the skin reach the eyes and here they produce the most pathological damage that is linked with *Onchocerca*. The final stage of this is blindness, the 'river blindness' especially common in the savannah areas of West and Central Africa. In heavily infected villages close to rivers with high *Simulium* densities as many as 30% of the population may become blind because of this parasite. Total blindness, however, is only the distressing end point of a progressive and accumulative series of changes that over a number of years involve all portions of the eyes.

The different strains of *Onchocerca* have skin distributions of microfilarial densities that broadly correspond with the preferred biting areas of their specific vector species. These distributions influence the choice of skin area used for removing the skin snips, 2–3 mm in diameter, that are used for the microfilarial diagnosis of onchocerciasis.

(c)   Other human filarial infections

Loiasis is caused by *Loa loa* in the rain forest zones of West and Central Africa. It is transmitted by large day-feeding tabanid flies in the genus *Chrysops*. Adult worms live subcutaneously but, unlike those of *Onchocerca*, do not form permanent nodules. Instead they move around inducing the formation of transient 'calabar swellings'. The commonest symptoms of infection are the result of allergic reactions to these wandering adults, which sometimes visibly cross the front of the eye under the conjunctiva. Infrequently, encephalitis and ocular lesions have been associated with loiasis.

Dipetalonema streptocerca, like *Loa loa*, is confined to the rain forests of Africa.

Adults live in subcutaneous connective tissues and microfilariae are found in the skin. Neither cause much damage to the host. Careful microscopical examination is needed to make the important differentiation between the microfilariae of *D. strepto-cera* and *O. volvulus* in skin snips.

Another species of *Dipetalonema*—*D. perstans*—is common in Central and South America as well as Africa. It is found in adult form in the peritoneal and pleural cavities, as is *Mansonella ozzardi* from the Caribbean and South America. Neither of these filarial infections causes serious pathological damage.

2.6.3   Other human nematode diseases

Dracunculiasis, or guinea worm disease, is caused by *Dracunculus medinensis*, the mature females of which may reach almost a metre in length. Dracunculiasis is widespread in much of India as well as parts of West and Central Africa, with more restricted foci in Pakistan, Iraq, Iran and Saudi Arabia. The parasites have an indirect life cycle and man becomes infected when he consumes drinking water contaminated with freshwater copepods containing L_3 larvae of the parasite. Ingested L_3 larvae penetrate the duodenal wall and spend approximately 12 weeks growing, moulting to adulthood and mating in subcutaneous tissues. After copulation male worms die. Females, however, move down through the body reaching a lower extremity like the ankle or foot about 8 or 10 months after the original infection with L_3 forms. Here the mature female worm, with its uterus packed with about a million L_1 larvae, produces a blister in the skin which subsequently bursts. This enables large numbers of actively swimming L_1 larvae to leave the lesion each time it is immersed in water, over a period of three to four weeks. Copepod species such as *Cyclops leukarti* ingest the larvae which then penetrate the crustacean gut wall and develop into L_2 then L_3 larvae in the haemocoele.

This indirect life cycle pattern means that the disease is usually focally transmitted. Foci of infection are often small discrete water sources such as pools with gently shelving sides in Africa, or constructed watering places such as step wells in India. Their shared characteristic is that persons washing, drinking or collecting water from them are required to stand in the water. This contact enables L_1 larvae from infected persons to enter the water system and infect copepods.

Blister formation in dracunculiasis can be an extremely painful process and the open wound of the blister often becomes secondarily infected. Adult female worm infections closely associated with bony joints can lead to arthritis.

Trichinosis, caused by *Trichinella spiralis*, is a cosmopolitan nematode disease demonstrating very low vertebrate-host specificity. The worm's mode of transmission is unusual. Short-lived adult infections in the guts of a wide range of carnivorous and omnivorous mammals give rise to large numbers of invasive L_1 larvae which migrate to voluntary muscle sites throughout the bodies of these same hosts. Here they encyst. The cysts are the infective stages which can be transmitted to any new host when infected flesh is eaten. In domestic cycles throughout the world man usually becomes infected by eating cyst-containing pork from domesticated pigs. In feral cycles meat from wild boar, bears, bushpigs or warthogs can give rise to infections.

Although adult worms in the small intestine do give rise to some gut damage, the main pathogenic phase of the *Trichinella* life cycle in man is the population of migrating and encysting larvae. Usually no symptoms occur until the L_1 larvae reach the muscles, and then, in heavy infections, a confusingly diverse range of serious symptoms can arise. Usually, however, a marked eosinophilia is apparent, with vomiting and diarrhoea followed by a high fever, muscle pain, and in severe cases, evidence of cardiac and central nervous system pathological damage.

Toxocariasis in humans is a zoonotic infection brought about by the inadvertent ingestion, usually by children, of infective eggs of the nematode species *Toxocara canis* and *T. cati*. These are normally found as adults in cats and dogs. The L_2 larvae which hatch from the eggs migrate round the body causing widespread small granulomas in the sites where they occur. The disease is a form of visceral larval migrans. The lesions are commonest in the liver and lungs but also occur in muscles, brain, skin and eyes ocular pathological damage, being probably the most serious consequence of human toxocariasis. Such changes occur in only a small proportion of infected children in which the larvae can cause chronic granulomatous endophthalmitis, with retinal degeneration occurring.

2.6.4   Other nematodes

In addition to those species which are the causative agents of medically important human diseases, a number of other nematodes are of significance, either because they infect domesticated animals or because they have been utilized extensively as laboratory models. Table 2.11 lists such species.

Table 2.11. Nematodes of domesticated animals (including species utilized as laboratory models).

Name	Final hosts	Comments
Order Strongylida		
Angiostrongylus cantonensis	Rats	'Lungworm' of rats; larvae ingested in land snails by man and cause eosinophilic meningitis
Dictyocaulus viviparus	Cattle	Adult worms parasitic in lungs
Haemonchus contortus	Sheep	'Stomach worm'; blood-feeding injurious parasite, particularly pathogenic in young hosts
Nippostrongylus brasiliensis	Rats	Adults parasitic in rat intestine; much used laboratory nematode in immunological, developmental and physiological studies
Oesophagostomum apiostomum	Monkeys and apes	Adults parasitic in primate gut causing nodular host reactions; occasionally infects man
Oesophagostomum radiatum	Cattle	Adults parasitic in intestine of cows causing nodular reactions
Ostertagia ostertagi	Sheep	Stomach inhabiting trichostrongylid
Stephanurus dentatus	Pigs	Adults in kidney of pigs; eggs passed out in urine
Strongylus edentatus	Horses	Adults parasitic in large intestine
Syngamus trachea	Turkeys, chickens, pheasants	'Gapeworms' adults inhabit pharynx or trachea of birds causing nodules
Trichostrongylus spp.	Sheep, goats, horses	Stomach inhabiting trichostrongylids; some occasionally infect man
Order Ascaridida		
Ascaridia galli	Chickens	Adults parasitic in small intestine
Ascaris suum	Pigs	Adults parasitic in the intestine of pigs; closely related to *Ascaris lumbricoides*
Heterakis gallinarum	Chickens and turkeys	Large numbers found in the intestinal caecae of turkeys; important as the carrier of the infective agent of the protozoan disease 'black spot', *Histomonas meleagridis* (see section 1.5.2)

continues

Table 2.11. *continued*

Name	Final hosts	Comments
Parascaris equorum	Horses	Adults parasitic in the small intestine of horses
Order Oxyurida		
Oxyurus equi	Horses	Adults parasitic in the large intestine
Syphacia obvelata	Rodents	Adults parasitic in the gut of rats and mice; used in laboratory studies
Order Spirurida		
Dirofilaria spp.	Dogs	Adult filarial worms in the heart and pulmonary artery of dogs; immature worms occasionally found in lungs or pulmonary artery of man
Onchocerca gutterosa	Cattle	Adult filarial worms in connective tissue on the surface of the nuchal ligament
Gnathostoma spinigerum	Fish-eating carnivores	Man occasionally becomes infected with larvae by eating infected raw fish
Order Enoplida		
Capillaria hepatica	Rats and other rodents	Adults in liver of final host; occasional human cases reported
Dioctophyma renale	Mink, dogs, etc.	'Giant kidney worm' in kidneys of final host

FURTHER READING

Chabaud A.G. (1974) *Keys to the Nematode Parasites of Vertebrates*, Slough, Commonwealth Agricultural Bureaux.

Chandler A.C. & Read C.P. (1961) *Introduction to Parasitology: With Special Reference to Parasites of Man*, 10th ed. New York, John Wiley and Sons.

Crompton D.W.T. (1970) *An Ecological Approach to Acanthocephalan Physiology*, Cambridge, Cambridge University Press.

Crompton D.W.T. & Joyner S.M. (1980) *Parasitic Worms*, London, Wykeham Publications.

Erasmus D.A. (1972) *The Biology of Trematodes*, London, Edward Arnold.

Grasse P-P. (ed.) (1961) Platyhelminthes, Mésozoaires, Acanthocéphales, Némertiens. *Traite de Zoologie*, vol.IV. Paris, Masson.

La Rue G.R. (1957) The classification of digenetic trematodes. *Expl. Parasit.* **6,** 306–44.

Lee D.L. & Atkinson H.J. (1976) *Physiology of Nematodes*. 2nd ed. London, Macmillan.

Muller R. (1975) *Worms and Disease*, London, Heinemann.

Nelson G.S. (1966) The pathology of filarial infections. *Helminth. Abstr.* **35,** 311–36.

Nelson G.S. (1970) Onchocerciasis. In B. Dawes (ed.) *Advances in Parasitology*, vol.8, pp.173–224. London, Academic Press.

Read C.P. (1970) *Parasitism and Symbiology*, New York, Ronald Press.

Schmidt G.D. (1971) Acanthocephalan infections in man, with two new records. *J. Parasit.* **57,** 282–4.

Schmidt G.D. & Roberts L.S. (1977) *Foundations of Parasitology*, St. Louis, C.V. Mosby.

Smyth J.D. (1966) *The Physiology of Trematodes*, Edinburgh, Oliver and Boyd.

Smyth J.D. (1969) *The Physiology of Cestodes*, Edinburgh, Oliver and Boyd.

Smyth J.D. (1976) *Introduction to Animal Parasitology*, 2nd ed. London, Hodder and Stoughton.

Smyth J.D. & Heath D.D. (1970) Pathogenesis of larval cestodes in mammals. *Helminth. Abstr.* **39,** 1–23.

Whitfield P.J. (1979) *The Biology of Parasitism: An Introduction to the Study of Associating Organisms*, London, Edward Arnold.

Woodruff A.W. (1970) Toxocariasis, *Brit. med. J.* **iii,** 663–9.

Wright C.A. (1971) *Flukes and Snails*, London, Allen and Unwin.

Chapter 3
Biochemistry
C. Bryant

3.1 INTRODUCTION

This chapter gives an account of the major biochemical processes which take place in parasitic protozoa and helminths, as far as they are known. The reader may immediately point out that there are other sorts of parasites. However, space is limited and, even with certain omissions, the groups discussed are still diverse. They include members of the protozoan phyla Sarcomastigophora and Apicomplexa, and of the helminth phyla Platyhelminthes, Acanthocephala and Nematoda. Generalizations are of necessity probably restricted to these groups; little is known of the biochemistry of parasitic arthropods.

Another compelling reason for the selection of material is that the study of the dynamic aspects of the biochemistry of parasitic protozoa and helminths, whilst not quite coming of age, has at least entered adolescence. This chapter is confined to these aspects and disregards much of what may be called 'structural' biochemistry, such as the detailed analysis of amino acid or carbohydrate composition of parasites. This is not to belittle these studies; there is simply such a plethora of information that it is impossible to condense it here. The following pages concentrate on concepts; for many of the supporting data the reader is referred to the references and especially to Von Brand's heroic compendia *The Biochemistry of Parasites* and *Biochemistry and Physiology of Endoparasites*. Finally, the reader will notice that a large part of this chapter is given to catabolism and the formation of ATP. This reflects faithfully the proportion of the biochemical literature on parasites which is devoted to this topic.

The following abbreviations are used in the text: ATP, ADP, AMP—adenosine tri-, di- and monophosphates; CoA—coenzyme A; FBP—fructose-1,6-bisphosphate; GTP, GDP—guanosine tri- and di- phosphates; $NAD(H_2)$—nicotinamide adenine dinucleotide (reduced form); PEP—phosphoenolpyruvate; PEPCK—phosphoenolpyruvate carboxykinase; PK—pyruvate kinase; DNA, RNA—deoxyribonucleic acid, ribonucleic acid.

3.2 ENERGY METABOLISM

'Energy metabolism' refers to those biochemical processes that result in the formation of ATP which, in turn, is employed in many energy-dependent reactions. Energy metabolism is of particular importance because the establishment of a parasite in a host organism depends initially on its ability to sustain life processes in its new environment. Other problems, such as overcoming the immune response of the host, are subordinated to this first crisis of survival.

3.2.1   Environments and life cycles

The environments of parasites are legion. Parasitic protozoa and helminths may be found in the vertebrate intestine and its ancillary organs, in the invertebrate intestine, in vascular, nervous, muscular and reproductive systems. Each environment has its own special characteristics. It may be rich in oxygen or carbon dioxide. It may provide the parasite with a well-regulated supply of metabolic precursors, as in the vascular system, or, as in the intestine, availability of nutrients may depend on the host's diet. It is not surprising that there is diversity in the pathways of energy metabolism of internal parasites, but it is superimposed upon a conformity which makes certain generalizations possible. One is that whether the parasite is aerobic or anaerobic (and even this apparently simple fact is contentious) it requires a source of highly reduced organic compounds, an efficient mechanism for the effective release and capture of the energy it contains, and the capacity to maintain its intracellular environment at the right level of oxidation.

Parasites often occupy more than one environment during their life cycles, which adds further complications to the study of their biochemistry. Biochemical strategies which enable survival in one environment may not be appropriate to the second, but the parasite must have the genetic capacity to respond to each. There must be a complex programme for the expression of different genes at different times, leading to the elaboration of different biochemical pathways at each of the life stages. This is achieved by the use of 'trigger' stimuli. Many parasites embark on the adult stages of their life cycles in response to the high carbon dioxide concentrations, the reducing conditions or the high temperatures encountered in their definitive hosts.

It is about the adult stages that we know most. The following sections therefore concentrate on energy metabolism in parasitic protozoa and helminths of the vertebrate bloodstream and intestine.

3.2.2   Energy stores

There is not much information available about energy stores in parasitic protozoa. In trichomonads and in *Entamoeba histolytica*, glycogen accounts for 10–30% of dry weight, yet there is little, if any, storage carbohydrate in trypanosomes or malarial parasites. This difference is probably related to environment: trypanosomes or malarial parasites, living in the bloodstream, have access to a constant pool of glucose. Of interest is a polymer composed of phosphate monomers found in *Crithidia fasciculata*, a kinetoplastid flagellate, which may represent an energy store. Alternatively, it may have a role in the regulation of phosphate concentrations within the parasite cell.

Large quantities of glycogen have been demonstrated in all species of parasitic helminths so far examined. Generally, glycogen stores are depleted during 'starvation' of helminth parasites in *in vitro* culture, which is good evidence that they are energy reserves. In addition, some helminth parasites possess substantial stores of trehalose, a soluble disaccharide, in their tissues. In the acanthocephalan *Moniliformis dubius* and in larvae of *Trichinella spiralis,* for example, trehalose accounts for about 2.5% of tissue solids. Glucose, too, is universally present: there are active transport mechanisms for glucose uptake in cestodes and nematodes while trematodes rely on simple diffusion. However, glucose is not an energy *store,* but an intracellular metabolic pool which is maintained by absorption from the environment and is destined to be phosphorylated to yield glucose-6-phosphate, and either converted to polysaccharide or oxidized immediately.

In adult helminths and protozoa, lipids generally do not form an energy store. Almost all parasites, except, possibly, larval nematodes, lack the enzymes necessary for their oxidation (see section 3.4).

3.2.3   The formation of phosphoenolpyruvate from carbohydrate

All protozoan and helminth parasites are capable of oxidizing glucose. The metabolic pathway by which this is achieved is similar to the glycolytic pathway of free-living organisms, to the level of phosphoenolpyruvate (PEP) (Barrett, 1977). There may, however, be some important differences. For example, phosphofructo-kinase from *Schistosoma* is much more sensitive to antimonial compounds than is the same enzyme from the host, which may contribute to the antischistosomal activity of the antimonial drugs.

At the level of PEP a number of alternative pathways are possible. They are illustrated in Fig. 3.1. The alternatives are manifested as products of metabolism which are excreted.

3.2.4   Further metabolism of phosphoenolpyruvate

In mammals, PEP is converted to pyruvate, which in turn is converted to acetyl CoA by pyruvate dehydrogenase, and the subsequent metabolism of acetyl CoA is by the tricarboxylic acid cycle in mitochondria. The operation of this aerobic system permits the synthesis of large amounts of ATP and the ultimate reoxidation of reduced cofactors by oxygen. Oxygen thus maintains the redox potential of cytosolic and mitochondrial compartments. The role of phosphoenolpyruvate carboxykinase (PEPCK) in mammals is the *decarboxylation* of oxaloacetate during gluconeogenesis. It serves as a bypass of the irreversible pyruvate dehydrogenase step.

A mammalian tissue may, for a brief spell, operate anaerobically. In muscle, for example, there is no mitochondrial involvement at all under such conditions. Pyruvate is converted to lactate in the cytosol; the lactate may accumulate to await subsequent oxidation. During the formation of lactate, $NADH_2$ is reoxidized. The production of lactate is a biochemical strategy to prevent the build-up of the more toxic pyruvate and to maintain a supply of NAD.

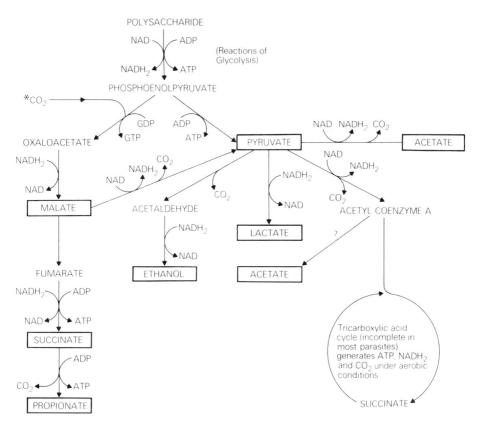

Fig. 3.1. Alternative pathways of carbon flow in energy metabolism of parasitic protozoa and helminths. Metabolites in boxes may be excreted, but each parasite does not excrete every metabolite (see Table 3.1). No attempt has been made to show stoichiometry, but sites of ATP generation and $NAD(H_2)$ involvement are indicated. In some parasites (*Ascaris*, *Hymenolepis*, *Fasciola*), $NADH_2$ generated in the conversion of malate to pyruvate and acetate is used to drive the fumarate to succinate reaction (fumarate reductase). ATP generation in the succinate/propionate conversion has only been shown for *Fasciola*, in sub-mitochondrial preparations. The reactions leading from pyruvate through acetyl coenzyme A are aerobic. Some parasites (*Trypanosoma*) may produce some of their excreted succinate in this way. The more usual route is that which is initiated by CO_2 fixation (asterisked) by phosphoenolpyruvate carboxykinase.

Few, if any, parasites possess a tricarboxylic acid cycle as active as that of mammals. Generally, where the cycle is complete, it operates at a very low activity. Important enzymes of the cycle are often missing or present at activities below the level of detection of the assay systems employed. There appear to be no rules as to which ones are absent. Citrate synthase, aconitate hydratase and isocitrate dehydrogenase are most often absent; this is true, for example, for some sporozoans, flagellates, digeneans and cestodes. Other parasites may lack 2-oxoglutarate dehydrogenase or fumarate hydratase. The inescapable conclusion is that the tricarboxylic acid cycle is of less importance to a majority of parasites than to mammals.

The end-products of phosphoenolpyruvate metabolism are widely encountered in parasites. Table 3.1 lists some of them, together with glycerol which is important in *Trypanosoma*. Their formation usually results in the synthesis of ATP by substrate-linked phosphorylation. However, few parasites depend solely on this process and electron transport mediated phosphorylation is common (see section 3.3). An example of a parasite which depends primarily on glycolysis for its energy requirements is *Schistosoma*; it has been called a 'homolactic' fermenter.

Table 3.1. Major products of energy metabolism in some representative parasites.

Parasite	Glycerol	Ethanol	Lactate	Pyruvate	Acetate	Formate	Succinate	Propionate
Trypanosoma vivax	×		×	×	×			
Trypanosoma rhodesiense	×			×				
Trypanosoma cruzi			×	×	×		×	
Entamoeba histolytica		×			×			
Plasmodium knowlesi			×		×	×		
Trichomonas spp.			×		×		×	
Fasciola hepatica			×		×		×	×
Hymenolepis diminuta			×		×		×	
Ascaris lumbricoides					×		×	×
Moniliformis dubius		×	×		×	×	×	×

There are three enzymes of the tricarboxylic acid cycle which *are*, almost invariably, present in parasites. They are malate-dehydrogenase, fumarate hydratase and fumarate reductase. They catalyse the following reaction, which is a reversed sequence of a portion of the tricarboxylic acid cycle:

$$\text{oxaloacetate} \xrightarrow[\text{NADH}_2 \quad \text{NAD}]{\substack{\text{malate} \\ \text{dehydrogenase}}} \text{malate} \xrightarrow[\text{H}_2\text{O}]{\substack{\text{fumarate} \\ \text{hydratase}}} \text{fumarate} \xrightarrow[\text{NADH}_2 \quad \text{NAD}]{\substack{\text{fumarate} \\ \text{reductase}}} \text{succinate.}$$

Malate dehydrogenase and fumarate hydratase catalyse reversible reactions. The status of fumarate reductase is unclear. Effectively, it is succinate dehydrogenase working in reverse, but it is not known whether it is the same enzyme. However, the evidence strongly suggests that a specialized electron transport system is associated with fumarate reductase activity (see section 3.3.3).

There are also a number of enzymes of carbon dioxide metabolism; most important are PEPCK and malic enzyme (Bryant, 1975). The reactions they catalyse are as follows:

$$\begin{array}{c} \text{PEPCK} \\ \text{a) PEP} + \text{CO}_2 + \text{GDP} \xleftrightarrow{\hspace{2cm}} \text{oxaloacetate} + \text{GTP} \end{array}$$

$$\begin{array}{c} \text{malic enzyme} \\ \text{b) Malate} + \text{NAD} \xleftrightarrow{\hspace{2cm}} \text{pyruvate} + \text{CO}_2 + \text{NADH}_2. \\ \text{(NADP)} \hspace{4cm} \text{(NADPH}_2) \end{array}$$

This distribution of enzymes and the excretion of the metabolites succinate, propionate and acetate, are accounted for by a metabolic pathway in which the initial step is the fixation of carbon dioxide into oxaloacetate by PEPCK (accompanied by a substrate-linked phosphorylation). Oxaloacetate is then reduced to malate, with the reoxidation of cytosolic NADH_2. Malate may then be converted to fumarate and succinate by the reactions discussed above. Succinate may be decarboxylated further to yield propionate. Alternatively, malate may be converted to pyruvate by malic enzyme; pyruvate, in turn, can be decarboxylated to acetate. These alternatives are not necessarily mutually exclusive and are discussed further in section 3.3.2.

There is an interesting variation on this pattern to be found in *Ascaris lumbricoides*. The terminal reactions of energy metabolism in this organism are unique. It ferments carbohydrates to two major end-products: 2-methyl butyrate and 2-methyl valerate. Propionyl CoA may be the direct precursor of these branched-chain fatty acids (Fig. 3.2). The pathway of synthesis is similar to a reversed β-oxidation pathway (but see section 3.4) and includes two novel enzymes: NADH_2-linked 2-methylacetoacetate reductase and NADH_2-linked propionyl CoA reductase.

The conversion of succinate to propionate which occurs in many parasites is also of great interest because it is an energy yielding process in *Fasciola hepatica* (Fig. 3.3); the key features are the recycling of coenzyme A and the synthesis of ATP at the

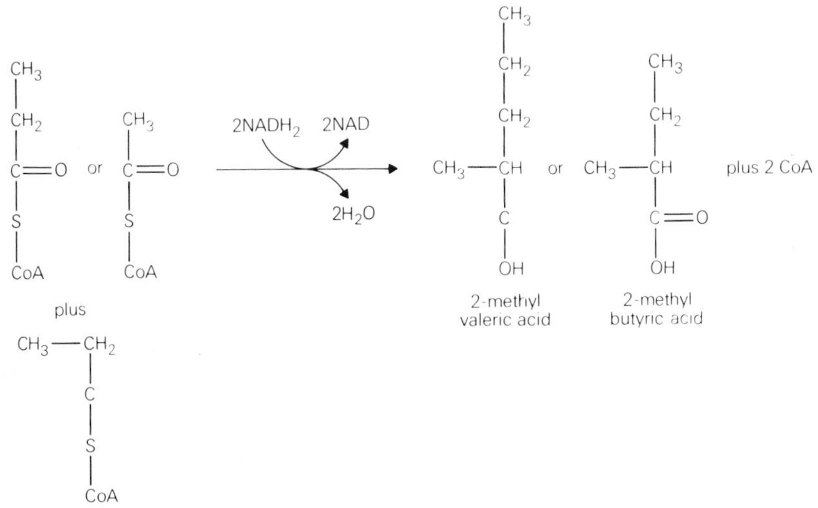

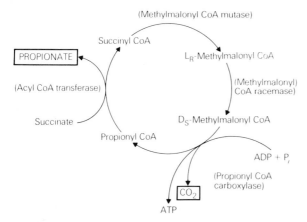

Fig. 3.2. End-product formation in *Ascaris lumbricoides*. Propionyl or acetyl CoA condenses with another molecule of propionyl coenzyme A to yield 2-methyl valeric or 2-methyl butyric acid. Two enzymes are involved, a propionyl CoA 'condensing enzyme' and 2-methyl acetoacetate reductase. As CoA does not recycle by means of a transfer reaction, as in *Fasciola* (Fig. 3.3), propionate formation from succinate in *Ascaris* may not lead to the synthesis of ATP. (After de Mata, Saz & Pasto, 1977.)

Fig. 3.3. Propionate production by the succinate decarboxylase system from the mitochondria of *Fasciola hepatica*. CoA is recycled by the transferase. In the absence of propionyl CoA the cycle needs 'priming'; energy (ATP) must be expended to synthesize a catalytic amount of succinyl CoA. (After Köhler, Bryant & Behm, 1978.)

propionyl CoA carboxylase step. It may also help to explain the tendency of many intestinal helminths to concentrate vitamin B_{12} to the detriment of their hosts, since the mutase and racemase in the cycle are B_{12}-dependent enzymes.

Pathways from PEP to succinate are common in protozoan parasites. They probably occur in *Trypanosoma cruzi*, although the picture is complicated by uncertainty about the exact fate of pyruvate. Culture forms of *Trypanosoma brucei* also produce succinate by this route. The trichomonads carry out the same series of reactions, but in the cytosol alone rather than in cytosol and mitochondria (see section 3.3). Carbon dioxide fixation into oxaloacetate also occurs in *Entamoeba histolytica*. The malate which is formed by reduction of oxaloacetate is not converted to succinate, but decarboxylated to pyruvate and subsequently metabolized to a variety of end-products (Fig. 3.1).

There is no totally satisfactory explanation for the widespread distribution of CO_2 fixation by PEPCK amongst parasites. Mettrick and co-workers (Podesta *et al.*, 1976) suggest that the prevalence of such pathways is due to the high levels of CO_2 frequently encountered in the environments of parasites. Their detailed hypothesis refers to *Hymenolepis diminuta*. They suggest that CO_2 diffuses down its concentration gradient into the parasite, and acidifies the worm tissue for the following reasons. As the carbon dioxide concentration increases, hydration and dissociation elevate the concentrations of H^+ and HCO_3^-:

$$H_2O + CO_2 = H^+ + HCO_3^-.$$

As the HCO_3^- concentration in the parasite rises, it follows its concentration gradient out of the worm. This, in turn, maintains the inward flow of CO_2, according to the Le Chatelier principle, leading to increased tissue acidification. Podesta *et al.* suggest that high levels of tissue CO_2 then promote carboxylation by PEPCK, with the ultimate formation of succinic acid. Succinic acid is excreted; as it is a dicarboxylic acid, its excretion is twice as effective in reducing the H^+ concentration as the excretion of the monocarboxylic lactic and acetic acids.

Attractive though this hypothesis is, recent work by Ovington and Bryant (1981) indicates that its application may be very limited. In a series of experiments designed to test the idea that CO_2 concentrations regulate the anaerobic pathway, they found that their strain of *Hymenolepis diminuta* produced only small amounts of succinic acid and that lactic and acetic acid excretion predominated. Further, they found that lactic acid excretion alone was sufficient to regulate the concentration of H^+ within the worm.

There are other parasites, such as *Fasciola hepatica*, which also do not excrete substantial amounts of succinic acid. Instead, they decarboxylate succinic to propionic acid, and pyruvic to acetic acid. Other advantages of these processes evidently outweigh any advantage accruing from pH regulation by succinic acid excretion (see section 3.2.6). In addition, there is a heterogeneous group of helminths, which includes the schistosomes and filarial worms, which apparently produce only lactate.

3.2.5   Regulation of the PK/PEPCK branchpoint

The PK/PEPCK branchpoint is an important locus in the metabolism of carbohydrate by parasites. The flow of carbon from carbohydrate through PEP must be regulated so that appropriate amounts of end-products may be formed. The nature of this regulation is dynamic—that is, it is not determined by the absolute concentrations of PK and PEPCK. This is demonstrated by the observation that, in parasites under different environmental conditions, there are changes in the ratios of the amounts of end-products they form. The two enzymes are influenced allosterically by cofactors such as purine nucleotides and by metabolic intermediates (Table 3.2). *Moniezia expansa* provides an excellent example. Under anaerobic conditions it produces 50% more lactate than when incubated in the presence of oxygen, while succinate production remains unchanged. The regulating factor is malate. Under aerobic conditions internal concentrations of malate rise, as it is produced both by PEPCK and malate dehydrogenase activity and by the aerobic oxidation of succinate. Malate inhibits the fructose bisphosphate-activated PK, thus reducing the flow of carbon from PEP to lactate. Anaerobically, the malate pool drains into succinate, allowing the derepression of PK. The sensitivity of PK to malate also occurs in several digeneans and cestodes but, except for *Moniezia expansa*, the details of its regulatory significance have not been worked out.

Table 3.2. Effectors of pyruvate kinase (PK) and phosphoenolpyruvate carboxykinase (PEPCK) from parasites.

	Activators	Inhibitors
PK	Cations (Mg^{2+}, Mn^{2+}) PEP, FBP	Malate, ATP, HCO_3^-
PEPCK	Cations (Mg^{2+}, Mn^{2+}) CO_2	ATP

3.2.6   End-products of energy metabolism

End-products of energy metabolism in parasitic protozoa and helminths include ethanol, lactate, pyruvate, acetate, succinate, propionate (Table 3.1) and, in the notable case of *Ascaris lumbricoides,* low molecular weight branched-chain fatty acids (Fig. 3.2). Respiratory end-products which do not quite fit into this pattern are those of the trypanosomes. The pathway of *Trypanosoma brucei* (bloodstream form) is illustrated in Fig. 3.4. The end-products, glycerol and pyruvate, are formed earlier in the pathway than PEP and involve a specialized series of reactions.

Fructose-6-phosphate is split by a unique aldolase to triose and glyceraldehyde-3-phosphate. The reduction of triose to glycerol is then achieved by an NAD-linked oxidation of glyceraldehyde-3-phosphate with the concomitant production of ATP (Bowman & Flynn, 1976).

The formation of end-products can be explained in terms of either 'energetic advantage' or 'redox advantage' but it is much more difficult, at the present state of knowledge, to understand why a particular set of end-products has been adopted by a particular organism.

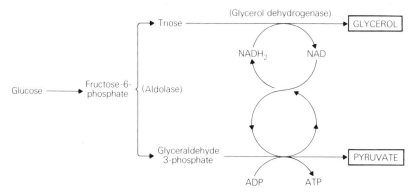

Fig. 3.4. The formation of glycerol and pyruvate by bloodstream *Trypanosoma brucei* under anaerobic conditions.

'Energetic advantage' implies that the specialized pathway to a particular end-product involves the net synthesis of a high energy compound—ATP or GTP—which can be employed in anabolic reactions by the parasite. 'Redox advantage' means that reduced cofactors, such as $NADH_2$, generated in other parts of the pathway, are reoxidized during the formation of the respiratory end-products. Recycling of the cofactors occurs and the subcellular compartments are maintained in an oxidized state. This permits the continued oxidation of highly reduced storage molecules such as glycogen. Thus, the production of either ethanol or lactate from PEP (Fig. 3.1) is equivalent in that their formation involves the synthesis of one molecule of ATP and the reoxidation of one molecule of reduced cofactor. Yet some organisms produce lactate, others produce ethanol and a few produce both.

A number of suggestions have been offered to explain the diversity of end-products of energy metabolism encountered in parasitic organisms. One is that parasites live in the midst of plenty and have simply not experienced selection pressures in favour of terminal respiratory processes which act at maximum efficiency. Thus, those processes which eventually were established depended on phylogeny and evolutionary accident. This proposal does not stand up to examination. There are, no doubt, phylogenetic considerations. However, many parasites which exhibit fermentative pathways as adults live in environments with sufficient available oxygen to permit full oxidation of foodstuffs. Aerobic oxidation is more efficient than anaerobic; the increase in efficiency would surely confer a substantial selective advantage on aerobic parasites in competition with those that depend on fermentation. Parasites may also possess a fermentative type of respiration as adults but have free-living aerobic larvae. The mechanisms which permit aerobic metabolism must therefore be suppressed in response to conditions which occur in the environment of the adult. Fermentation pathways must therefore be considered to be adaptive, rather than occurring by default.

A second suggestion, that excretion of highly reduced end-products is the direct result of living in environments deficient in oxygen, also does not hold. The bloodstream of mammals is certainly not oxygen-deficient and is occupied by many organisms (trypanosomes, schistosomes) which do not completely oxidize carbohydrates. The small intestine of the rat possesses a luminal oxygen tension equivalent to that of venous blood yet *Hymenolepis diminuta* displays the characteristic metabolism of cestodes. In the small intestine of the sheep, oxygen tensions of 35 mmHg occur. It is therefore possible that the metabolism of the sheep tape-worm, *Moniezia expansa*, may be a consequence of low or fluctuating oxygen tensions. The same may be true of *Hymenolepis diminuta*, which is often found in intertwined masses in the rat small intestine. The centres of such masses may well be oxygen-deficient.

A third suggestion is that of Fairbairn (1970) who points out that the energetic burden of removing weaker acids, such as propionic, acetic or succinic acid, is less than that of removing stronger ones such as lactic acid. In addition, there is a distinct energetic advantage—in ATP production—in producing, say, propionic acid rather than lactic acid. Interaction of these factors with the genetic potential of the parasite may bring about specific responses to specific environments.

Finally, recent work on *Hymenolepis diminuta* (see section 3.2.4) has identified a problem which few have suspected. The difference between the North American strain referred to by Podesta *et al.* (1976), which excretes a large amount of succinic acid, and the Australian strain referred to by Ovington & Bryant (1981), which does not, is disturbing for the parasite biochemist. This is not an isolated case. Similar differences are detectable in *Echinococcus granulosus*, the fox and dog strains of which are metabolically distinct. The differences presumably arise from the genetic isolation of the strains. In the case of laboratory strains, the 'founder principle' has removed the parasite from the gene pool of the species, and further selection in the laboratory has intensified the separation. In the case of *Echinococcus*, diversity is assured by the differences between the two species of definitive host. The warning is clear for those whose research is the physiology and biochemistry of parasites. Generalizations based on work done with a single laboratory or field strain may not be valid; and the alternative, of working with several strains simultaneously, may pose enormous logistical problems. It is a dilemma which will have to be faced in the next decade.

3.3   MITOCHONDRIAL METABOLISM

In mammals, the mitochondrion is the organelle which contains the enzymes of the tricarboxylic acid cycle and the carriers of the electron transport system. It is strictly aerobic and the oxidation of one molecule of acetyl coenzyme A brings about the synthesis of 12 molecules of ATP. In parasites, profound modifications of mitochondrial function have evolved in response to the exigencies of their environments. The mitochondrion is, however, still the site of some of the reactions of the tricarboxylic acid cycle and electron transport. It has recently been well reviewed by Köhler (1980).

3.3.1   Mitochondrion and hydrogenosome

Helminth mitochondria generally possess fewer cristae than mammalian mitochondria. This feature is generally accepted as diagnostic of organisms with reduced dependence on oxygen. Protozoan mitochondria are even more remarkable; tubular cristae are frequently encountered. Perhaps the most surprising adaptation is that of *Tritrichomonas foetus*, which has no mitochondria at all. Instead, the cytoplasm contains bodies called hydrogenosomes, whose function is the reoxidation of cofactors and the synthesis of ATP accompanied by the production of molecular hydrogen. Hydrogen production by hydrogenosomes (Fig. 3.5) is apparently a unique feature of the trichomonads (although hydrogen production also occurs in

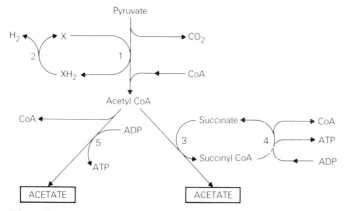

Fig. 3.5. The role of the hydrogenosome in *Tritrichomonas foetus*. These reactions take place within the hydrogenosome. The enzymes concerned are: 1: pyruvate dehydrogenase; 2: hydrogenase, which accepts electrons from an unknown carrier $\times$; 3: acetate-succinate CoA transferase; 4: succinate thiokinase; 5: acetate thiokinase.

Entamoeba histolytica). If the symbiotic hypothesis for the origin of semi-autonomous organelles is correct, it is tempting to speculate that the hydrogenosome is an ancient symbiotic *Clostridium,* the members of which genus depend on hydrogen production for the reoxidation of reduced cofactors.

Little is known about the functions of mitochondria in protozoa. Probably, some of the reactions illustrated in Fig. 3.1 take place within the mitochondrial compartment, but the dynamics of the organelle remain obscure. Much more is known about the metabolism of mitochondria from parasitic helminths, but even this is a tiny amount compared with what is known about mammalian mitochondria.

3.3.2   The dismutation of malate by helminths

In *Ascaris*, the mitochondrion is concerned with the further oxidation of malate. The key enzymes are fumarate hydratase and malic enzyme (they are present in the intermembrane space, not in the mitochondrial matrix, as in mammals), a transhydrogenase and the fumarate reductase system. The last two are associated with the inner mitochondrial membrane.

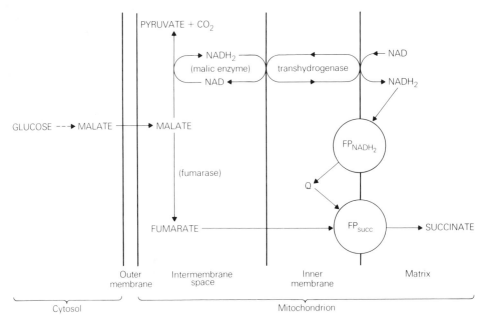

Fig. 3.6. The metabolism of malate by *Ascaris*. (After Rew & Saz, 1974; and Köhler, 1976.) Electrons are transferred from $NADH_2$, generated by malic enzyme activity, across the membrane by the transhydrogenase. They are then passed to FP_{NADH_2} ($NADH_2$ dehydrogenase), ubiquinone (Q) and FP_{succ} (succinate dehydrogenase or fumarate reductase). In this scheme there is no role for cytochromes. Another view (Cheah, 1976) suggests that cytochrome mediated electron transport intervenes at the level of Q.

Malate enters the mitochondrion from the cytosol, and undergoes a dismutation reaction (Fig. 3.6), that is, one in which the oxidation of part of the substrate is counterbalanced by reduction of the remainder. In this case, part of the malate is oxidatively decarboxylated to yield $NADH_2$, pyruvate and carbon dioxide. The other portion is converted to fumarate by fumarate hydratase. The reducing equivalents generated by malic enzyme are transferred across the inner membrane to the mitochondrial matrix by a transhydrogenase. At the same time, fumarate is transported to the matrix where, in the presence of $NADH_2$ and fumarate reductase, succinate is formed. Thus, the reducing equivalents generated by malic enzyme are ultimately used for succinate production with the concurrent synthesis of ATP. In *Ascaris*, the end-products undergo further reactions as outlined in Fig. 3.2.

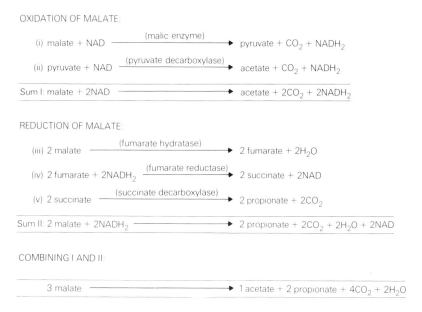

OXIDATION OF MALATE:

(i) malate + NAD $\xrightarrow{\text{(malic enzyme)}}$ pyruvate + CO_2 + $NADH_2$

(ii) pyruvate + NAD $\xrightarrow{\text{(pyruvate decarboxylase)}}$ acetate + CO_2 + $NADH_2$

Sum I: malate + 2NAD $\longrightarrow$ acetate + $2CO_2$ + $2NADH_2$

REDUCTION OF MALATE:

(iii) 2 malate $\xrightarrow{\text{(fumarate hydratase)}}$ 2 fumarate + $2H_2O$

(iv) 2 fumarate + $2NADH_2$ $\xrightarrow{\text{(fumarate reductase)}}$ 2 succinate + 2NAD

(v) 2 succinate $\xrightarrow{\text{(succinate decarboxylase)}}$ 2 propionate + $2CO_2$

Sum II: 2 malate + $2NADH_2$ $\longrightarrow$ 2 propionate + $2CO_2$ + $2H_2O$ + 2NAD

COMBINING I AND II:

3 malate $\longrightarrow$ 1 acetate + 2 propionate + $4CO_2$ + $2H_2O$

Fig. 3.7. The dismutation of malate by *Fasciola hepatica*. The reactions are mitochondrial. $NADH_2$ generated in the oxidative pathway is reoxidized in the reductive pathway, resulting in a propionate : acetate ratio of 2 : 1. ATP yielding steps are (iv) and (v). (After Cornish & Bryant, 1976.)

A similar system, involving dismutation of malate, also occurs in *Hymenolepis diminuta* and, probably, in *Fasciola hepatica*. The evidence for the latter is indirect, and rests upon the ratio of the amount of propionate to that of acetate produced in culture. Cornish & Bryant (1976) found this to be exactly 2 in accordance with the scheme illustrated in Fig. 3.7.

3.3.3   Electron transport

The mechanism of electron transport in mammals involves the reoxidation of reduced cofactors by a system of enzymes and electron carriers. The latter include flavoprotein dehydrogenases, a quinonoid electron carrier, cytochromes b, c and a and, finally, cytochrome oxidase which transfers the electrons to oxygen with the formation of water. During electron transfer, phosphorylation occurs at the levels of $NADH_2$ dehydrogenase, cytochrome b and cytochrome a (Fig. 3.8).

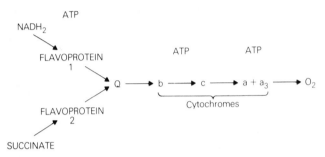

Fig. 3.8. A simplified diagram of the electron transport system in mammals, showing phosphorylation sites. (Flavoproteins 1 and 2 are $NADH_2$-dehydrogenase and succinate dehydrogenase respectively. Q is ubiquinone, or coenzyme Q).

Oxygen is the terminal electron acceptor. It is therefore not surprising that in anaerobic organisms, or in organisms to which the availability of oxygen is restricted, profound modifications of the process of electron transport occur. Alternative terminal electron acceptors must be provided; one commonly employed is fumarate. This appears to be true for a large number of parasitic protozoa and helminths. In helminths at least, this modification is not due to an incapacity to synthesize the carriers and enzymes of the aerobic electron transport system, as it is frequently found that free-living stages possess them.

It is *not* clear why the electron transport systems of parasites occupying environments apparently rich in oxygen should also be profoundly modified, but this does seem to be the case. There is little useful information about protozoan electron transport in this regard. Cytochrome systems have merely been identified as present in the stages parasitic in vertebrates of the following species: *Crithidia, Leishmania, Eimeria* and perhaps *Plasmodium*. However, in *Plasmodium* the system may not be associated with respiration but linked to pyrimidine biosynthesis.

The respiration of culture forms of *Trypanosoma brucei* is partially inhibited by cyanide. Inhibition by cyanide at concentrations less than 10^{-6}M is usually taken to mean that an aerobic cytochrome oxidase system is present. In turn, this is diagnostic of the presence of the classical electron transfer system. In the culture forms, cytochromes b, c and a + a_3 are present, which accounts for the aerobic component of respiration. These cytochromes are generally similar to mammalian ones, differ from them in some details of their physical and chemical characteristics, and perform the same function.

The cyanide insensitive fraction of respiration in culture forms of *Trypanosoma brucei* is probably an anaerobic component; it is mitochondrial and is mediated by cytochrome o (Bowman & Flynn, 1976). Cytochrome o is an alternative oxidase which has been identified in prokaryotes and parasitic helminths. These two pathways are illustrated in Fig. 3.9. An observation which may explain the occurrence of a double system in the culture form, and the fact that the bloodstream form is aerobic, is that the oxygen tension in the tsetse fly intestine is much less than in the vertebrate bloodstream.

Studies of electron transport in helminths are as old as studies of cytochromes. *Ascaris* was one of the animals in which Keilin demonstrated cytochrome in 1925, and reported in his seminal paper *On Cytochrome*. Eight years later, the cestode *Diphyllobothrium* was found to possess an unusual cytochrome system. In recent years, studies of electron transport in helminths have been mostly profitably pursued on two parasite models: muscle mitochondria from *Ascaris* and mitochondria from *Moniezia*.

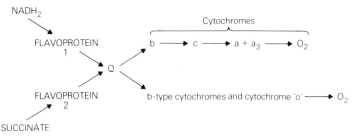

Fig. 3.9. Electron transport in parasitic protozoa and helminths, showing the alternative pathway with cytochrome o. This pathway transfers electrons to oxygen. It is probable that, in the absence of oxygen, it transfers electrons to another acceptor, such as fumarate. Under these circumstances, the succinate branch would, of course, be inoperative. Similar pathways occur in *Trypanosoma brucei*, *Ascaris lumbricoides*, *Moniezia expansa*, *Taenia hydatigena*, *Moniliformis dubius* and *Fasciola hepatica*.

A substantial controversy has centred upon *Ascaris*. It was widely agreed that it possessed a fumarate reductase, and that fumarate accepted electrons from $NADH_2$. The subject of the dispute was whether the transfer of electrons was mediated by a flavoprotein dehydrogenase only, or by a flavoprotein dehydrogenase plus cytochromes. Studies by Cheah (1976) have put the matter beyond question. Cytochromes are involved; disagreement is now on details of transport. Cheah found that *Ascaris* muscle mitochondria contained two terminal oxidases. As in *Trypanosoma* they are cytochrome o and cytochrome a_3. In addition, there are at least three other b-type cytochromes. The cyanide sensitive fraction of respiration accounts for about a quarter of the total, and resembles the classical mammalian system. There is also a major, cyanide insensitive component, terminating in cytochrome o, which transfers electrons to oxygen, with the production of hydrogen peroxide. The production of peroxide may be a consequence of high partial pressure of oxygen in the assay system. This does not affect the general scheme. Evidence suggests that *Ascaris lumbricoides* does make use of its cytochromes *in vivo*: they are readily reduced by endogenous mitochondrial substrates.

Cheah considers that the pathways bifurcate at the cytochrome b level (Fig. 3.9). *Moniezia expansa, Taenia hydatigena*, the acanthocephalan *Moniliformis dubius* and *Fasciola hepatica* probably have very similar electron transport systems.

Electron transport as illustrated in Fig. 3.9 refers only to the behaviour of the system in the presence of oxygen. The helminths mentioned in the preceding paragraphs react uniformly to their environments in that they depend on carbon dioxide fixation by PEPCK, with the eventual production of fumarate to act as an electron acceptor. $NADH_2$ is oxidized by the fumarate reductase system which involves electron-flow mediated oxidative phosphorylation. Superficially, it seems as if the parasite is getting something for nothing. Aerobic organisms synthesize two molecules of ATP for each molecule of succinate converted to fumarate. How, then, is it possible to synthesize ATP by the reverse reaction? The answer lies in summing the overall reaction. The conversion of a molecule of $NADH_2$ to NAD by the electron transport system of aerobic organisms results in the synthesis of three molecules of ATP. To reverse the succinate-fumarate conversion would consume two. In the fumarate reductase system as illustrated in section 3.2.4, therefore, a theoretical net gain of one molecule of ATP is possible. This has yet to be definitely proved, but indirect evidence suggests that fumarate reductase activity is accompanied by the phosphorylation of ADP under anaerobic conditions.

There is evidence from work with *Moniezia expansa, Echinococcus granulosus* and *Fasciola hepatica* that one of the b-type cytochromes (probably cytochrome o, as this also belongs to the b group) transfers electrons directly to fumarate, forming an anaerobic pathway. This aspect of the electron transport system needs much more work. It is, however, extremely difficult to devise the proper experiments.

It is probable that the modified electron transport pathways encountered in parasitic protozoa and helminths are not directly related to the parasitic habit. Many free-living protozoa (e.g. *Tetrahymena, Paramecium* and *Amoeba*) have alternative pathways of electron transport; freshwater turbellarians and soil nematodes possess a cyanide-insensitive component of respiration and high concentrations of the b-type cytochromes.

There are several possible explanations for the existence of such systems. First, the anaerobic pathway may be primitive and the 'classical' electron transport system is a later evolutionary adaptation. In this context, it is interesting that all the carriers to the level of cytochrome are iron based, whereas cytochrome a_3 contains copper. It is almost as if it were a late addition in response to the oxygenation of the primeval atmosphere. Similarities between the free-living and parasitic protozoa and helminths may therefore be generic, derived from their early anaerobic ancestors. Second, there is the possibility that some common component of the environments of protozoa and helminths has elicited similar, but not necessarily homologous, adaptive responses from them. If this is so, we can only speculate as to the critical factor. It may be low or fluctuating oxygen tensions or high carbon dioxide levels, or something entirely unsuspected. Much more information is necessary before we begin to understand the phenomenon. One promising field is the study of the 'sulphide layer'. This is an anaerobic or partially anaerobic biome of enormous area but relatively small thickness, which lies under the surface sediments at the bottom of all major bodies of water. It is inhabited by a primitive anaerobic fauna which may well be derived from the earliest free-living ancestors of modern parasites.

3.4   LIPIDS

All parasites contain lipids, but different parasites contain different amounts. There is no observable correlation of lipid content with the site occupied by the parasite. Nor does it seem that phylogenetic relationships offer any indication of the types and amounts of lipids that a given parasite may possess. Thus, the lipid content of five species of *Trypanosoma* ranges from 11 to 20% of dry weight, and for parasitic protozoa as a whole the average seems to be about 14%. Helminth parasites show much greater variation: 1–34%. Details of the lipid content of parasites may be found in Von Brand (1973).

Lipids can generally be divided into three fractions: (i) glycerides (esters of glycerol and fatty acids) and free fatty acids; (ii) phospholipids; and (iii) unsaponifiable matter, which includes sterols and related substances. In the majority of cases, the functions of the various lipid components in parasites is understood only by analogy with other organisms. Parasites require an external source of lipids for their maintenance in culture. For protozoa, the addition of whole serum to the culture medium is sufficient. Essential components of the serum are cholesterol and one or more fatty acids. Trypanosomes are even capable of absorbing fat droplets when they are available. Once absorbed, however, the fate of the droplets is obscure; presumably lipolysis occurs to yield fatty acids and alcohols. Lipases have been demonstrated in species of *Entamoeba* and *Plasmodium* (Fig. 3.10).

Parasitic helminths also take up lipids and fatty acids, including acetate, from incubation media. The cestodes, *Spirometra* and *Hymenolepis*, absorb triglycerides and phosphatidyl choline. For their prolonged maintenance in culture, a source of lipid is essential.

In many animals, glycerides and free fatty acids form an energy store which may

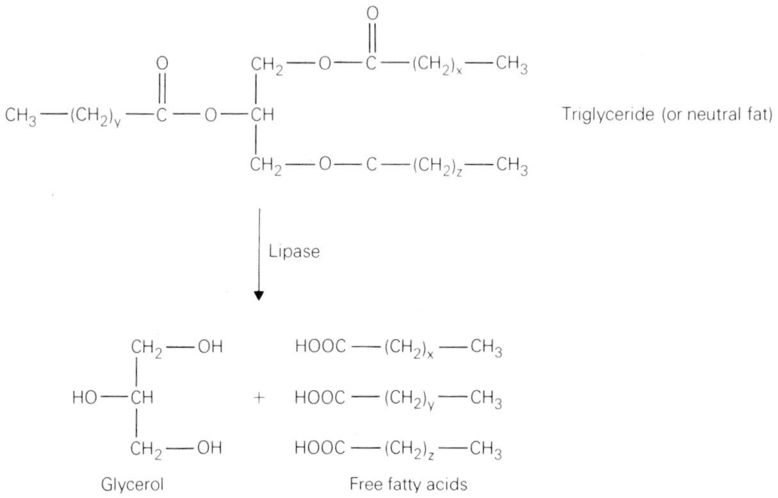

$$CH_3-(CH_2)_y-\overset{\overset{\displaystyle O}{\|}}{C}-O-\overset{\displaystyle CH_2-O-\overset{\overset{\displaystyle O}{\|}}{C}-(CH_2)_x-CH_3}{\underset{\displaystyle CH_2-O-C-(CH_2)_z-CH_3}{CH}}$$

Triglyceride (or neutral fat)

$\downarrow$ Lipase

$$\begin{array}{ccc}
CH_2-OH & & HOOC-(CH_2)_x-CH_3 \\
HO-CH & + & HOOC-(CH_2)_y-CH_3 \\
CH_2-OH & & HOOC-(CH_2)_z-CH_3 \\
\text{Glycerol} & & \text{Free fatty acids}
\end{array}$$

Fig. 3.10. The conversion of triglyceride (or neutral fat) to glycerol and free fatty acids. x, y and z may be any number up to 14.

be drawn upon in times of starvation. While parasites have considerable quantities of glycerides and free fatty acids—from 10 to 80% of total lipid depending on the group—they are, almost certainly, not used in the synthesis of ATP. In *Hymenolepis diminuta,* unsaturated fatty acids predominate. This probably reflects the parasite's circumstances: host dietary fats made of unsaturated fatty acids, and the acids themselves, are more easily emulsified by host bile and more easily absorbed by the tapeworm than those made up of saturated fatty acids. However, while bile salts improve the absorption of long-chain fatty acids and cholesterol by *Hymenolepis,* they are not absolutely necessary for uptake to occur. Once absorbed, digestion of fats apparently proceeds via lipases, which are widely distributed among the helminth groups. Short chain fatty acids, such as acetate, have a different fate and are actively transported into the parasite, where they may be used for lengthening the carbon chain of pre-existing long-chain fatty acids.

Cestodes, of course, have no gut, and their external surfaces perform the function of absorption. Digeneans and nematodes do possess guts and it is possible that the early stages of lipid digestion are extracellular, and take place in the gut lumen. Lipases and other esterases have been demonstrated in the intestinal tracts of digeneans and within their tissues.

No group of parasitic protozoa or helminths seems capable of synthesizing long-chain fatty acids *de novo*—that is, from simple precursors. Although many incorporate labelled acetate into long-chain fatty acids, or carbon, derived from glucose or glycerol, into the lipid fraction, the process usually involves a comparatively slight modification of an existing lipid precursor. *Ascaris* may be an exception; it is possible that it is capable of a very limited amount of *de novo* synthesis, but elongation of pre-existing fatty-acid chains is a much more active process. Protozoa and cestodes are capable only of chain elongation, using acetate for the purpose.

Other components of the lipid fraction, such as glycerol or choline, are freely synthesized. They may then be used in the synthesis of more complex lipids. For example, glycerol is produced from glucose by *Plasmodium* and *Trypanosoma* spp., cestodes and *Ascaris*. It thus appears that most parasites can put together complex lipids provided that they have access to fatty acids. Phospholipids, too, are readily manufactured. They are most often associated with membrane systems. It is therefore not surprising that they are found widely distributed in the parasitic groups and that the protozoa are especially rich in them. In trypanosomes, about 70% of total lipids is phospholipid. In helminths, the range is commonly 10–40%.

In contrast, few, if any, parasites are capable of synthesizing sterols. Neither helminth parasites nor *Plasmodium* proved capable of synthesizing cholesterol; a rare exception is *Crithidia fasciculata* which may be able to synthesize ergosterol *de novo*. It should be noted, however, that these deficiencies in synthetic capacity do not necessarily relate to the parasitic habit; some free-living platyhelminths are also deficient in them. Sterols and other components of the non-saponifiable fraction are also involved in the formation and maintenance of membranes. Adult helminths generally do not mobilize their lipid stores during prolonged starvation, although some larval nematodes do. Little is known about fat catabolism in parasitic protozoa. Bloodstreams forms of *Trypanosoma cruzi* may oxidize fats by an as yet undescribed pathway, while other protozoa do not seem to depend much on fats as an energy store.

This apparent neglect of a resource widely exploited in the animal kingdom is no doubt because parasites possess neither all the enzymes necessary for the β-oxidation of fatty acids, nor active tricarboxylicx acid cycles essential for the oxidation of acetyl CoA produced during β-oxidation. This pathway consists of the sequence of reactions shown in Fig. 3.11.

By repetition of reactions 2–5 shown in Fig. 3.11 fatty acids are oxidized to acetyl CoA. However, *Fasciola hepatica* and *Ascaris lumbricoides* are unable to oxidize exogenous palmitate even though a β-oxidation pathway is present, while *Hymenolepis diminuta* and the acanthocephalan *Moniliformis dubius* lack a complete β-oxidation of fatty acids, nor active tricarboxylic acid cycles essential for the oxidation of acetyl CoA produced during β-oxidation. The latter pathway consists of the sequence of reactions shown in Fig. 3.11.

Many of the free-living larvae of parasitic nematodes are certainly capable of oxidizing stored lipids in the production of energy. Developing eggs of *Ascaris lumbricoides*, free-living larvae and adults of *Strongyloides ratti* oxidize palmitic acid by the β-oxidation pathway. Similarly, there is evidence for lipid oxidation in larval

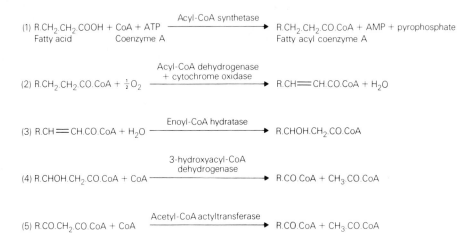

Fig. 3.11. The oxidation of fatty acids to acetyl CoA.

trematodes. Cestode larvae are different; they are parasitic and might therefore be expected to resemble the adults more closely. Only plerocercoids of *Schistocephalus solidus* and *Ligula intestinalis* have been comprehensively studied. In the former, all the enzymes of β-oxidation are present; in the latter they are incomplete. However, neither parasite oxidizes exogenous palmitic acid, incorporating it instead into neutral and phospholipid fractions. The role of the β-oxidation enzymes still remains to be clarified.

3.5   THE METABOLISM OF NITROGENOUS COMPOUNDS

About 20 amino acids are found free in the cytosol or incorporated into proteins in free-living organisms. There is also a limited number of purine and pyrimidine bases. In the many studies of the composition of parasites, the same range of substances has been found. Some parasites are dependent on the host for their supply of these compounds; less often, they are capable of synthesizing nitrogenous compounds *de novo*.

Some definitions are essential for the proper understanding of this section. *Diffusion* is the movement of a solute into a parasite due only to the kinetic energy of the molecules. It occurs only from high concentrations to low ones and, under ideal conditions, will cease when outside and inside concentrations are the same. This equilibrium position may be obscured if the solute in question is rapidly metabolized by the parasite, thus causing it to pass into the parasite continuously. *Facilitated diffusion* involves a carrier which 'picks up' the solute on one side of the cell membrane, moves in across the membrane and there releases it. The carrier then returns to 'pick up' another molecule. Again, kinetic energy provides the motive force and the equilibrium achieved is the same as for diffusion. The advantage of facilitated diffusion is that it reaches that equilibrium more rapidly. In *active transport* a carrier is again involved, but the energy of transport is derived from ATP. In this case, the parasite is able to concentrate a solute within itself against the concentration gradient. Active transport is inhibited by substances which impair energy metabolism. Some parasitic helminths may absorb a compound by a combination of mediated uptake (facilitated diffusion or active transport) and diffusion. An excellent treatment of this subject is to be found in Pappas & Read (1975).

3.5.1   Amino acid uptake and metabolism

Amino acids are absorbed by *Trypanosoma brucei* by a simple diffusion and by mediated processes. There are four transport sites. One is specific for serine, threonine and alanine, the second is specific for aromatic, the third for acidic and the fourth for basic amino acids.

Cestodes also possess mediated mechanisms for amino acid uptake. The transport sites are remarkable as they are stereo-specific for D- and L-amino acids and, unlike mammalian systems, amino acid uptake is independent of ion transport. The acanthocephalan, *Moniliformis dubius*, also possesses both mediated and passive amino acid transport mechanisms but the evidence for the occurrence of mediated processes in digeneans is conflicting. Present information suggests that only passive processes occur in *Fasciola hepatica*, while in schistosomes ion interactions with amino acid transport point to an active process. Nematodes possess a cuticle, so that amino acid uptake occurs through the intestinal epithelium. Uptake is apparently mediated, but detailed data are lacking.

All parasites so far studied can synthesize amino acids. *Trypanosoma rhodesiense* and *Trypanosoma cruzi* manufacture alanine, glycine, serine, aspartate and glutamate: the former utilizes carbohydrate and a nitrogen source while the latter employs the amino acid serine as an initial substrate. *Plasmodium knowlesi* synthesizes alanine, aspartate, glutamate and the sulphur-containing amino acids from various precursors. Some cestodes and nematodes can incorporate ammonia directly into pyruvate and 2-oxoglutarate to form alanine and glutamate, respectively.

Amino acids are readily metabolized by transamination. The two most important reactions, because they interact with pathways of energy metabolism, that are catalysed by aminotransferases are

(i) 2-oxoglutarate + amino acid → glutamate + oxoacid;
(ii) pyruvate + amino acid → alanine + oxoacid.

The reactions are reversible and have been demonstrated in many parasitic protozoa and helminths. The enzymes act upon a large number of different amino acids.

Degradation of amino acids takes place in the presence of L-amino acid oxidases. They catalyse the following general reaction:

$$\text{L-amino acid} + H_2O + O_2 \rightarrow \text{2-oxoacid} + NH_3 + H_2O_2.$$

The ammonia is excreted and the oxoacid may be metabolized further during respiration. Amino acid oxidases have been demonstrated in *Plasmodium berghei*, *Hymenolepis diminuta* and *Ascaris lumbricoides*.

Another end-product of amino acid and protein metabolism is urea. A survey of several parasites showed that none of them possessed all the enzymes of the Krebs'–Henseleit urea cycle, although all possessed one or two (see Fig. 3.12). There is thus no evidence that any internal parasite possesses the urea cycle. Urea presumably originates from purine catabolism (see section 3.5.3) or from the activity of arginase.

Arginase, which is widely distributed among parasites, splits arginine into ornithine and urea. Kurelec (1975) suggested a unique role for arginine metabolism

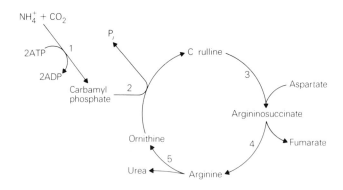

	1 Carbamyl phosphate synthetase	2 Ornithine transcarbamylase	3 Argininosuccinate synthetase	4 Argininosuccinate lyase	5 Arginase
Taenia pisiformis	−	+	+	+	+
Fasciola hepatica	+	+	−	+	+
Toxocara canis	−	+	−	?	+
Moniliformis dubius	−	+	−	−	−

+ Enzyme detected

− Enzyme not detected

? Uncertain

Fig. 3.12. The urea (Krebs–Henseleit) cycle. This cycle has not been demonstrated in parasites, although some of the enzymes have been found.

in *Fasciola hepatica*. He proposed the scheme outlined in Fig. 3.13, to account both for urea formation and proline synthesis by the liver fluke. The proline synthetic pathway has since been investigated in some detail. In particular, it was found that the activity of the worm enzyme which catalyses the final step in the production of proline was four times that of the host. Unlike the mammalian enzyme, it was not subject to end-product inhibition. Several suggestions have been made to account for this pathway. The first suggestion is that reoxidation of $NADH_2$ maintains the redox potential of the cell. A second possibility is that proline is an important vehicle for nitrogen excretion.

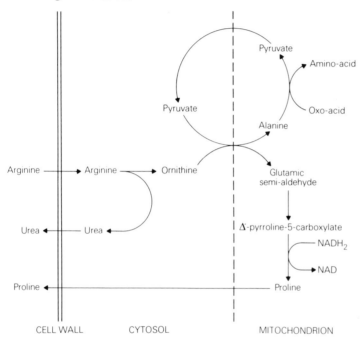

Fig. 3.13. A scheme for arginine catabolism and the production of proline and urea in *Fasciola hepatica*. Arginine is taken up from the environment, converted to ornithine and then, by interaction with a transamination cycle, to glutamic semi-aldehyde. This is eventually converted to proline in the mitochondrion. Proline and urea, a product of the first step in this pathway, are excreted. (After Kurelec, 1975.)

A third suggestion is much more recent. Proline is produced in large quantities by liver fluke. Isseroff and coworkers (Sawma, Isseroff & Reino, 1977) have shown that proline infused into the peritoneal cavity of rats causes bile-duct hyperplasia similar to that produced in the early stages of fascioliasis. It is therefore possible that proline excretion is a strategy by which the parasite improves its definitive environment. If proline has the same effect on bile ducts in ruminants, then proline synthesis takes on an important role in the host–parasite relationship.

3.5.2   Protein synthesis

Little is known about protein synthesis in parasitic helminths and protozoa. What evidence there is suggests that it does not differ significantly from that found in other organisms.

3.5.3   Purines and pyrimidines

Purines and pyrimidines are bases which possess the heterocyclic ring structure illustrated in Figs 3.14 and 3.15. Adenine and guanine are purine derivatives; thymine and cytosine are pyrimidines. A *nucleoside* is the combination of a heterocyclic base with a sugar, usually D-ribose. A *nucleotide* is the combination of a heterocyclic base with a sugar phosphate. ATP is a nucleotide.

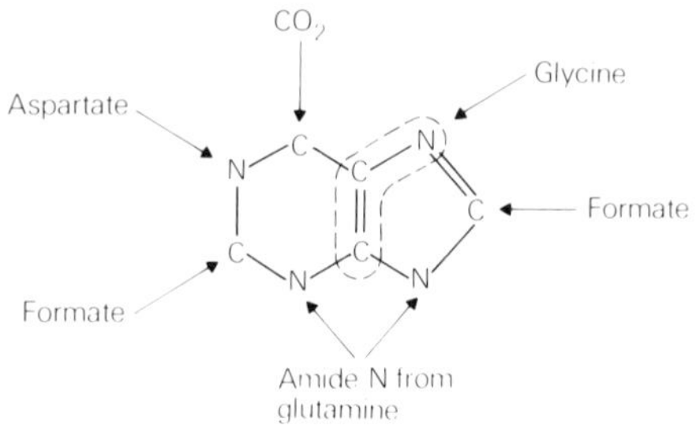

Fig. 3.14. The origins of the atoms which form the purine ring during *de novo* synthesis.

Many organisms synthesize purines from simple precursors. In pigeon liver, it has been found that the purine ring is assembled on ribose phosphate, so that the final product is a nucleotide, not a free purine. The components of the purine ring derive from carbon dioxide, formate, glycine, aspartate and glutamine (Fig. 3.14) and the initial product is inosine monophosphate. Once formed, there are several possible enzyme reactions which catalyse the interconversion of the various purine derivatives.

It is doubtful whether any of the protozoan or helminth parasites so far examined has the capacity to synthesize the purine ring *de novo*. A possible exception is *Crithidia oncopelti*; but, for the remainder, studies of radioactive carbon uptake from the simple precursors lead one to the conclusion that parasites rely on their environments to provide a source of purines. In the absence of *de novo* synthesis, it is not surprising to find elaborate systems for absorption and interconversion of existing purines. The latter are the so-called 'salvage' pathways, widely distributed in parasites.

Evidence, scanty though it is, suggests, however, that parasitic protozoa and some helminths are capable of synthesizing pyrimidines *de novo* (Fig. 3.15). For protozoa, this information derives from studies of nutritional requirements in

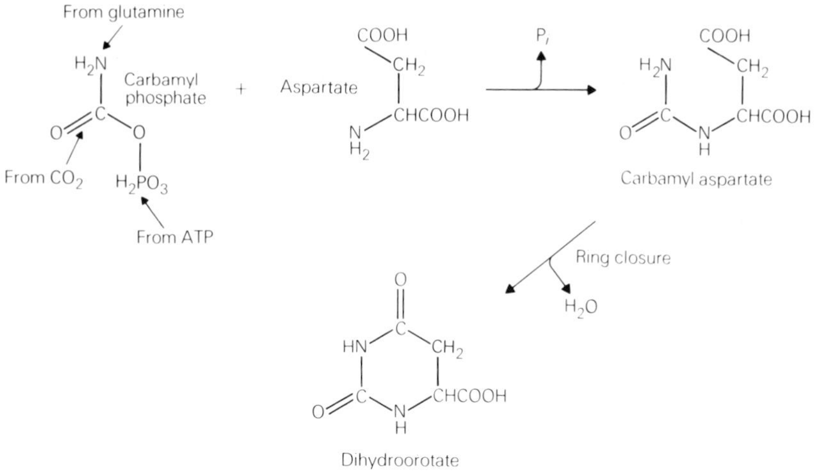

Fig. 3.15. The *de novo* pathway for the synthesis of pyrimidines. The enzymes responsible for these initial steps are carbamyl phosphate synthetase (for the synthesis of carbamyl phosphate), aspartate carbamyl transferase and dihydroorotase.

culture and from radiocarbon experiments in which labelled bicarbonate is followed into pyrimidine components of nucleic acids. Similarly, in at least one tapeworm, regeneration experiments in media free of pyrimidines suggest that *de novo* synthesis does occur.

3.5.4   Absorption of purines and pyrimidines

The mechanisms for absorption of nutrients by parasitic helminths have been comprehensively reviewed by Pappas & Read (1975). The information relating to protozoan parasites is virtually nonexistent. Most of the information on purine absorption in helminths is derived primarily from *Hymenolepis diminuta*. However, there is good reason to believe that what is true for *Hymenolepis diminuta* will be true for other cestodes. Moreover, similarities between the 'salvage' pathways in parasitic helminths and protozoa encourage the belief that complex absorption mechanisms also occur in the latter.

In *Hymenolepis diminuta*, mechanisms for the absorption of purines and pyrimidines are complex. There seem to be at least three carrier systems, two of which bind several substrate molecules simultaneously. The uptake of uracil, adenine and hypoxanthine occurs both by diffusion and mediated transport. Either purines or pyrimidines inhibit uracil uptake. In addition, purines, but not pyrimidines, inhibit hypoxanthine uptake; and uracil or thymine stimulates radioactive uracil uptake. However, uracil, under certain conditions can also inhibit the uptake of radioactive uracil! When the rate of thymine uptake is plotted against thymine concentration, the resulting curve is sigmoid in shape. Sigmoidicity is an indication of cooperativity—that is, the binding of one substrate molecule facilitates the binding of a second. From studies such as those of Pappas & Read (1975) it is possible to calculate the number of binding sites which, in the present instance, proved to be at least two. One site was designated an 'activator', the other a 'transport' site.

This information on purine and pyrimidine uptake by *Hymenolepis diminuta* is summarized in the model which is illustrated in Table 3.3. It identifies three distinct loci for absorption. At the thymine/uracil locus, thymine or uracil binds to activator and transport sites, resulting in cooperative uptake. Adenine and hypoxanthine are bound at this locus without accelerating the transport of pyrimidines. At hypoxanthine locus no. 1, only adenine attaches to activator and transport sites and thus shows cooperativity. Guanine and hypoxanthine bind only to the transport site, and display simple, hyperbolic, kinetics. At hypoxanthine locus no. 2, hypoxanthine is transported, while adenine acts a competitive inhibitor.

Table 3.3. Uptake of purines and pyrimidines of *Hymenolepis diminuta*. The thymine-uracil and hypoxanthine no. 1 loci possess two binding sites. Binding of bases to the 'activator site' increases transport of the bases indicated under 'transport site'. Those in italics inhibit transport. Hypoxanthine no. 2 locus possesses no activator site.

Thymine-Uracil locus		Hypoxanthine locus no. 1		Hypoxanthine locus no. 2
Activator site	Transport site	Activator site	Transport site	transport site
Thymine	Thymine	Adenine	Adenine	Hypoxanthine
Uracil	Uracil		Guanine	
			Hypoxanthine	
	(Adenine)			*(Adenine)*
	(Hypoxanthine)			

Almost the only other parasite in which purine and pyrimidine uptake has been investigated is *Schistosoma mansoni*. Pyrimidines are taken up by simple diffusion, while purines are absorbed by a combination of mediated transport and diffusion. Adenosine also interacts in this system, as it too can be taken up. Adenosine partially inhibits adenine uptake and *vice-versa*. These observations are consistent with the view that *Schistosoma mansoni* possesses a single purine transport system, a single nucleoside transport system and a third system which transports both purines and nucleosides.

3.5.5   Salvage pathways for purines

Parasites are found to possess the same spectrum of purines encountered in other organisms. They depend, therefore, on the interconversion of pre-existing purines. Experiments with media containing the minimum number of components necessary for maintenance of the parasites may identify what purines are necessary for maintenance and growth. Alternatively, studies with radioactively labelled precursors provide evidence for interconversion.

Of the protozoa, the purine salvage pathways have been elucidated only in *Trypanosoma gambiense* and *Plasmodium chabaudi*. The results are indicated in Fig. 3.16. Those of parasitic helminths are equally poorly known, but it appears that the capacity for purine synthesis in *Schistosoma mansoni* is comparable to that of the protozoa. If purines are not fully utilized, there is evidence that, in helminths at least, many of them are degraded to ammonia. A degradation pathway is illustrated in Fig. 3.17. The full pathway is presumed to be present in *Ascaris* as urea is produced from purines and the nematode lacks an ornithine–urea cycle.

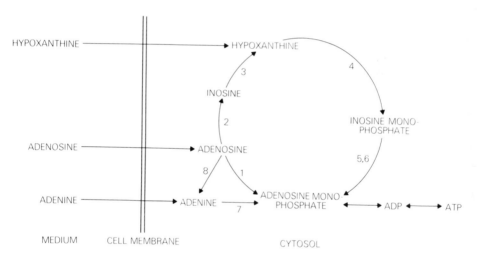

Fig. 3.16. The purine salvage pathways in some parasitic protozoa and helminths. The enzymes concerned are: 1: adenosine kinase; 2: adenosine deaminase; 3: inosine phosphorylase; 4: hypoxanthine phosphoribosyl transferase; 5, 6: adenylo-succinate lyase and synthetase; 7: adenine phosphoribosyl transferase; 8: purine nucleoside hydrolase. They are all present in *Schistosoma mansoni; Plasmodium chabaudi* lacks 8, and *Trypanosoma gambiense* lacks 2 and 3.

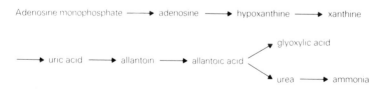

Fig. 3.17. The probable pathway of purine degradation in parasitic nematodes, inferred from the detection of the end-products after the administration of purine compounds.

3.5.6   Pyrimidine metabolism

Pyrimidine synthesis *de novo* involves incorporation of glutamine, bicarbonate and aspartate into uridine monophosphate in accordance with the reaction scheme outlined in Fig. 3.15. There is circumstantial evidence, mainly derived from culture and incorporation studies, that this pathway is widely distributed in protozoa and in the tetrathyridia larvae of the tapeworm *Mesocestoides*. In addition, the first three enzymes of the *de novo* pathway have been detected in *Ascaris*. There is also evidence of the existence of the *de novo* pyrimidine synthesis pathway in the digeneans *Opisthorchis sinensis* and *Paragonimus ohirae*.

'Salvage' pathways for pyrimidines, by which one can be converted into another, also exist in parasitic protozoa. They are of different importance in different parasites: *Plasmodium* spp. make little use of them, whereas *Trypanosoma* spp. are reliant equally on salvage and on *de novo* synthesis of pyrimidines.

3.6   RNA AND DNA METABOLISM

Protein synthesis in mammals is mediated by three functional types of RNA. Although only transfer and ribosomal RNA have as yet been isolated from parasitic protozoa, it is generally accepted that messenger RNA is also present. Similarly, protein synthesis in parasitic helminths is thought to follow the mammalian pattern.

The DNA of parasites is unremarkable. There is no evidence for the presence of any unusual base, neither is there evidence to suggest that the organization of the genome is unusual. The argument that parasites, which depend for many of their requirements on the genetic information of their hosts, should possess a diminished genome, is not borne out by observation. In fact, parasitic nematodes and flatworms have more complex genomes than their free-living relatives.

Mitochondrial DNA from parasites is likewise unremarkable. However, the DNA from the trypanosome kinetoplast shows some unusual features. The major structural element is the minicircle, less than $1.0\,\mu$m in diameter. Minicircles tend to form links with each other so that the whole DNA content of the kinetoplast can be removed intact as a gigantic circular network with a mass of 2×10^{22} daltons. Maxicircles, about 5–$12\,\mu$m in diameter are also found in several species. The function of this complex system remains unknown.

3.7   SUMMARY AND CONCLUSIONS

The biochemistry of parasites is different in many ways from that of higher metazoa. Respiratory metabolism places greater emphasis on fermentative processes, and parasites characteristically excrete a wide range of incompletely oxidized respiratory end-products. In particular, there is an emphasis on pathways of carbon dioxide fixation leading to the production of acetate and succinate or propionate, often by the dismutation of malate. Synthesis of ATP takes place by substrate-linked and electron transport-mediated processes. The tricarboxylic acid cycle is rarely encountered in a completely active form and electron transport is profoundly modified. However, an 'orthodox' aerobic electron transport system is often present in parasitic organisms, but usually subordinated to an alternative system in which cytochromes of the b type and perhaps o cytochromes figure. The latter is the anaerobic system, and may include a fumarate reductase which generates ATP during the $NADH_2$-dependent reduction of fumarate to succinate.

Lipid metabolism is not clearly understood. All parasites require an external source of lipids for proper maintenance. They may be capable of synthesizing some of the components of the lipid fraction but, generally, synthetic activity is limited to lengthening the carbon chain of pre-existing fatty acids. The current state of knowledge suggests that only larval nematodes are capable of oxidizing fatty acids.

Parasite amino acid and DNA metabolism are not very remarkable. The capacity for purine synthesis, however, is absent from the majority of parasites, which perforce rely on external sources of purines. It is not known whether they once, in their evolutionary past, did possess this ability. Pyrimidine synthesis probably occurs in protozoa and nematodes.

None of the biochemical strategies described in this chapter can be unequivocally ascribed to the parasitic habit. There is some evidence which suggests that many of the adaptations may also be encountered in free-living organisms, especially protozoa, nematodes and flatworms, which occupy habitats with low or fluctuating oxygen tensions and high CO_2 concentrations. The environments of parasites may be considered to be an extension of these.

If a particular metabolic capacity is absent, such as synthetic or oxidative pathways for purines or fatty acids, one may *suspect* that excision has occurred to effect economies in the energy expenditure of the parasite. However, as Fairbairn (1970) writes of helminths 'No unequivocal loss of genetic capacity is known. Either . . . the genetic information is present but repressed, or an insufficient study of all stages of a life cycle has been made'.

REFERENCES AND FURTHER READING

Barrett J. (1977) Energy metabolism and infection in helminths. In A.E.R Taylor & R. Müller (eds.) *Parasite Invasion*, pp. 121–44. Oxford, Blackwell Scientific Publications.

Borst P. & Fairlamb A.H. (1976) DNA of parasites, with special reference to kinetoplast DNA. In H. Van den Bossche (ed.) *Biochemistry of Parasites and Host-parasite Relationships*, pp. 89–94. Amsterdam, North Holland Publishing Co.

Bowman I.B.R. & Flynn I.W. (1976) Oxidative metabolism of trypanosomes. In W.H.R. Lumsden & D.A. Evans (eds.) *Biology of the Kinetoplastida*, vol.1, pp. 435–76. London, Academic Press.

Bryant C. (1970) Electron transport in parasitic helminths and protozoa. In B. Dawes (ed.) *Advances in Parasitology*, vol.8, pp. 139–71. London, Academic Press.

Bryant C. (1975) Carbon dioxide utilisation and the regulation of respiratory metabolic pathways in parasitic helminths. In B. Dawes (ed.) *Advances in Parasitology*, vol.13, pp. 35–69. London, Academic Press.

Bryant C. & Behm C.A. (1976) Regulation of respiratory metabolism in *Moniezia expansa* under aerobic and anaerobic conditions. In H. Van den Bossche (ed.) *Biochemistry of Parasites and Host-parasite Relationships*, pp. 89–94. Amsterdam, North Holland Publishing Co.

Cheah K.S. (1976) Electron transport system of *Ascaris* muscle mitochondria. In H. Van den Bossche (ed.) *Biochemistry of Parasites and Host-parasite Relationships*, pp. 133–44. Amsterdam, North Holland Publishing Co.

Cornish R.A. & Bryant C. (1976) The metabolic integrity of *Fasciola hepatica* during *in vitro* maintenance. *Int. J. Parasit.* **6**, 387–92.

Fairbairn D. (1970) Biochemical adaptation and loss of genetic capacity in helminth parasites. *Biol. Rev.* **45**, 29–72.

Friedman M.J. & Trager W. (1981) The biochemistry of resistance to malaria. *Scient. Am.* **244** (3), 112–20.

Gutteridge W.E. & Coombs G.H. (1977) *Biochemistry of Parasitic Protozoa*. London, Macmillan.

Kennedy C.R. (ed.) (1976) *Ecological Aspects of Parasitology*. Amsterdam, North Holland Publishing Co.

Köhler P. (1976) Hydrogen transport in the muscle mitochondria of *Ascaris suum*. In H. Van den Bossche (ed.) *Biochemistry of Parasites and Host-parasite Relationships*, pp. 125–32. Amsterdam, North Holland Publishing Co.

Köhler P. (1980) The function of mitochondrial enzymes. In L. Vitale & V. Simeon (eds.) *Industrial and Clinical Enzymology*, pp. 243–56. Oxford, Pergamon Press.

Köhler P., Bryant C. & Behm C.A. (1978) ATP synthesis in a succinate decarboxylase system from *Fasciola hepatica* mitochondria. *Int. J. Parasit.* **8**, 399–404.

Körting W. & Barrett J. (1978) Studies on β-oxidation in the plerocercoids of *Ligula intestinalis* (Cestoda: Pseudophyllidea). *Z. Parasit Kde.* **57**, 243–6.

Kurelec B. (1975) Catabolic path of arginine and NAD regeneration in the parasite *Fasciola hepatica*. *Comp. Biochem. Physiol.* **51B**, 151–6.

de Mata Z.S., Saz H.J. & Pasto D. (1977) 2-methylacetoacetate reductase and possible propionyl coenzyme A condensing enzyme activity in branched chain volatile fatty acid synthesis by *Ascaris lumbricoides*. *J. biol. Chem.* **252**, 4215–24.

Müller M. (1975) Biochemistry of protozoan microbodies. *A. Rev. Microbiol.* **29**, 467–83.

Ovington K.S. & Bryant C. (1981) The role of carbon dioxide in the formation of end-products by *Hymenolepis diminuta*. *Int. J. Parasitol.* **11**, 221–8.

Pappas P.W. & Read C.P. (1975) Membrane transport in helminth parasites: a review. *Expl Parasit.* **37**, 469–530.

Podesta R.B. & Mettrick D.F. (1974) Pathophysiology of cestode infections: effects of *Hymenolepis diminuta* on oxygen tensions, pH and gastrointestinal function. *Int. J. Parasit.* **4**, 277–92.

Podesta R.B., Mustafa T., Moon T.W., Hulbert W.C. & Mettrick D.F. (1976) Anaerobes in an aerobic environment; role of CO_2 in energy metabolism of *Hymenolepis diminuta*. In H. Van den Bossche (ed.) *Biochemistry of Parasites and Host-parasite Relationships*, pp. 81–8. Amsterdam, North Holland Publishing Co.

Rew R.S. & Saz H.J. (1974) Enzyme localisation in the anaerobic mitochondria of *Ascaris lumbricoides*. *J. Cell Biol.* **63**, 125–35.

Rogers W.P. (1949) On the relative importance of aerobic metabolism in small nematode parasites of the alimentary canal. I. Oxygen tensions in the normal environment of the parasites. *Aust. J. scient Res.* **2B**, 157–65.

Rogers W.P. (1952) Nitrogen catabolism in some nematode parasites. *Aust. J. Sci. Res.* **5B**, 210–22.

Sawma J.T., Isseroff H. & Reino D. (1977) Proline in fascioliasis—IV. Induction of bile duct hyperplasia. *Comp. Biochem. Physiol.* **61A**, 239–43.

Searcy D.G. & McInnis A.J. (1970) Measurements by DNA renaturation of the genetic basis of parasitic reduction. *Evolution N.Y.* **24**, 796–806.

Von Brand T. (1973) *Biochemistry of Parasites.* London, Academic Press.

Von Brand T. (1979) *Biochemistry and Physiology of Endoparasites.* Amsterdam, Elsevier/North Holland.

Chapter 4
Physiology
L.H. Chappell

4.1 INTRODUCTION

The scope of parasite physiology is enormous. It involves parasitic animals that belong to several invertebrate phyla, interactions with hosts in all plant and animal phyla, and the complete range of biological regulatory and control mechanisms that can be included under the general term physiology. This chapter is an attempt to introduce the range of parasite physiology at the inevitable expense of detail and, as a consequence, few examples can be treated in depth.

A knowledge and understanding of parasite physiology is fundamental to both academic and applied parasitology, but there are large areas where it lags behind the physiology of free-living animals. Parasite physiology is, however, an exciting and complex discipline that offers many unique opportunities for investigation and a challenge to the research scientist.

4.2 TRANSMISSION OF PARASITES BETWEEN HOSTS

There are three basic ways by which parasites are transmitted to new hosts:
1 the prospective host feeds on the egg or larval stage of the parasite or on an intermediate host that harbours the larval parasite;
2 an intermediate host (often termed vector) acquires and subsequently transmits the parasite while feeding on host blood or tissues;
3 the larval parasite actively locates and penetrates (or settles upon) the intermediate or final host in the life cycle.
The first two mechanisms are passive processes from the parasite's standpoint, while the third involves the active participation of the larval parasite (Table 4.1). The majority of larval parasites that are transmitted through oral ingestion are enclosed within a cyst or within the protective egg membranes. Cysts can be found both in the external environment or within the tissues of an intermediate host animal.

4.2.1 Parasite cysts

Parasitic amoebae of the alimentary canal, e.g. *Entamoeba histolytica*, commonly produce resistant cysts that contain quiescent, infective forms and which pass to the outside with host faeces to await ingestion by the next host. Little is known of the physiology of cyst formation in alimentary canal amoebae.

Table 4.1. Transmission stages of parasites: a synopsis.

	Parasite eaten by host	Arthropod vector transmits parasite	Parasite actively locates host
Protozoa	Coccidian cysts	Babesias	—
	Amoebic cysts	Trypanosomes	
		Malaria	
Monogenea	—	—	Oncomiracidium
Digenea	Metacercaria	—	Miracidium
	Cercaria (some)		Cercaria
Cestoda	Egg	—	—
	Cysticercoid		
	Cysticercus		
	Coenurus		
	Hydatid cyst		
	Coracidium		
	Procercoid		
	Plerocercoid		
Acanthocephala	Egg	—	—
	Cystacanth		
Nematoda	Egg		
	Larvae (L_3)	Larvae	Larvae
	(ensheathed or free)	(microfilariae)	(e.g. hookworms)

Amongst the sporozoans both coccidians and gregarines form resistant, infective cysts. The gregarines, which are mostly parasitic in the gut of arthropods, synchronize cyst formation with the host's moulting cycle (e.g. *Gregarina garnhami* in desert locusts) and these cysts are liberated along with host faeces. Some gregarines encyst as the host reaches sexual maturity and the cysts are shed along with the germinal products of the host (e.g. *Gonospora arenicola* in *Arenicola*). The transmission of such parasites is controlled by hormonal cycles of host origin.

Coccidians form resistant oocysts that contain the sporocyst stages; these are voided with the faeces (e.g. *Eimeria, Isospora, Toxoplasma*). Reinfection occurs on ingestion of the oocyst by a new host animal.

Some of the parasitic flagellates have cystic stages that are involved in transmission between hosts (e.g. *Giardia*). An unusual case is that of *Histomonas*, which is transmitted between bird hosts within the developing eggs of the parasitic nematode *Heterakis gallinarum*. In the Opalinatea, cysts are produced only during the breeding season of the amphibian host; encystment can be inhibited experimentally by keeping sexually mature frogs in hibernation by enforced drought. Ciliates possess encysted stages in their life cycles (e.g. *Balantidium coli* in man and pigs and *Nyctotherus* in frogs and toads). Cyst formation in both *Opalina ranarum* and *Nyctotherus cordiformis* is controlled by host sex hormones.

Amongst the helminth parasites encysted transmission stages are common. In the Digenea, metacercarial cysts may be found either in the external environment or within the body of an intermediate host. The liver fluke, *Fasciola hepatica*, encysts as a metacercaria on vegetation, where it awaits ingestion by the final host. This cyst has a thick, highly resistant structure. The morphology of the cyst wall of digenean metacercariae varies considerably, particularly with regard to the number of distinct layers that are present, which can range from one to four (*Fasciola hepatica* has four). Very little is known about the relationship between the morphology of the metacercarial cyst wall and the physiological conditions for optimum excystation (see section 4.3.1).

Encysted tapeworm larvae only occur within the body of an intermediate host. These larvae are frequently proliferative, containing large numbers of larvae formed by asexual budding (see section 4.5.1). Cystic stages of cestodes include cysticercoids in the Hymenolepididae, cysticerci and coenuri in the Taeniidae and the hydatid cysts of *Echinococcus*. Hydatid cysts may be simple (unilocular) or more complex in their structure (multivesicular, alveolar or multilocular). Regardless of their structure, each cyst can contain between 12 and 18 million larval scoleces, each of which is a potential adult tapeworm if ingested by a suitable final host.

Several nematode genera produce cystic forms that are concerned with transmission. Larval *Trichinella spiralis* encysts in mammalian muscles; *Syngamus* may encyst in the haemocoel of an invertebrate transport host. Some plant parasitic nematodes develop cysts with a remarkably high resistance to desiccation. *Heterodera rostochiensis* cysts, for example, contain viable eggs after 8 years of drying and many of the pastoral nematodes, such as the cattle and sheep parasitic trichostrongyles, have desiccation resistant eggs and third stage larvae. Ensheathment of the L_3 larva involves protection of the infective stage in the cuticle of the previous moult (e.g. *Haemonchus contortus*).

The life cycle of acanthocephalans typically includes the formation of an encysted, parasitic larva—the cystacanth. This stage inhabits the haemocoel of the arthropod intermediate host: a second phase of encystment may occur if the first intermediate host is eaten by a transport host in which development to maturity cannot be completed. The cystacanth is surrounded by a very thin cyst wall.

4.2.2   Mechanisms for location of the host

Active location of either the intermediate or the final host is a function carried out by a variety of larval parasite stages. These include oncomiracidia larvae (and adults) in the Monogenea, miracidia and cercariae in the Digenea, coracidia in the Cestoda, and infective L_3 larvae in the Nematoda. With the single exception of the coracidia of pseudophyllidean cestodes, these larvae all actively seek out and attach to, or penetrate, the next host in the life cycle. Although considerable research effort has been invested in mechanisms of host locations, the physiology of these processes remains largely unexplained.

(a)   Monogenea

Little information has been gathered on host location in the Monogenea, with one exception, *Entobdella soleae*, a parasite of the gills and body surface of European marine flatfish. The comprehensive studies of Kearn have revealed the importance of chemotaxis in host recognition by the oncomiracidia of *Entobdella*. These larvae are active swimmers with a strongly ciliated epidermis, and possess four eye-spots (Fig. 2.1). Epidemiological evidence shows clearly that *E. soleae* has a marked preference for the sole (*Solea solea*) over alternative cohabiting flatfish. This preference is mediated, in experimental conditions, by chemotactic recognition of a suitable host; the skin itself possibly produces the chemical signal for miracidial attraction.

(b)   Digenea

Two distinct kinds of larvae are concerned with active location of the host—the miracidium and the cercaria (see section 2.4.4). The miracidium is a ciliated, swimming larvae of limited life-span that hatches from the egg in water and attempts to locate and penetrate the molluscan intermediate host. The cercaria can be involved in transmission in one of several ways, for example it can encyst on vegetation as a metacercaria (e.g. *Fasciola hepatica*) or it may swim or crawl and locate the next host in the life cycle and then actively penetrate through the epidermis (e.g. *Schistosoma mansoni*).

The ciliated miracidium larva possesses a variety of sensory structures including eye-spots and epidermal papillae. Miracidial responses to environmental stimuli are thought to favour the larval parasite entering the close proximity of a snail. Miracidia react variously to light, temperature, gravity, water currents and to changes in pCO_2, pO_2 and pH. The extent to which chemotaxis is involved in locating a suitable snail is a matter of considerable controversy. There is experimental evidence that miracidia of many species of digenean identify and approach chemoattractants released by the snail, which are possibly mucoid in composition. Contradictory evidence also exists to support the assertion that host-finding by miracidia is a random, trial-and-error process.

Miracidia of *Schistosoma mansoni* detect and approach intact snails, crushed snails and agar blocks impregnated with snail extract. Certain fatty acids, amino acids and sialic acid in agar will induce detectable changes in miracidial swimming behaviour. Although snail mucus is almost universally regarded as the most likely chemoattractant for digenean miracidia, there is little indication as to which component of this complex secretion might specifically be involved. On the other hand, experimental observations on a number of different miracidia including *Fasciola hepatica*, *Fascioloides magna*, *Gigantobilharzia huronensis*, *Schistosoma mansoni*, *Schistosomatium douthitti*, *Trichobilharzia elvae* and *T. physellae*) refute the chemoattraction hypothesis, stressing the importance of the effects of environmental stimuli that bring host and parasite together, as well as the element of accidental discovery.

The mechanisms of location of the host by the cercaria are also surrounded by controversy, although current evidence swings in favour of chemoattraction as the major component. Cercariae, like miracidia, have pronounced responses to the physical elements of their environment. For example, many of the swimming cercariae are positively phototactic; superimposed upon this may be a positive response to shadows (e.g. *Posthodiplostomum cuticola*, a strigeid that infects fishes). Schistosome cercariae, by contrast, appear to lack chemotaxis, although attachment and penetration may be aided by host secretions such as sebum or cholesterol.

(c)   Cestoda

The coracidium of the Pseudophyllidea is a ciliated, swimming larva that hatches from the egg. It is infective to copepods to whom it presents itself as food. In this case transmission may be regarded as a passive process.

(d)   Nematoda

Chemical attraction is probably an important component of host location by many larval plant and animal parasitic nematodes. Nematode larvae are well endowed with sensory structures and show complex patterns of behaviour.

4.2.3   Mechanisms for penetration of the host

Active penetration of the host through its epidermis is typical of miracidia, cercariae and some nematode larvae.

Penetration of a suitable snail by a miracidium is effected by secretions from the complex of apical glands of the miracidium. These secretions contain both lubricants and lytic enzymes. Some miracidia shed their ciliated epidermis during the act of penetration (e.g. *Fasciola hepatica* and *Fascioloides magna*), while many species retain their cilia. These differences in behaviour are unexplained.

The penetration of avian and mammalian skin by schistosome cercariae has attracted considerable research interest. Skin lipids are important stimulants for penetration (e.g. free fatty acids in mammalian schistosomes). Secretions from the cercarial acetabular glands, along with vigorous body movements, are essential components for successful penetration.

The infective larvae of hookworms and their relatives actively penetrate the skin of the vertebrate final host. The involvement of lytic enzymes of parasite origin in penetration has been examined using a variety of techniques, including the Goodey 'floating raft' of excised skin. Despite extensive observations, it is not clear whether these larval nematodes penetrate the host aided by enzyme secretion.

4.2.4   Circadian rhythms in parasite transmission

Transmission to a new host may in some cases be related to patterns of circadian (24 h) rhythms in either adult or larval parasites. Hawking (1975) classified these rhythms as follows:
1   synchronous cell division (e.g. malaria parasites);
2   release of infective forms:
(a) from the definitive (final) host (e.g. coccidia, pinworms, schistosomes),
(b) from the intermediate host (e.g. schistosomes);
3   migratory behaviour (e.g. malaria parasites, trypanosomes, microfilariae).

(a)   Synchronous cell division

Asexual reproduction (i.e. schizogony) is profoundly periodic in occurrence in many species of malaria parasite. Cell division may occur every 24 h (e.g. *Plasmodium knowlesi*), 48 h (e.g. *P. vivax*) or 72 h (e.g. *P. malariae*). This is related to the production of gametocyctes in the circulatory system, which are infective to the mosquito vector. There is evidence that exflagellation of the gametocyte takes place at a time of day that coincides with the feeding activities of the appropriate species of mosquito. Circadian rhythms of this type are possibly entrained to the daily temperature cycle of homoiothermic hosts; experimental hypothermia in monkeys disrupts the circadian pattern of malarial development.

(b)   Release of infective forms

There are several examples of the circadian release of infective parasites, timed so as to optimize transmission. Amongst the Coccidia, the oocysts of *Isospora* are released from the gut of the bird host at the time of day when roosting occurs (i.e. late afternoon). This greatly increases the chances of a new host accidentally ingesting the oocysts and becoming infected.

Mammalian pinworms (e.g. *Syphacia muris* in rats and *Enterobius vermicularis* in man) migrate diurnally from the rectum to the perianal region to lay eggs. The migration is related to the lowering of the rectal temperature of mammals during sleep; it serves to release eggs that will not become contaminated by host faeces until infection by the hand-to-mouth route has been accomplished.

Schistosome cercariae are released from snails on a diurnal basis; release may be during the day (e.g. *Schistosoma bovis, S. haematobium, S. mattheei* and *S. mansoni*) or at night (e.g. *S. japonicum*).

(c)   Migratory behaviour

Certain types of parasite migration within the body of the host are associated with transmission. Larval filarial worms (microfilariae) present one such example. The adult nematode inhabits deep tissues of the mammal and transmission is by mosquitoes that feed on peripheral blood. Microfilariae are liberated from the adult worms on a diurnal basis according to the feeding activities of the vector. Several distinct categories have been recognized:
1   microfilariae numerous in peripheral blood at night only (e.g. *Wuchereria bancrofti, Brugia malayi*);
2   microfilariae numerous in peripheral blood by day only (e.g. *Loa loa*);
3   microfilariae more numerous in peripheral blood in the evening (e.g. *Dirofilaria immitis*);
4   microfilariae in the peripheral blood over the entire 24 h, but more numerous in the afternoon (e.g. *W. bancrofti* Pacific form).
When the microfilariae are not in the peripheral blood they accumulate within the pulmonary circulation at the arteriole-capillary junctions. The difference in oxygen tension (ΔpO_2) between pulmonary arterial and venous blood is responsible for the diurnal migration of the microfilariae. The larvae of *W. bancrofti* accumulate in the pulmonary circulation when the ΔpO_2 is 55 mmHg or greater; decrease of ΔpO_2 to 47 mmHg or below results in the migration of microfilariae to the peripheral blood (Table 4.2 and Fig. 4.1).

Table 4.2. The effects of human venous and arterial oxygen tension on the distribution of *Wuchereria bancrofti* microfilariae. (Based on data from Hawking, 1975.)

Activity of host	Arterial pO_2 (mmHg)	Venous pO_2 (mmHg)	Venous-arterial difference (mmHg)	Microfilarial distribution
Resting (day)	95	40	55	Lungs
Sleeping (night)	85–90	43	42–47	Peripheral blood
Breathing 100% O_2	640	53	587	Lungs
Breathing 14% O_2	51	32	19	Peripheral blood (partial release)
Vigorous exercise	91	20	71	Lungs

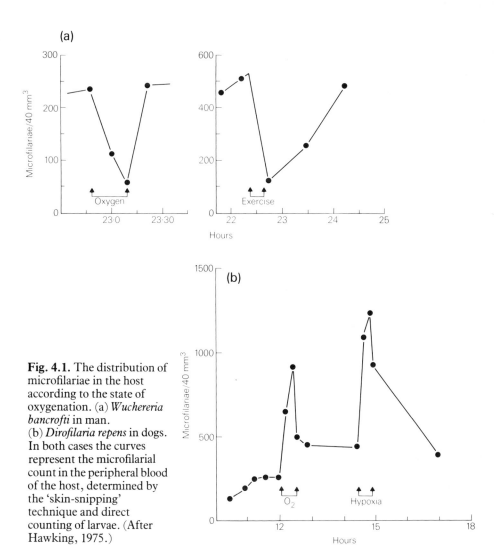

Fig. 4.1. The distribution of microfilariae in the host according to the state of oxygenation. (a) *Wuchereria bancrofti* in man. (b) *Dirofilaria repens* in dogs. In both cases the curves represent the microfilarial count in the peripheral blood of the host, determined by the 'skin-snipping' technique and direct counting of larvae. (After Hawking, 1975.)

Some trypanosomes of amphibians show circadian variation in their distribution within the host in a manner related to transmission by a blood-feeding invertebrate. *Trypanosoma rotatorium* appears in the peripheral blood of *Rana clamitans* by day and accumulates in the renal circulation by night. Transmission is by a day-feeding leech.

4.3   ESTABLISHMENT AND GROWTH

After locating and gaining entry into a suitable host, whether by active or passive means, the parasite becomes established and grows, either to maturity or to a larval stage whose continued development occurs in the next host. Establishment and growth require a complex series of physiological conditions to be met. These are summarized in Fig. 4.2.

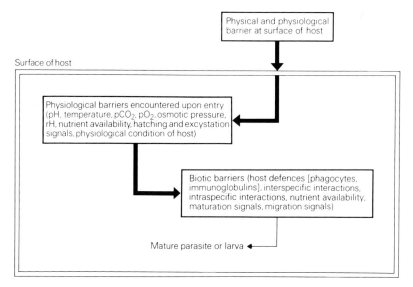

Fig. 4.2. Barriers to establishment encountered by invading parasites.

4.3.1   Hatching and excystation

Many parasites enter their hosts encapsulated either within egg membranes or within cysts (see section 4.2.1). Such parasites inevitably enter the host via the alimentary canal, within which organ system they must become activated and liberated from their capsules before any further development can take place. This applies to oocysts and other cysts in the Protozoa, metacercarial cysts in the Digenea, eggs and a variety of cysts in the Cestoda, eggs and cystacanths in the Acanthocephala, and eggs and ensheathed larvae in the Nematoda. It is worth noting that not all parasites acquired through ingestion are encapsulated; many parasite larvae are found free in the tissues of a host animal that is eaten by the next host (e.g. metacercariae of several strigeid digeneans, pseudophyllidean procercoids and plerocercoids and many nematode larvae).

(a)   Protozoa

Activation and excystation of protozoan cysts has been examined using only a small range of species *in vitro* (Table 4.3). It is generally found that optimum conditions include elevation of the ambient temperature to the appropriate level (for parasites of homoiotherms), employing a medium of neutral pH with a low pO_2, high

Table 4.3. Conditions for *in vitro* excystation of selected protozoan parasites (data from Lackie, 1975).

Species	Temperature (°C)	pH	Gas phase	Enzymes added	Bile	Host
Entamoeba histolytica	37	—	Air or anaerobic	Reducing agents	—	Man
E. invadens	8–24	—	—	—	—	Reptiles
Eimeria bovis	40	7.5–8.5	Air or 50% Air/CO_2	Trypsin+ reducing agents	1%	Cattle
E. tenella	37–41	7.6	Air or CO_2	Trypsin, HCO_3^-, pancreatin	Present	Poultry
Cystoisospora canis	22–37	—	Air or CO_2	Trypsin	0.5%	Dogs

pCO_2 and containing reducing agents. Activation of the encysted parasite may be a process distinct from excystation, the former depending particularly upon a high pCO_2 and the latter requiring the action of proteolytic enzymes.

In the Coccidia, excystation of the sporocyst after release from the oocyst may involve the breakdown of a localized region of the cyst wall—the Stieda body. This is effected by the action of bile and trypsin (e.g. *Eimeria* and *Isospora*). Some species lack a Stieda body and excyst following the action of proteolytic enzymes on the entire sporocyst wall.

(b)   Digenea

The eggs of the majority of digeneans hatch in water under suitable environmental conditions; temperature, salinity and light are the major factors.

The metacercariae of many digeneans are enclosed within cysts of varying wall architecture and dimensions (see section 4.2.1). Where cyst walls are particularly thin, excystation is brought about simply by elevation of the temperature (if the host is a bird or mammal). Metacercarial cysts of more complex structure require, in addition, serial treatment with pepsin and trypsin. Excystation in some species (e.g. *Fasciola hepatica*) involves the action of bile salts. In general, metacercariae are activated by temperature, high pCO_2 and, perhaps, bile salts, while excystation is brought about by proteolytic enzymes of exogenous and, possibly, endogenous origin. Factors affecting activation and excystation of parasites of poikilotherms have rarely been examined.

(c)   *Cestoda*

Although many tapeworm eggs hatch in the external environment on receipt of suitable stimuli, those of the Cyclophyllidea hatch in the alimentary canal of the host (invertebrate and verebrate) after oral ingestion. The cyclophyllidean egg has a thin outer capsule but the oncosphere larva is enclosed by a thick, protective embryophore; this is especially thick in the Taeniidae (Fig. 2.3). Hatching of some cyclophyllidean eggs (e.g. Taeniidae) is normally a biphasic process: the hexacanth larva is activated, it disrupts the oncospheral membrane and host proteolytic enzymes digest the outer capsule. In non-taeniids hatching is largely a mechanical event dependent upon the action of the host mouthparts; hatching of these eggs *in vitro* can be accomplished in simple physiological saline. In *Hymenolepis*, however, activation of the oncosphere requires HCO_3^-, high pCO_2 and digestive enzymes. Hatching of the taeniid egg depends upon the presence of either pepsin (*Taenia saginata*) or pancreatin (*T. pisiformis*). Bile salts are probably responsible for activation of the larval tapeworm.

Excystation of cestode cysts always takes place in the alimentary canal of the vertebrate definitive host. Normally pepsin, trypsin and bile salts are required to expedite this process (e.g. *H. diminuta*), though some species require pancreatin (e.g. *Echinoccoccus granulosus*).

(d)   *Acanthocephala*

Activation of the cystacanth larva depends upon temperature increase to the appropriate level and may require the presence of bile salts (e.g. *Moniliformis dubius*). Excystation is due either to mechanical (e.g. *Polymorphus minutus*) or enzymic (e.g. *M. dubius*) disruption of the thin outer capsule. The egg (or shelled acanthor larva) hatches in the midgut of arthropods. Hatching *in vitro* depends upon the ionic strength of the medium used, the concentration of HCO_3^-, and the pH. Enzymes, such as insect chitinases, are without effect.

(e)   *Nematoda*

The eggs of many nematodes hatch in the external environment to release infective larvae (e.g. *Ancylostoma, Nippostrongylus*). Upon receipt of the requisite environmental stimuli (water, temperature, pO_2), the enclosed larva liberates digestive enzymes whose action may facilitate the uptake of water by the egg: hatching, in such cases, may therefore be due to an increased turgor pressure within the egg (e.g. *Trichostrongylus*).

The eggs of many species of parasitic nematodes hatch only after ingestion by a suitable host (e.g. *Ascaris, Toxocara*). *Ascaris* eggs hatch *in vitro* at 37°C in a medium with a high pCO_2, neutral pH, HCO_3^- and reducing agents. The larva within the egg is stimulated to produce a hatching fluid, comprising enzymes capable of digesting the ascaroside and chitin layers of the egg shell.

Exsheathment of trichostrongyle larvae, enclosed within the cuticle of the second ecdysis, takes place in the alimentary canal of the host and *in vitro* under the influence of CO_2, HCO_3^- and reducing agents, at neutral pH and at the appropriate temperature. Suitable stimuli induce production of exsheathing fluid by the larval parasite, which is thought to contain proteolytic enzymes (Fig. 4.3).

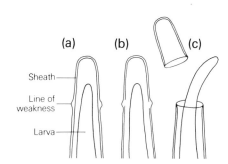

Fig. 4.3. Exsheathment in infective trichostrongyle larvae (e.g. *Haemonchus*). (a) A line of cuticular weakness is developed by localized anterior swelling of the sheath. (b) Digestion of the inner layers of line of weakness. (c) Rupture of sheath along the line of weakness and release of larvae. (After Lee & Atkinson, 1976).

4.3.2   The role of bile in parasite establishment

Bile, a complex mixture of organic acids, is released into the upper small intestine of vertebrates through the opening of the bile duct. Bile salts are of considerable importance to the establishment and development of parasites both of the alimentary canal itself, and to those of other regions of the vertebrate body that enter the host via the mouth. The effects of bile salts on parasites include (i) effects on membrane permeability; (ii) initiation of activation of encysted larvae; (iii) lysis of parasite surfaces; (iv) synergistic action with host digestive enzymes; and (v) metabolic effects.

It has been postulated that, through their various actions, bile salts may act as determinants of host specificity in many parasitic infections. Although there is little direct evidence to support this notion, a possible mode of action is exemplified by the effects of bile salts from a range of potential host animals on the protoscoleces of *Echinococcus granulosus* (Table 4.4). Chemical analysis of the composition of the various biles reveals that lysis of larval tapeworms occurs with bile that is rich in deoxycholate. Dog bile is low in deoxycholate and carnivores, in general, possess deoxycholate conjugated with taurine; herbivores alternatively use glycine as a conjugant. The lytic action of bile acids from unsuitable hosts therefore provides a possible mechanism by which host specificity might be mediated at the physiological level.

Table 4.4. *In vitro* survival of protoscoleces of *Echinococcus granulosus* in 10% bile from various vertebrates. (Data obtained from curves by Smyth & Haslewood 1963.)

Survival time of protoscoleces (days)	Percentage survival (source of bile)				
	Dog	Sheep	Pig	Ox	Fish
1	100	100	100	100	100
2	100	100	100	100	75
3	100	95	88	92	—
4	100	80	52	36	0

In addition, bile salts can exert an influence upon both establishing and established parasites. Experimental cannulation of the bile duct of rats infected with *Hymenolepis diminuta* causes a reduction in size and fecundity of the parasite; cannulation of the bile duct before infection precludes the establishment of the tapeworm.

Bile salts are involved in both activation and excystation of many cystic stages of parasites including protozoans (e.g. *Eimeria*), digeneans (e.g. *Fasciola*), cestodes (e.g. *Taenia pisiformis*), and acanthocephalans (e.g. *Moniliformis*, *Polymorphus*). The physiology of these mechanisms is poorly understood.

4.3.3   Migration and site selection

Once within the body of the host, the majority of parasites migrate away from the point of entry to a preferred target organ or microhabitat. Migrations of this type are *ontogenetic* since they are normally accompanied by growth and development of the parasite. They may culminate in a sexually mature adult parasite or a 'mature' larva; in either case the migration over a fixed route is mandatory for normal parasite development. The physiological determinants of these often highly complex patterns of migration are not well documented. It is probable that sequential stimuli from the host are recognized by the migrating parasite and assist with the determination of the precise migratory pattern. Aberrant ontogenetic migration may occur if a parasite enters an unsuitable host and cannot complete its normal development. Examples of this include cutaneous and visceral *larva migrans*. These are migratory hookworm larvae (e.g. *Ancylostoma braziliense* and *Toxocara canis* in man) that wander in the deep or superficial tissues (respectively) of the wrong host and eventually die. In such cases the host fails to provide the necessary physiological signals for normal migration and development to take place. Some common examples of normal ontogenetic migrations are shown in Fig. 4.4.

(a) Entry to the host via the mouth

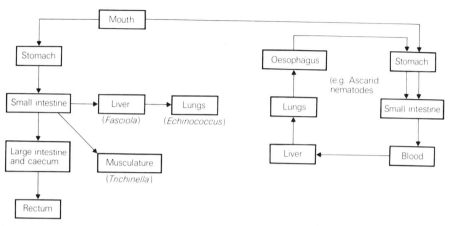

(Many protozoans and helminths inhabit the gut; the exact site selected varies)

(b) Entry to the host via the skin

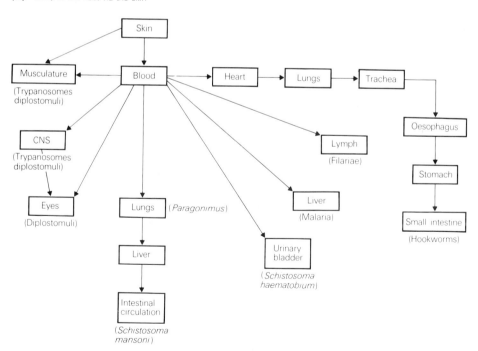

Fig. 4.4. Common patterns of ontogenetic migrations by parasites in vertebrate hosts.

Other patterns of parasite migration within the host include diurnal migration, often associated with transmission (see section 4.2.4) and diurnal migration within the preferred microhabitat in a manner related to the nutritional physiology of the host. The latter pattern has so far only been described for the rat tapeworm *Hymenolepis diminuta*, which migrates diurnally along the length of the host's small intestine. It is postulated that the worm responds to various chemical gradients that develop in the rat intestine as a result of the normal feeding cycle, but the exact nature of the migratory stimuli has yet to be elucidated.

A fundamental feature of both ontogenetic and diurnal migrations of parasites is the ability of the parasite to recognize its whereabouts within the host body. The sensory physiology associated with migrations and with site selection is virtually unknown, but it must be relatively sophisticated since ectopic parasitisms are rare.

4.3.4   Invasion of tissues

During the processes of migration and site selection, many parasites penetrate and invade the tissues of the host, in some cases as the final stage of their establishment sequence. The physiological factors that govern cell recognition and penetration are both interesting and obscure in all but a few cases. Examples of tissue-invading parasites include malaria and babesia parasites (red blood cells), leishmanias (macrophages), coccidians, cestodes and nematodes (the *muscularis mucosa* of the gut), schistosomes (circulatory system), trypanosomes (nervous tissue) and larval digeneans, cestodes and nematodes (the musculature).

The invasion of mammalian erythrocytes by malarial parasites has attracted considerable recent research interest which has set out to answer the questions, How do the malarial merozoites recognize red cells and what is the mechanism of penetration? Recognition of the red cell depends upon the presence of specific receptors on the erythrocyte surface membranes. These receptors are insensitive to neuraminidase treatment but can be removed by proteases. Lectin treatment, using concanavalin A or wheat germ agglutinin, reduces the success of red cell invasion by merozoites. The surface receptors may be associated with blood group antigens since negroid races lacking certain Duffy group determinants are resistant to *Plasmodium vivax*. Host specificity in malaria is determined, in part, by the efficacy of red cell recognition by the merozoite; mammalian malarias are normally specific for red cell invasion while merozoites of malarial species infecting lower vertebrates are less specific and invade a wide range of cell types.

The process of invasion of the red cell by the merozoite of *Plasmodium* is complex (Fig. 4.5). First, the merozoite attaches to the red cell and orientates so that it becomes attached by its apical protruberance; this structure contains organelles with secretory function. Following this, the merozoite induces the erythrocyte surface membrane to invaginate. Entry of the merozoite into the cell is exclusively by

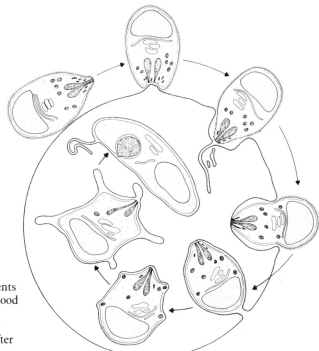

Fig. 4.5. Sequence of events in the invasion of a red blood cell by the merozoite of *Plasmodium knowlesi* (see text for explanation). (After Bannister, 1977).

invagination and there is no penetration of the cell membranes. Invagination is probably due to the secretions of apical organelles since these become emptied during the process of invasion. A histidine-rich protein has been isolated which stimulates cupping of red cell membranes at low concentrations and lysis at higher concentrations. Once invasion of the red cell is completed the merozoite develops into the trophozoite still residing within the invaginated red cell membrane which forms the parasitophorous vacuole.

Many other protozoan parasites invade and inhabit host cells and they also reside within a parasitophorous vacuole formed from the host cell surface. Invaginative entry is typical of invasion by coccidians (e.g. *Eimeria* and *Toxoplasma*) and some gregarines. In *Babesia*, the parasitophorous vacuole is a temporary structure which regresses during or shortly after invasion. *Toxoplasma* and *Eimeria* may invade host cells by inducing phagocytosis; host cells treated with drugs that inhibit phagocytosis (e.g. colchicine, cytochalasin B) are invaded normally, whereas drug treatment of the merozoite itself inhibits invasion.

There is virtually no information on tissue invasion by helminth parasites.

4.3.5   Factors that inhibit parasite establishment and growth

Apart from the nonspecific (phagocytic) and specific (immunological) defences of animals (see Chapter 6) a variety of factors can act to reduce or inhibit parasite viability within a host.

(a)   *Crowding effect*

The rate of growth, the maximum size attained and the fecundity of parasites can be reduced by the effects of intraspecific crowding of individuals within a single host. The best known example of this phenomenon is with *Hymenolepis diminuta* in the laboratory rat; here the effects are cumulative with increasing numbers of tapeworms present. Suggestions to account for the crowding effect in *H. diminuta* infections include intraspecific competition for a limiting resource (e.g. oxygen, space, carbohydrates), toxin production by the tapeworms, and immunologically mediated responses from the host. There is no widely accepted explanation at present. Crowding effects have also been recorded in some infections of nematodes in vertebrate hosts (e.g. *Skrjabingylus nasicola*, *Ancylostoma caninum*).

(b)   *Interspecific interactions*

Parasites of different species may coexist within the same site in a host, and may interact in such a way as to affect growth and site selectivity of either or both species. Examples of this phenomenon are rare; they come from both laboratory studies (e.g. *H. diminuta* and *Moniliformis dubius* in the rat) and from natural populations (e.g. *Proteocephalus* and *Neoechinorhynchus* in sticklebacks). These are all parasites of the alimentary canal, which may be a significant feature. Among protozoa, babesias and malaria parasites inhibit the development of one another.

4.3.6   Labile growth

Platyhelminth parasites, particularly cestodes, often respond to adverse physiological conditions within the host by the active loss of tissue (i.e. degrowth). This process is called *destrobilation* in the adult tapeworm and involves the shedding of the body segments (proglottids) leaving only the neck and scolex intact. Destrobilation is a response to nutrient shortage; deprivation of dietary carbohydrate in laboratory infections of *Raillietina cesticillus* or *Davainea proglottina* induces destrobilation, while *Dibothriocephalus* destrobilates in wild bears during the period of hibernation. Some cestodes respond to nutrient deprivation by reduction in size without destrobilation (e.g. *H. diminuta*).

Another pattern of labile growth occurs in the hydatid larval stage of *Echinococcus granulosus*. The hydatid cyst contains protoscoleces that can differentiate and develop in one of two ways according to the nature of environmental stimuli. Protoscoleces liberated from the cyst in the alimentary canal of a suitable canine host develop into adult tapeworms but should the cyst burst *in situ* or become damaged during surgery and the protoscoleces be released into the viscera of the host, each protoscolex can develop into a new, secondary hydatid cyst. In experimental cultures, protoscoleces grown in a liquid medium always develop to secondary cysts; protoscoleces grown in a biphasic medium, with a solid protein base and a liquid overlay, develop to adult tapeworms. This dichotomous pattern of development results from the effects of different external stimuli upon a complex of operator genes that control the precise direction of development.

4.4   NEUROPHYSIOLOGY

Parasite neurophysiology is a much neglected area of research. It will be obvious to the reader that parasites must have relatively sophisticated levels of nervous coordination related particularly to their host finding, invasion and migratory behaviour patterns.

4.4.1   Parasite nervous systems

All platyhelminths have a basically similar type of nervous system comprising an anterior cerebral complex of ganglia, proximal to the pharynx (where present), and a series of bilaterally symmetrical nerves which extend forwards and backwards from the cerebral ganglia and innervate the various regions of the body. Typically there is a considerable degree of lateral branching of the trunk nerves. In the Monogenea and Digenea, trunk nerves are developed to innervate the suckers and any additional organs of attachment (e.g. opisthaptor of monogeneans). In the Cestoda, the paired cerebral ganglia give rise to a pair of lateral nerve trunks that extend along the entire length of the strobila and which are interconnected by numerous lateral branches. The platyhelminth nervous system is a nerve net containing unmyelinated fibres.

The acanthocephalan nervous system comprises a cerebral ganglion from which arise a variety of both paired and single nerves. A second ganglion is formed in the reproductive system of male acanthocephalans but not in females.

The nervous system of nematodes does not radically differ in free-living or parasitic forms; it is rather more complex than that of the other helminth parasites. Six or more ganglia are located on a circumoesophageal commissure, from which six nerves extend anteriorly to supply the head and six to eight posteriorly to supply the organs and various regions of the body. The major (ventral) trunk nerve is paired and ganglionated along its length. Sensory activity is a function of the lateral and ventral trunk nerves, and motor activity of the dorsal and ventral nerves.

4.4.2   Sense organs and sensory physiology

There is a general paucity of information on the physiological activities of most parasite sense organs, but it is evident that sensory physiology is an important facet of a parasitic mode of life. Most information on sense organ function derives from behavioural observations and electron microscopy rather than from experimental manipulation.

(a)   Photoreception

Monogeneans frequently, but not always, have eye spots; these usually occur in the oncomiracidia rather than in the adult worm. One or two pairs can be present and they may have an oil-droplet lens. Positive phototaxis occurs in some oncomiracidia but it has been suggested that the photoreceptors act primarily in dorso-ventral orientation during swimming rather than in host location. Ciliated sense organs have been described in *Entobdella soleae*, which are located close to the eyes and are thought to be photoreceptors.

Larval digeneans (particularly miracidia and cercariae) and a few adults possess eyes, and phototaxis has been frequently reported to occur. Most larvae that have eyes react to light but there are some (e.g. cercariae of *Schistosomatium douthitti*) that do not. Detailed studies are rare; changes in light intensity alter the swimming activity of *Cryptocotyle lingua* and *Diplostomum spathaceum* cercariae. In all of these, a reduction in light intensity causes an increase in swimming activity, though factors other than light may also be involved. Such responses are of obvious importance to cercariae such as these that invade fishes and to whose shadows they respond positively. Some miracidia respond positively to shade (e.g. *Schistosoma haematobium*), while many others are positively phototactic.

Light is responsible for stimulating hatching of many helminth larvae from the egg (e.g. *Fasciola hepatica*, *Diphyllobothrium latum*); presumably the encapsulated larvae are photosensitive.

Nematodes do not possess eyes as such, but some species can be shown to respond to light.

(b)   Chemoreception

Putative chemoreceptors have been identified in many helminth parasites. They take the form of ciliated sensillae (Monogenea), ciliated pits and papillae (Digenea), tegumental protrusions (Cestoda) and amphids, papillae and ciliated pits (Nematoda). There is little direct experimental evidence for the physiological functioning of these sense organs and their role is deduced primarily from their ultrastructure.

Chemical recognition is of undoubted importance to all parasites. Amongst the Protozoa, activities such as feeding, attraction between gametes and recognition of cells for invasion will all involve chemoreception, though little is known about surface chemoreceptors of protozoans. Helminths similarly rely to a considerable extent upon chemoreception (e.g. host location mechanisms, host penetration mechanisms). Sexual attraction between adult helminths probably involves the interpretation of chemical signals; possible pheromones have been demonstrated in several nematode parasites (e.g. *Ancylostoma caninum*, *Nippostrongylus brasiliensis*).

(c)   Temperature reception (thermotaxis)

Many parasites respond to thermal gradients, commonly as one aspect of locating the host (e.g. larval hookworms, larval *Nippostrongylus brasiliensis*, schistosome cercariae).

(d)   Other sensory perceptions

There is a variety of sense organs on the tegument of helminth parasites which are thought to be mechanoreceptors; these are typically ciliated pits (platyhelminths) or papillae and spicules (nematodes).

Geotaxis (responses to gravity) is thought to occur in many larval helminths. Digenean cercariae are either positively geotactic (i.e. bottom-dwelling cercariae) or negatively geotactic (i.e. swimming cercariae), though it is difficult to exclude the role of light in eliciting these responses. Negative geotaxis occurs in *Schistosoma mansoni*, *S. japonicum* and in some nematodes such as adult *Ostertagia*. Positive geotaxis has been identified in a few species (e.g. *Amphilodera amnicolae* cercariae and *Cercaria tuckerensis*).

Thigmotaxis is not uncommon in parasites. Aggregation of nematodes is thought to be due to thigmotaxis, enhancing copulatory events and invasion of new hosts. Rheotaxis may be important to free-swimming larval helminths and to blood-dwelling adult worms.

Proprioreceptors must be present in many parasites but only those associated with organs of attachment have been described to date (e.g. stretch receptors in the cestode scolex).

4.4.3   Nerve transmission

Biochemical and histochemical evidence strongly suggests that the nervous system of helminth parasites is almost exclusively cholinergic. Acetylcholinesterase activity has been localized histochemically in many helminths, and the presence of acetylcholine has been demonstrated by chemical determination. Nerve-muscle preparations have only been examined in the larger nematodes (e.g. *Ascaris*). Acetylcholine decreases the muscle resting potential; physostigmine and neostigmine increase the sensitivity to acetylcholine, while piperazine (a commonly used anthelminthic, see Table 9.3) blocks the stimulatory effect of acetylcholine. Piperazine and GABA (γ-amino butyric acid) induce muscle relaxation.

Adrenergic activity may also feature in the nematode nervous system; noradrenergic, dopaminergic and tryptaminergic neurons have been identified.

Studies on the neuromuscular physiology of other helminth parasites are limited. Cholinergic relaxation of muscles has been demonstrated in *Fasciola*; cholinesterase inhibitors reduce schistosome motility. Platyhelminth parasites may produce serotonin which stimulates movement; large quantities of serotonin are present in *Schistosoma mansoni*, while in *Hymenolepis diminuta* and *H. nana* acetylcholinesterase and serotonin are distributed equally, implying antagonistic activity.

Neurosecretion has been identified in a small number of parasites using histochemical techniques (e.g. *Dicrocoelium dendriticum*, *Echinococcus granulosus*, *Hymenolepis diminuta*). In the nematodes, moulting and neurosecretory activity are closely linked.

4.4.4   Muscular and locomotory physiology

Very little is known about muscle physiology in the platyhelminth parasites. By contrast, the muscles of nematodes have been the focus of considerable attention. The muscle cells of *Ascaris* contain both nervous and contractile elements (Fig. 4.6); the latter are composed of regular arrangements of thick and thin

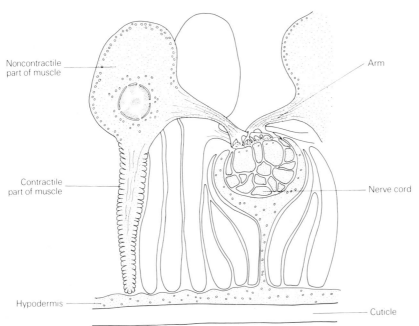

Noncontractile part of muscle

Arm

Contractile part of muscle

Nerve cord

Hypodermis

Cuticle

Fig. 4.6. The nematode muscle cell and myoneural junction in cross-section. (After Lee & Atkinson, 1976).

myofilaments, typical of cross-striated muscle, forming H, A and I, but not Z, bands. Actin and myosin are probably present in the thick and thin myofilaments, respectively. Contraction of *Ascaris* muscle involves the myofilaments sliding past one another and in a folding of the supporting fibres of the muscle cell. These two distinct modes of contraction confer on the nematode muscle cell a greater degree of plasticity than that found in more typical cross-striated muscle.

The resting potential of *Ascaris* somatic muscle averages 30 mV; nervous stimulation produces rhythmic muscle potentials that are myogenic in origin. Both ambient temperature and inorganic ions, particularly Cl^-, affect the resting potential. The electrophysiology of *Ascaris* oesophageal cells has also been examined; the resting potential is 30 mV and, once again, the most important ion during depolarization is Cl^-. Electrophysiological data are not available for other parasites.

Motility and locomotory activity are important facets of almost all parasite life-styles. Information on locomotory physiology is, however, sparse, and tends to be restricted to observations on the effects of various external stimuli upon activity and speed of movement. In the Protozoa, flagellar movement has been examined in *Opalina* and in various haemoflagellates (e.g. *Crithidia oncopelti*, *Trypanosoma lewisi*, *T. brucei*, *T. cruzi*). The available evidence suggests no major departure from the equivalent types of movement in free-living forms. The curious gliding movements of some sporozoans (e.g. gregarines) are thought to be due to the myonemes of the pellicle and their involvement in coordinated undulations of the entire surface.

Ciliary movement is found in some helminth larvae (e.g. oncomiracidia, miracidia and coracidia). Patterns of locomotory behaviour have been examined in detail for schistosome miracidia and shown to be complex. Movement in other helminth larvae and adults is through muscular action; locomotion in the platyhelminths takes a variety of forms (swimming, crawling, burrowing) but little information has been gathered on the physiology of each type. By contrast, nematode locomotion has been extensively examined. Nematodes lack circular muscles in their body wall but they possess dorsal and ventral longitudinal muscles that work against the hydrostatic skeleton of pseudocoelomic fluid, itself contained within an elastic cuticle. The resting pseudocoelomic fluid pressure of *Ascaris* is approximately 70 mmHg and varies from 16 to 225 mmHg during normal alternating waves of posteriad contraction of the longitudinal muscles. The body waves are dorso-ventral in plane and the animal lies on its side during locomotion. The three basic mechanisms concerned with nematode locomotion, spontaneous myogenic depolarization, neuromuscular coordination and local pressure changes in the hydrostatic skeleton, are thought to be controlled and coordinated by serotonin and epinephrine. Nematode locomotory behaviour is concerned with hatching from the egg, location of the host, penetration of the host, migration within the host, sexual reproduction and oviposition.

4.5   REPRODUCTIVE PHYSIOLOGY

Many parasites have complex life cycles which often involve stages that reproduce sexually in one host and have asexual, proliferative, stages in a second host.

4.5.1   Asexual reproduction

Asexual splitting, or budding, is typical of many parasitic Protozoa, all of the Digenea and a few of the Cestoda; it is not a feature of the Monogenea, Acanthocephala or Nematoda, although a small number of parthenogenetic nematodes are known.

Asexual reproduction in the Protozoa may involve binary fission, multiple fission, schizogony, endodyogeny and, more rarely, single budding. In the helminths, asexual reproduction involves internal budding (polyembryony) almost exclusively. The asexual phase of the digenean life cycle is located only within the molluscan intermediate host; it concerns the sporocyst and redia stages. Normally there are two distinct asexual generations that are passed within the snail (mother sporocyst to daughter sporocyst, or sporocyst to redia); from a single miracidium many hundreds of thousands of cercariae can be generated by asexual budding.

Asexual multiplication in the Cestoda is often numerically less dramatic than in the Digenea; the great majority of tapeworms form only a single larva from the egg while proliferative budding is a feature of the urocystis and urocystidium larvae (external budding) and the polycercus, coenurus and hydatid larvae (internal budding), typical of the Taeniidae. The hydatid cyst of *Echinococcus* can generate several millions of protoscoleces by asexual budding within brood capsules; the coenurus larva rarely produces more than a few hundreds of larval tapeworms.

4.5.2   Sexual reproduction

Many protozoans reproduce by a form of sexual reproduction (e.g. Apicomplexa, Ciliophora, Opalinata, Hypermastigida) but it is often difficult to distinguish between the fusion of gametes and the fusion of individuals (e.g. conjugation). Some species produce gametes that are morphologically distinguishable, such as 'male' microgametes and 'female' macrogametes. It is not uncommon to find an alteration of sexual and asexual generations in the parasitic protozoa, particularly where more than one host is involved in the life cycle. In malarial parasites, sexual reproduction (gamogony) takes place in the invertebrate vector and asexual schizogony in the vertebrate liver and circulatory system. The trypanosomes, by contrast, reproduce asexually in both invertebrate and vertebrate hosts.

All monogeneans are hermaphrodites, possessing a common opening for the male and female reproductive systems. Cross-fertilization between separate individuals is usual but self-fertilization may occur. Egg production in monogeneans may be prolific (e.g. *Polystoma integerrimum* lays up to 2500 eggs). The eggs of many monogeneans contain one or two long filaments, presumably for attachment to the substrate when released from the parent worm.

The majority of digeneans are hermaphrodites, but members of the Schistosomatidae have separate sexes. Both cross- and self-fertilization take place. The physiology of egg production in the Digenea is well studied (Fig. 4.7). Eggs are released from the mature ovary and enter the oviduct; spermatozoa from the partner are stored, after copulation, in the seminal receptacle. Vitelline cells (30–40 in number), and spermatozoa, are released simultaneously and make their way to the ootype where the ova become fertilized. Shell precursor material is then released from the vitelline cells and a soft shell is formed around the developing egg. The secretions of associated glands, such as the Mehlis' gland, once thought to furnish

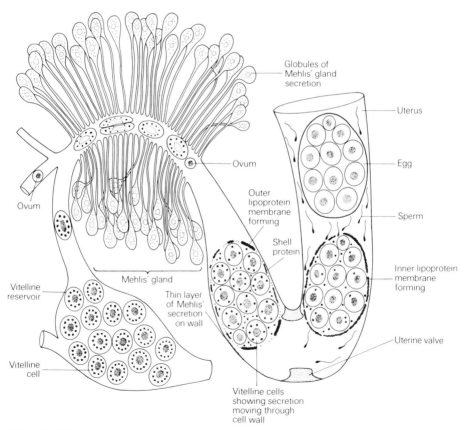

Fig. 4.7. The mechanisms of egg formation in the Digenea, based upon *Fasciola hepatica*. (After Smyth, 1966).

egg shell material, are probably sources of nourishment for the developing egg. The egg shell, upon release from the worm, is composed of quinone-tanned sclerotin, formed by the oxidation of an o-phenol by phenolase to yield an o-quinone. The o-quinone groups react with $-NH_2$ groups on adjacent proteins to form stable cross-linkages. Although the majority of digenean eggs are protected by the products of a quinone-tanning mechanism, alternative modes of cross-linkage have been detected (e.g. dityrosine and disulphide bridges in *Fasciola hepatica*).

Almost all of the cestodes are hermaphrodites and each proglottid contains a complete male and female reproductive system (Fig. 2.3). Cestodes mature posteriorly so that the terminal segments contain ripe eggs and are gravid. Fertilization can involve eggs and spermatozoa originating from the same proglottid or from adjacent proglottids. The cestode egg is not quinone-tanned, but is surrounded by a capsule of differing dimensions and constituent layers (Fig. 2.3).

Acanthocephalans have separate sexes and display considerable sexual dimorphism. Spermatozoa are introduced to the pseudocoelom of the female at copulation and the ova are associated with ovarian balls. After copulation, the male plugs the vaginal opening of the partner with secretions from the cement glands. Eggs are fertilized and subsequently liberated from the ovarian balls to complete their development free in the pseudocoelom. Mature eggs enter the uterus, controlled by a uterine bell which prevents immature eggs from leaving the pseudocoelom. Large numbers of eggs are released from female acanthocephalans; these eggs are surrounded by a protective covering of protein and chitin.

Most species of parasitic nematode have separate sexes and overt sexual dimorphism. During copulation the male inserts cuticular spicules into the vagina of the female prior to ejaculation of spermatozoa which pass into the seminal receptacle where fertilization of the oocyte takes place. The nematode egg shell is a tough, protective covering consisting of an inner lipid (ascaroside) layer, a thick, median chitinous layer, and a thin outer layer; all these layers derive from the egg itself and the uterus may contribute a fourth layer. In general the egg shell of nematodes confers a considerable degree of impermeability and resistance to damage.

4.5.3   Reproductive synchrony with host cycles

There are a few examples of synchronized reproduction in both parasite and host; such synchrony serves to liberate infective parasites and susceptible juvenile host animals concurrently. Among the Protozoa, the Opalinata release their gametes only during the breeding season of their amphibian hosts and fertilization takes place in the gut of the newly infected tadpole. Experimental evidence suggests that the sex hormones of the host directly induce gamete formation in these parasites. The Hypermastigida that inhabit the gut of arthropods can be stimulated to reproduce sexually under the influence of host moulting hormones. For example, termite flagellates are lost with each moult, since they inhabit the cuticular hind gut, and synchrony of sexual reproduction in the parasites with moulting in the host is essential for reinfection. The host, in this case, relies exclusively on the parasite to produce cellulases and therefore reinfection is mandatory for the continued existence of the host.

In the helminths, few examples of sexual synchrony have been described. *Polystoma integerrimum* inhabits the urinary bladder of amphibians; sexual maturation of this monogenean is controlled by gonadotrophin released by the host. This ensures that infective parasites and amphibian tadpoles occur together and thus infection is facilitated.

4.6   EXCRETORY PHYSIOLOGY

Since the life-cycle patterns of many parasites include alternating parasitic and free-living stages, we might expect the excretory and osmoregulatory systems to be of considerable importance. Surprisingly little is known of the physiology of these systems in the majority of parasites.

4.6.1   Excretory systems

Two fundamental mechanisms are known for the formation of excreta, active transport and ultrafiltration. Often both mechanisms can be employed by an excretory system, i.e. the initial process of excretory fluid formation is by ultrafiltration, while modification of the ultrafiltrate is by active transport (e.g. tubular secretion or reabsorption). The evidence for the occurrence of either of these fundamental mechanisms in parasite tissues is not yet available.

In parasites two types of excretory system are found, the protozoan contractile vacuole and the helminth protonephridial system (though the nematode excretory system is not strictly protonephridial).

Contractile vacuoles are present in many parasitic ciliates but are absent in the amoebae and sporozoans. The physiological role of the contractile vacuole in either excretion of nitrogenous waste or in osmoregulation is not known, but it seems likely that toxic metabolic end products are removed over the entire body surface.

The protonephridial system of platyhelminths comprises numerous blind-ending tubules that interconnect and open to the outside via a single nephridiopore. At the terminus of each tubule is a flame cell or cluster of cells, so called because the wave-like beating of the flagella is reminiscent of a flickering candle (Fig. 4.8). There are between 50 and 100 flagella in each 'flame' and their rhythmic beating is thought to initiate and maintain the flow of fluid in the excretory tubule and possibly draw solutes into the protonephridial terminal organ from the surrounding parenchyma. The latter process may be associated with ultrafiltration, but this remains to be

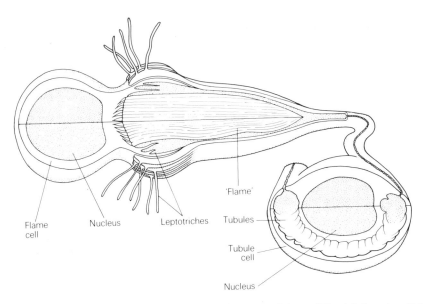

Fig. 4.8. A flame cell of a digenean, based on the miracidium of *Fasciola hepatica*. (After Wilson, 1974).

demonstrated experimentally. Wilson and Webster (1974) applied Pappenheimer's equation to show that a sufficiently high filtration pressure could be developed by the flagellar beat of the flame cell:

$$Q_f = \frac{K_f A}{\eta} \times \frac{\Delta P}{\Delta x},$$

where Q_f is the volume of fluid entering the flame cell in $m^3 s^{-1}$, η the viscosity of the fluid ($N\ s\ m^{-2}$), A the area of filtration (m^2), Δx the length of the diffusion path (m), K_f a flow constant and Δp the pressure difference generated ($N\ m^{-2}$). A calculated Δp of 12.4 cm H_2O ($1.21 \times 10^3\ N\ m^{-2}$) can be obtained for the top of the flame cell barrel, but the effectiveness of such a pressure difference in developing ultrafiltration would depend upon a low interstitial fluid colloid pressure.

Excretion of nitrogenous waste by the platyhelminth protonephridial system is not well documented. The cestode *Moniezia expansa* is thought to remove ammonia by outwards diffusion across the entire tegument. The protonephridial canal fluid of *Hymenolepis diminuta* has been subjected to chemical analysis using samples of 10 μl or less. The tubule fluid contains inorganic ions (NA^+, K^+, Cl^-, CO_3^-) equivalent to 1.15% NaCl, amino acids (12 mg ml^{-1}), ammonia (0.04 mg ml^{-1}), urea (0.5 mg ml^{-1}) and lactic acid (0.7 mg ml^{-1}). This analysis accounts for 90% of the total dry matter. The pH of the canal fluid is 4.5 and the pCO_2 120 mmHg. These data suggest that the protonephridial system of *H. diminuta* has an excretory role, though ultrafiltration and active transport components have not been demonstrated. Lipid droplets have been recorded in the protonephridia of several parasites (e.g. *Fasciola hepatica, H. diminuta*) and amino acids, ammonia and urea have been detected in the canal fluid of *F. gigantica*.

Only one order of the Acanthocephala—the Archiacanthocephala—possesses a protonephridial system, while the other orders lack a discrete excretory system. There is no evidence concerning the mode of excretion of nitrogenous material in acanthocephalans.

The excretory system of nematodes is not truly protonephridial but consists of either gland cells that open at an excretory pore or of a canal system. There is considerable doubt whether this system is in fact excretory and it is proposed that organic waste is lost by outwards diffusion across the body surface.

4.6.2   Excretory products

The end products of nitrogen metabolism are highly toxic. They are derived from amino acid, protein, purine and pyrimidine metabolism and include ammonia, uric acid and urea. Ammonia is the major end product of parasite nitrogen metabolism, although both urea and uric acid have been detected. Few parasites have a fully functional urea cycle.

4.6.3   Osmoregulation

The osmoregulatory role of the contractile vacuole in the parasitic protozoa is not at all clear since vacuoles are not found in all parasites. Similarly there is inadequate information on the platyhelminth protonephridial system to determine its osmoregulatory function. The majority of parasitic helminths are osmoconformers, though some species may be capable of limited ionic regulation (e.g. *Hymenolepis diminuta*). Some of the parasitic nematodes (e.g. *Ancylostoma, Nippostrongylus*) possess an ampulla associated with the excretory system; the beat frequency of the ampulla decreases with increased ambient osmotic pressure.

4.7   PATHOPHYSIOLOGY

Parasites can react with their hosts at the physiological level in a number of ways. When these interactions are sufficiently severe so as to cause overt deviation from normal physiological function in the host, the parasite is regarded as a pathogen. The process of disease production is called pathogenesis.

4.7.1   Immunopathogenesis

A variety of parasitic pathological developments can be attributed to the immunological responses of the host to the parasite (i.e. immunopathology). Such changes result from the allergic mechanisms of parasitic disease (see section 6.8).

4.7.2   General pathophysiology

(a)   *Mechanical injury*

Many parasites may cause physiological disturbances simply by their presence and normal activities within host tissues; examples include occlusion of ducts or blood vessels (e.g. *Fasciola* in the bile duct) and damage due to parasite feeding (e.g. hookworm ulcerations in the intestine).

(b)   *Toxins*

Few parasites release toxins; there is disputed evidence that toxic substances released from malaria parasites can inhibit host liver mitochondrial energy metabolism. Toxins are possibly produced by *Ascaris, Schistosoma* and *Moniezia*.

(c)   *Growth effects*

Hyperplasia (cell growth without cell proliferation) results from some parasitic infections (e.g. *Eimeria, Fasciola hepatica, Paragonimus westermani, Schistosoma haematobium*). Neoplasia (new cell growth or tumour formation) has been documented in rodents infected with *Taenia taeniaeformis* and in humans infected with *Schistosoma haematobium*.

(d)   *Effects on the reproductive system*

'Castration' and various lesser effects on primary and secondary sex characters occur in a variety of different parasitic infections (e.g. *Ligula intestinalis* in cyprinid fishes, and many larval digeneans in molluscs). These parasites may release substances which can mimic the action of host sex hormones, but as yet none has been unequivocally demonstrated.

(e)   *Effects on metabolism*

There are many examples of parasitic disturbance of host metabolism. Included amongst these are (i) changes in carbohydrate metabolism caused by malaria parasites, trypanosomes, *Fasciola*, and schistosomes; (ii) changes in lipid metabolism caused by malaria parasites, trypanosomes, and schistosomes; (iii) changes in protein metabolism caused by *Eimeria, Histomonas, Leishmania, Fasciola, Schistosoma, Toxocara* and *Dirofilaria*; and (iv) changes in serum enzymes, such as transaminases, lactate dehydrogenase, glutamate dehydrogenase and sorbitol dehydrogenase, caused by *Histomonas*, trypanosomes, malaria parasites, *Fasciola, Schistosoma, Ascaris, Trichinella, Toxocara*. The metabolism of inorganic ions can be affected in certain parasitic infections (e.g. *Trypanosoma congolense, T. cruzi, Ostertagia*). Endocrine dysfunction of the suprarenals (e.g. trypanosomes, *Leishmania, Trichinella*), thyroid (e.g. *T. cruzi*) and pancreas (e.g. *Trichostrongylus*) has also been detected.

(f)   Nutritional effects

The effects of parasites on the nutritional physiology of the host animal include reduction in food uptake (e.g. malaria parasites, *Fasciola hepatica*), digestive malfunction (e.g. *Nippostrongylus, Ostertagia*) and malabsorption (e.g. *Eimeria, Plasmodium falciparum, Ascaris, Ancylostoma, Trichinella*).

4.8   CONCLUSIONS

In this chapter we have examined the physiological attributes of parasites from their transmission stages to the fully established adult. We have shown that parasite physiology involves interactions with the external environment and with host animals or plants. It will perhaps have become apparent that parasites are potentially more complex in their physiology than free-living animals because of the variety of habitats they may exploit during a single life cycle (i.e. alternating free-living and parasitic stages, invasion of a poikilotherm and a homoiotherm or an invertebrate and a vertebrate). The adaptive flexibility in the physiological mechanisms is indeed enormous.

We have considered here only the parasitic protozoans and helminths, but it should be remembered that many other invertebrate phyla contain parasitic members, whose physiology, unfortunately, has only rarely been examined.

REFERENCES AND FURTHER READING

Bannister L.H. (1977) The invasion of red cells by *Plasmodium*. In A.E.R. Taylor and R. Muller (eds.) *Parasite Invasion*, pp. 27–55. Oxford, Blackwell Scientific Publications.

Barrett J. (1981) *Biochemistry of Parasitic Helminths*, London, Macmillan.

Chappell L.H. (1980) *Physiology of Parasites*, Glasgow, Blackie.

Cohen S. & Sadun, E.H. (1976) *Immunology of Parasitic Infections*. Oxford, Blackwell Scientific Publications.

Crompton D.W.T. (1970) *An Ecological Approach to Acanthocephalan Physiology*, Cambridge, Cambridge University Press.

Crompton D.W.T. (1973) The sites occupied by some parasitic helminths in the alimentary tract of vertebrates. *Biol. Rev.* **48**, 27–83.

Grell K.G. (1967) Sexual reproduction in Protozoa. In T.T. Chen (ed.) *Research in Protozoology*, vol. 2, pp. 148–213. Oxford, Pergamon Press.

Hawking F. (1975) Circadian and other rhythms of parasites. In B. Dawes (ed.) *Advances in Parasitology*, vol. 13, pp. 123–82. London, Academic Press.

Irvin A.D. & Boarer C.D.H. (1980) Some implications of the sexual cycle in *Theileria*. *Parasitology*. **80**, 571–9

Jarman M. (1976) Neuromuscular physiology of nematodes. In N.A. Croll (ed.) *The Organisation of Nematodes*, pp. 293–312 London, Academic Press.

Kearn G.C. (1971) The physiology and behaviour of the monogenean skin parasite *Entobdella soleae* in relation to its host *(Solea solea)*. In A.M. Fallis (ed.) *Ecology and Physiology of Parasites*, pp. 161–87. Toronto, University of Toronto Press.

Lackie A.M. (1975) The activation of infective stages of endoparasites of vertebrates. *Biol. Rev.* **50**, 285–323.

Lee D.L. & Atkinson H.J. (1976) *The Physiology of Nematodes.* 2nd ed. London, Macmillan.

Llewellyn J. (1976) Behaviour of monogeneans. In E.U. Canning and C.A. Wright (eds.) *Behavioural Aspects of Parasite Transmission*, pp. 19–30. London, Linnean Society.

Lyons K.M. (1973) The epidermis and sense organs of the Monogenea and some related groups. In B. Dawes (ed.) *Advances in Parasitology*, vol. 11, pp. 193–232. London, Academic Press.

Mathews B.E. (1977) The passage of larval helminths through tissue barriers. In A.E.R. Taylor and R. Muller (eds.) *Parasite Invasion*, pp. 93–120. Oxford, Blackwell Scientific Publications.

MacInnis A.J. (1965) Responses of *Schistosoma mansoni* miracidia to chemical attractants. *J. Parasit.* **51**, 731–46.

McLaren D.J. (1976) Nematode sense organs. In B. Dawes (ed.) *Advances in Parasitology*, vol. 14, pp. 195–265. London, Academic Press.

Miller, G.C. (1981) Helminths and the transmammary route of infection. *Parasitology*, **82**, 335–42.

Read C.P. & Simmons J.E. (1963) Biochemistry and physiology of tapeworms. *Physiol. Rev.* **43**, 263–305.

Roberts L.S. (1961) The influence of population density on patterns and physiology of growth in *Hymenolepis diminuta* (Cestoda: Cyclophyllidea) in the definitive host. *Expl Parasit.* **11**, 332–71.

Roberts L.S. (1980) Development of *Hymenolepis diminuta* in its definitive host. In H.P. Arai (ed.) *Biology of the Tapeworm Hymenolepis diminuta*, pp. 357–423.

Rogers W.P. (1966) Exsheathment and hatching mechanisms in helminths. In E.J.L. Soulsby (ed.) *Biology of Parasites*, pp. 33–40. London, Academic Press.

Smyth J.D. (1966) *The Physiology of Trematodes*, Edinburgh, Oliver and Boyd.

Smyth J.D. (1969) *The Physiology of Cestodes*, Edinburgh, Oliver and Boyd.

Smyth J.D. (1976) *Introduction to Animal Parasitology*, 2nd ed. London, Hodder and Stoughton.

Smyth J.D. & Haslewood G.A.D. (1965) The biochemistry of bile as a factor determining host specificity in intestinal parasites, with particular reference to *Echinococcus granulosus*. *Ann. N.Y. Acad. Sci.* **113**, 234–60.

Stirewalt M.A. (1966) Skin penetration mechanisms in helminths. In E.J.L. Soulsby (ed.) *Biology of Parasites*, pp.41–60. London, Academic Press.

Ulmer M.J. (1971) Site finding behaviour in helminths in intermediate and definitive hosts. In A.M. Fallis (ed.) *Ecology and Physiology of Parasites*, pp. 123–60. Toronto, University of Toronto Press.

Von Brand T. (1979) *Biochemistry and Physiology of Endoparasites*, Amsterdam, Elsevier/North Holland.

Webster L.A. & Wilson R.A. (1970) The chemical composition of protonephridial canal fluid from the cestode *Hymenolepsis diminuta*. *Comp. Biochem. Physiol.* **35**, 201–9.

Wharton D. (1980) Nematode egg shells. *Parasitology*, **81**, 447–63.

Wilson R.A. & Webster L.A. (1974) Protonephridia. *Biol. Rev.* **49**, 127–60.

Wright D.J. & Newell D.P. (1976) Nitrogen excretion, osmotic and ionic regulation in nematodes. In N.A. Croll (ed.) *The Organisation of Nematodes*, pp. 163–210. London, Academic Press.

Chapter 5
Nutrition
C. Arme

5.1   INTRODUCTION

All living organisms interact to varying degrees with the physical, chemical and biological components of their environments. In free-living animals and plants there is little physiological intimacy between members of heterospecific associations. In parasitism, however, the environment of the parasite is wholly or partly another living organism, and associations of this type are typically characterized by a metabolic dependence of one of the partners—the parasite—upon the other—the host. Usually, but not invariably, this metabolic dependence involves a nutritional relationship.

Most studies on parasite nutrition have involved the removal of the parasite from the host and its subsequent investigation *in vitro*. There is no doubt that data so obtained are valuable in contributing to our understanding of basic mechanisms of nutrition. They should, however, be viewed with some caution since it is not possible to reproduce in the test tube the complex environment of, for example, the mammalian intestine which some parasites inhabit *in vivo*. *In vitro* studies therefore will tend to obscure the *interactions* known to occur between host and parasite. Such interactions should not be viewed solely with respect to effects upon the parasite (adsorption of macromolecules onto the surface of the parasite, possible immunological effects etc.). The host may also respond to the presence of the parasite to such an extent that information gained from studies on uninfected individuals may only have limited applicability to a parasitized host. Hence it should be the long-term aim of parasitologists to study the host–parasite unit as an entity in which the functioning of the whole cannot be entirely predicted by a consideration of the properties of the separate parts.

The systems utilized by parasites for nutrient acquisition may be reduced, at their simplest, to two. First, systems involving the transfer of nutrients directly across the outer membranes of organisms, e.g. diffusion, facilitated diffusion and active transport, the evolution of which has involved specialization primarily at the molecular level. Second, systems involving either temporary or permanent morphological specializations (cytostome, mouth, gut, accessory feeding structures etc.). Both of these systems are developed to a greater or lesser extent in the parasitic Protozoa and Metazoa.

5.2   MEMBRANE MECHANISMS OF NUTRITION

Absorption of nutrients across the cell membranes of Protozoa and the 'skin' of Metazoa is a well-documented phenomenon. Many free-living soft-bodied invertebrates are able to absorb low molecular-weight organic nutrients directly from the sea and, in a few instances, such uptake has been shown to be nutritionally significant. Studies on parasites have revealed similar membrane transport systems which, in the case of those Metazoa lacking a gut (the Cestoda and Acanthocephala), represent the sole means of nutrient acquisition.

5.2.1   Methods of study

To obtain reliable and reproducible results an adequate supply of physiologically homogeneous animals, grown under highly standardized conditions, is required. An example of the careful preparation required for such studies may be found in the work of Read, Rothman and Simmons (1963) who established methods for studying nutrient absorption in the rat tapeworm, *Hymenolepis diminuta*, which are still in use today, and which yield results that are reproducible the world over.

Having secured a supply of organisms it is possible to devise a set of *in vitro* experiments which will provide basic data on the nature of the uptake process. Thus, under suitable experimental conditions (osmolarity, temperature, pH, etc.), the absorption of a nutrient (e.g. an amino acid or hexose sugar) from a number of fixed

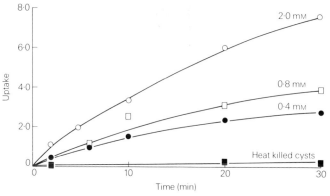

Fig. 5.1. A time-course study in which larval *Hymenolepis diminuta* were incubated for varying periods of time in a non-metabolizable amino acid α-aminoisobutyric acid (AIB). A control incubation with heat killed larvae was also carried out. In all three concentrations the levels of uptake declined with time and in this experiment the authors decided that an incubation time of 2 min in subsequent kinetic experiments would approximate to 'initial rates'. After 30 min incubation in 0.4 mM AIB, its concentration in the parasite was 6.2 mM, corresponding figures after incubation in 0.8 mM and 2.0 mM AIB were 8.8 mM and 17.6 mM respectively. Since accumulation against a concentration gradient had taken place it was concluded that AIB was absorbed into the larval worm by a process of active transport. (After Arme & Coates, 1973.)

concentrations, over varying periods of time, may be determined. When uptake is plotted against time a graph resembling that in Fig. 5.1 may be obtained. The decline in the apparent initial rates of uptake may be due to a variety of causes—the development of adverse conditions in the incubation medium, e.g. pH changes, anaerobiosis etc. which may deleteriously affect the physiology of the organism, or a decline in the external concentration of nutrient. Alternatively, the levelling off in the uptake curve may be due to the development of a steady-state condition in which the absorption of nutrient is balanced by its efflux from the animal.

Two important items of information can be derived from time-course experiments: (a) the internal concentration of nutrient can be compared with that in the incubation medium. If the ratio [nutrient int/nutrient ext] > unity, and if it can be demonstrated that no metabolism or compartmentalization of substrate has occurred, then it may be assumed that an active uptake process is involved; (b) a time interval can be determined (in Fig. 5.1 < 3 min) during which uptake occurs at 'initial rates'. In experiments designed to investigate the kinetics of uptake, incubation times should not exceed this value and in many instances incubation times of < 2 min are employed. Having selected a suitable fixed-time interval for subsequent incubation, uptake is determined from a series of substrate concentrations, preferably selected to lie within the physiological range of concentrations experienced by the parasite.

A number of possible relationships between uptake rate and substrate concentration may be revealed from such experiments, and these are illustrated in Fig. 5.2. A linear relationship between rate of uptake and substrate concentration, as in line A, strongly suggests that absorption is occurring by a process of simple diffusion, the quantitative expression of which is embodied is Fick's Law. Such a hypothesis could

Fig. 5.2. Possible relationships between uptake rate and sulstrate concentration. Line A indicates that the uptake rate is proportional to concentration—this is characteristic of diffusion processes. Line B on the other hand shows evidence of saturation, i.e. uptake is non-linear with respect to concentration and is indicative of a mediated transport process. Methods for determining K_t and V_{max} are indicated.

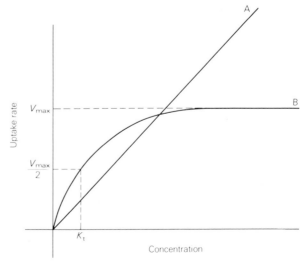

be further investigated by the use of inhibitors of uptake (see below). In contrast, in line B, at low substrate concentrations uptake is broadly proportional to concentration, whereas at higher substrate concentrations the rates of uptake decline until a maximum is reached, which does not increase despite increases in nutrient concentration.

It may be recalled that data similar to that depicted by line B are obtained when, under certain conditions, the rate of an enzyme-catalysed reaction is plotted against substrate concentration. The shape of line B is explained by analogy with enzyme kinetics; it is assumed that at high substrate concentrations the membrane components involved in transport are saturated. It must be emphasized however that, although the methods used in the kinetic analysis of transport are similar to those used in the study of enzyme-catalysed reactions, there is no evidence that enzymes are directly involved in uptake systems. Indeed, if transport phenomena had been discovered and analysed before enzyme systems we might have stated that the reactions of the latter follow transport kinetics! Little is known of the nature of the transport process. Many workers subscribe to the view that within cell membranes there are carriers which translocate substrates across plasma membranes in either direction. Such a view is consistent with the observed kinetics of transport and modern views of membrane structure (e.g. fluid mosaic model of Singer & Nicolson).

Two important parameters of transport systems can be calculated from data comprising line B, either directly (Fig. 5.3), or by replotting the data by a variety of methods used by enzyme-chemists, e.g. Lineweaver–Burk plots (Fig. 5.4). These are the maximum velocity of uptake V_{max}, and the transport constant K_t, which is analogous to the K_m of enzyme-kinetics (i.e. it represents the concentration of substrate which yields ½ maximum velocity of uptake). K_t is a measure of the affinity of a substrate for the transport system—the lower its value, the greater the affinity.

If, in an experiment, a curve of the shape of line B in Fig. 5.2 is obtained it may be postulated that adsorption of a substrate onto a component of the plasma membrane has occurred—in other words uptake is by a mediated process rather than by simple

Fig. 5.3. Uptake of AIB (0.1–3.0 mM) into larval *Hymenolepis diminuta*. Incubation times were of 2 min duration. Uptake is non-linear with respect to concentration. Saturation kinetics are characteristic of mediated uptake systems. (After Arme & Coates, 1973.)

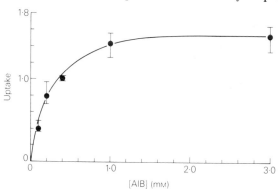

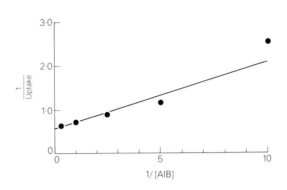

Fig. 5.4. Lineweaver-Burk plot of the data in Fig. 5.3. From these data a K_t of 0.27 mM and a V_{max} of 1.78 n moles/100 cysticercoids/2 min were calculated. The slope of the line equals K_m/V_{max} and its intercept on the $+y$ axis is $1/V_{max}$. If the line is extrapolated, the point where it crosses the $-x$ axis equals $-1/K_t$. (After Arme & Coates, 1973.)

diffusion. If, in a mediated uptake system, movement of substrate against a concentration gradient occurs, then *active transport* is said to occur. If substrate movement only goes in a 'downhill' direction so that an equilibrium is reached, with [nutrient int/nutrient ext] not exceeding unity, then the uptake process is termed *facilitated diffusion*.

Data from experiments in which uptake rates are studied at varying substrate concentrations may yield a third type of curve—line C (Fig. 5.5). Here absorption is

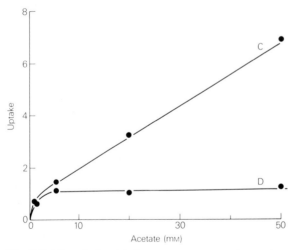

Fig. 5.5. The relationship between acetate uptake and its concentration using 10-day-old *Hymenolepis diminuta*. The raw data are plotted as line C in which it can be seen that at low substrate concentrations uptake is non-linear with respect to substrate concentrations whereas at acetate concentrations between 5.0–50.0 mM, uptake rate increases linearly with concentration. This suggests a dual mechanism of uptake with diffusion masking a mediated component at high concentrations of acetate. If it is assumed that between acetate concentrations of 30.0–50.0 mM uptake is largely diffusion then a K_d (diffusion constant) can be calculated. When this is subtracted from all the data and the points replotted a typical adsorption isotherm is obtained (line D). (After Arme & Read, 1968.)

occurring by a combination of mediated uptake and diffusion. If it is assumed that diffusion predominates at high substrate concentrations, then the linear part of line C can be used to calculate the diffusion component of uptake (K_d). By subtracting this value from all points on line C a typical 'saturation curve' (line D) is obtained.

Mediated absorptive systems are typically affected to greater or lesser degrees by variations in medium temperature and pH and by the presence of certain inhibitors of metabolism. Of most interest to a student of nutrition, however, is the fact that substrate uptake may be inhibited by other nutrients sharing the same transport system. This is explained (again by analogy with enzyme kinetics) by assuming that the two nutrients *compete* with one another for the same transport locus, and this characteristic may be utilized to determine variations in the specificity and number of transport systems in different organisms.

To illustrate this technique let us assume that it has been demonstrated in a particular organism that glucose is absorbed by a mediated uptake system. An indication of the specificity of the transport locus may be obtained by experiments in which uptake from a fixed concentration of glucose (say 0.1mM) is determined in the presence and absence of a number of other low molecular weight nutrients, for example galactose, fructose, alanine, lysine, and acetic acid at a concentration of 10mM. The relative molar ratios of inhibitor and substrate (I:S) should be large so that inhibition by compounds with only slight affinity for the glucose locus may be detected. If in such an experiment only galactose was found to significantly inhibit glucose uptake, then the nature of such inhibition should be investigated further.

There are a number of techniques available for such studies, but the one most frequently employed involves the study of uptake rates from a variety of concentrations of substrate in the presence and absence of a fixed concentration of inhibitor. The reciprocals of uptake rates are then plotted against the reciprocals of substrate concentrations by the methods of Lineweaver and Burk (Fig. 5.6). If the two lines so obtained have a common intercept at $1/V_{max}$ then it may be assumed that both glucose and galactose compete for a common binding site on a transport locus.

This experiment does not show that galactose is transported by the glucose locus since it is possible that *nonproductive* binding of galactose onto the glucose locus has occurred. The uptake of galactose would need to be studied independently to determine whether or not it was actually absorbed by the organism. The experiment also shows that if fructose, alanine, lysine and acetic acid are absorbed by membrane mechanisms, then these transport systems are distinct from that which absorbs glucose.

The above account represents only an outline of elementary transport kinetics, sufficient, it is hoped, to enable the reader to interpret data on nutrient absorption given below. The techniques described permit an analysis of transport phenomena at a superficial level only, because they ignore certain factors which are known to influence the process in certain parasites. Such factors include the adsorption of

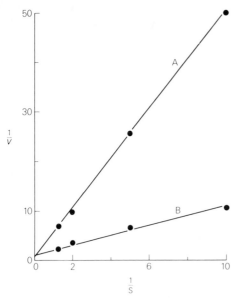

Fig. 5.6. This graph shows data when 10-day-old *Hymenolepis diminuta* were incubated in a range of concentrations of sodium acetate in the presence (line A) and absence (line B) of 4 mM sodium propionate, a short chain fatty acid salt which had been previously shown to inhibit acetate uptake. The data were plotted by the method of Lineweaver and Burk and two straight lines with a common intercept at $1/V_{max}$ were obtained. This indicates that the acetate inhibition by propionate is competitive in nature. From the graph the inhibition constant K_i can be calculated thus:

$$\text{slope of line acetate} + \text{propionate} = (K_t/V_{max})(1+[I]/K_i),$$

where K_t and V_{max} are determined for acetate in the absence of inhibitor and $[I]$ = inhibitor concentration. In this experiment K_i (propionate) was 1.25 mM. In other experiments K_i (formate) was found to be 6.9 mM, indicating that this substance had a low affinity for the acetate carrier when compared to propionate. (After Arme & Read, 1968.)

macromolecules onto parasite surfaces and the presence of the so called 'unstirred water' layers, known to be present on microvillar surfaces, and which may present diffusion barriers to solute movement.

The reader should not construe the fact that transport kinetics have been dealt with at some length to imply that membrane mechanisms *necessarily* play a dominant role in the nutrition of parasites. Rather, their emphasis reflects the fact that the methodology of transport studies is largely ignored in general textbooks.

5.3   NUTRITION IN PROTOZOA

A number of parasitic protozoa have been shown to possess mediated systems for nutrient uptake and often these operate in conjunction with endocytosis and diffusion to contribute to the nutritional physiology of a particular organism.

In the parasitic flagellates, membrane transport has been demonstated in *Crithidia* spp. and *Leishmania* spp., but most information is available for the bloodstream forms of the genus *Trypanosoma* and culture forms of *T. cruzi*. Thus, in *T. lewisi* for example, glucose, mannose, fructose, galactose, glucosamine and 3-*O*-methylglucose are absorbed by mediated mechanisms, apparently via two distinct transport sites.

In *T. equiperdum* three distinct systems are involved in monsaccharide absorption; to illustrate how the techniques of transport kinetics described above were used to arrive at this conclusion, a summary of the work of Ruff and Read (1974) is given below.

Using established techniques Ruff and Read incubated bloodstream forms of *T. equiperdum* in a variety of substrates. Prior to embarking on a detailed kinetic analysis, two important factors likely to influence data were determined, viz. the extent of substrate metabolism during incubations and also whether the post-incubation washing procedure was adequate to minimize 'carry-over' of isotope from incubation media to the ethanol used for substrate extraction. Four substrates were used in this study—glucose, fructose, mannose and glycerol; and 40 compounds (glucose analogues, fructose analogues, pentoses, heptoses, disaccharides and glycerol analogues) were tested as potential inhibitors at an I:S ratio of 40:1.

These preliminary studies indicated some specificity in the carbohydrate transport system of *T. equiperdum* since, although in general the results with glucose, fructose and mannose were similar, the effect of certain inhibitors of glycerol uptake was different from their effects on hexose transport (Table 5.1). This initial suggestion of a two-site system was further studied using reciprocal inhibition studies with the four substrates under study. Mannose and fructose were found to be completely competitive inhibitors of glucose uptake and also glucose competitively inhibited the uptake of mannose and fructose. These observations added weight to the concept of a single locus, 'the hexose site', via which absorption of glucose, mannose and fructose occurred. It was also noted that glycerol competitively inhibited glucose uptake (see below).

With regard to glycerol, it was found that glucose and 2-deoxyglucose were only partially competitive inhibitors of its uptake and that the maximum inhibition of glycerol transport by glucose was 80%. It was therefore assumed, since diffusion was not a detectable component of glycerol uptake, that two loci for glycerol uptake were present. That portion of glycerol uptake not susceptible to glucose inhibition was designated glycerol site II and the locus for that portion of glycerol uptake which was inhibited by glucose was termed glycerol site I. It is pertinent to ask the question that, since glucose and glycerol produce reciprocal inhibitions, do glycerol and hexoses share a common transport locus or is 'glycerol I' a distinct site? This question was resolved by a study of the effects of N-acetyl-D-glucosamine and 3-*O*-methylglucose on glucose and glycerol uptake. It was found that both these

Table 5.1. Effectiveness of various compounds as inhibitors of substrate transport* in *Trypanosoma equiperdum*.

Inhibitor (20mM)	Substrate (0.5mM)			
	Glucose	Fructose	Mannose	Glycerol
Glucose analogues				
D-Glucose	92.8	99.0	87.4	79.3
D-Mannose	96.4	99.3	94.1	72.3
D-Galactose	0†	0	0	0
D-Fucose	0	0	0	0
L-Rhamnose	0	0	0	0
D-Glucosamine	60.8	86.6	58.8	31.4
D-Mannosamine	72.6	66.2	41.4	34.0
N-Acetyl-D-glucosamine	72.3	84.8	67.4	0
N-Acetyl-D-mannosamine	0	0	0	0
D-Mannitol	0	0	0	0
D-Galacitol	0	0	0	0
2-Deoxy-D-glucose	99.0	100.0	99.2	48.8
3-O-Methylglucose	63.1	58.2	51.0	0
D-Gluconic acid	0	0	0	0
D-Gluconic acid lactone	0	0	0	0
α-Methyl-D-glucoside	0	0	0	0
Phenyl-D-glucopyranoside	0	0	0	0
Fructose analogues				
D-Tagatose	30.8	33.8	31.3	0
L-Sorbose	0	0	0	0
L-Fructose	80.2	90.7	82.0	62.9
D-Sorbitol	0	0	0	0
Pentoses				
D-Ribose	0	0	0	0
D-Arabinose	0	0	0	0
D-Xylose	0	0	0	0
L-Xylose	0	0	0	0
D-Xylitol	0	0	0	0
Heptoses				
Glucoheptose	0	0	0	0
Mannoheptulose	28.4	73.7	23.6	0
Disaccharides				
Sucrose	0	0	0	0
Lactose	0	0	0	0
Maltose	41.5	47.1	32.0	0
Trehalose	0	0	0	0

Table 5.1. *continued*

Inhibitor (20mM)	Substrate (0.5mM)			
	Glucose	Fructose	Mannose	Glycerol
Glycerol analogues				
Glycerol	87.4	92.7	84.9	96.5
1-Propanol	0	0	0	0
2-Propanol	0	0	0	0
1,2-Propanediol	0	0	0	0
1,3-Propanediol	0	0	0	0
Ethylene glycol	0	0	0	0
Glyceraldehyde	95.9	55.8	89.3	35.7

⋆ Values are percentage inhibition compared to uninhibited uptake. Each value is the mean of three to nine determinations.

† Indicates no significant inhibition ($P = 0.05$) compared with the uninhibited uptake (Ruff & Read, 1974).

substances were fully competitive inhibitors of glucose uptake, that is *they act at all the sites through which glucose is absorbed* but they had no effect on glycerol transport, even at I:S ratio of 400:1. Therefore glucose and glycerol could not be entering the parasite at the same locus even though they were mutual inhibitors of their respective transport!

Such a result can be explained if nonproductive binding were occurring (see section 5.2.1). Data in Table 5.1 permits certain tentative conclusions regarding the specificity of the three transport sites described above with respect to the chemical configuration of potential substrates. Thus variation in carbon atoms 1 and 6 rendered substrates incapable of interacting with the hexose site (lack of effect of gluconic acid, α-methyl-D-glucoside, D-mannitol) whereas changes at carbon atom 2 still resulted in the ability of certain compounds to inhibit glucose uptake (mannose, glucosamine, 2-deoxyglucose). Glycerol site II was very specific in its configurational binding requirements; transport could only be inhibited by glycerol and glyceraldehyde and glycerol analogues like ethylene glycol or 1-propanol lacked an inhibitory effect.

Amino acid uptake in bloodstream forms of *T. lewisi*, *T. equiperdum*, culture forms of *T. cruzi* and promastigotes of *Leishmania tropica* is also mediated, but at high substrate concentrations diffusion is often found to play an important role in solute absorption.

Detailed analysis of the amino acid uptake systems in *T. equiperdum* has revealed four systems with overlapping affinities, and the transport loci were defined thus: (a) arginine-phenylalanine locus; (b) arginine locus; (c) alanine-phenylalanine-glutamic acid locus; and (d) glutamic acid locus. In contrast to the broad specificity exhibited by the amino acid loci in *T. equiperdum*, in *T. cruzi* extreme specificity for the arginine uptake locus has been demonstrated. Indeed one of the two uptake systems for arginine is so specific for its substrate that homoarginine does not interact with it!

In addition to membrane transport and diffusion, macromolecular uptake has been demonstrated in several flagellate species. All members of the Kinetoplastida possess a deep invagination of the plasma membrane at the origin of the flagellum (see Fig. 1.1). From this flagellar pocket, endocytosis of macromolecules has been shown to occur. In addition, many kinetoplastid flagellates possess a cytostomal-cytopharynx complex, also involved in the uptake of large molecules, but such complexes have not been demonstrated in salivarian trypanosomes. Digestion in many species apparently occurs in lysosomes with a discharge of undigested material into the flagellar pocket occurring by exocytosis.

In the Apicomplexa, erythrocytic stages may feed by phagotrophy or mediated uptake systems. In the red cell the malarial parasite lies in a parasitophorous vacuole, surrounded by a membrane of host origin (see Fig. 4.5). Ingestion of host haemo-globin, often via a cytostome, therefore results initially in food vacuoles surrounded by two membranes, one of host and the other of parasite origin. As digestion progresses, acid hydrolases accumulate in the food vacuoles which eventually lose one of their membranes, presumably that of host origin. Digestion of globin yields amino acids, and the haem is converted into haemozoin (malaria pigment) which is stored in the parasite.

Studies on plasmodia freed from erythrocytes have demonstrated both diffusion and mediated uptake of amino acids. In *Plasmodium lophurae*, a malaria parasite of birds, infection of erythrocytes apparently results in striking alterations in the permeability of the red cell membrane. In the non-parasitized erythrocyte the uptake of many amino acids occurs by mediated systems. Following infection, however, with the single exception of glycine, all amino acids tested enter the erythrocyte by diffusion. Differences in the permeability of parasitized and non-parasitized erythrocytes to glucose have also been demonstrated. The reasons for these permeability changes are not known but may be associated with reduced intraerythrocytic ATP levels following infection. In support of this view is the fact that infected erythrocytes have an increased sodium content, the activity of the red cell sodium pump being presumably dependent directly or indirectly on ATP. Such alterations in the normal sodium gradient may affect the transport systems of the erythrocyte membrane since in many organisms the link between cation gradients and transport systems is well established.

An alternative view is that lipid synthesized by the parasite becomes incor-porated into the erythrocyte plasma membrane, and that this may cause an alteration in its permeability. It has been demonstrated that following infection the plasma membrane of red cells contains increased quantities of certain long-chain fatty acids. In addition to altering membrane permeability it has also been suggested that changes in erythrocyte membrane lipids may be associated with changes in its immunological properties and fragility.

In the Sarcodina, comparisons between certain free-living and parasitic forms have revealed interesting differences in structure and physiology. With particular reference to nutrition, specific transport systems for amino acids and mono-saccharides appear to be absent in non-parasitic amoebae and their nutritional demands are satisfied by endocytosis. In certain strains of the parasite *Entamoeba histolytica*, however, both endocytosis and mediated uptake systems contribute to nutrition of the organisms. Thus in the DKB strain of *E. histolytica*, glucose, 2-deoxyglucose, 3-*O*-methylglucose and xylose are all absorbed by a saturable process.

In experiments involving reciprocal inhibitions with pairs of different substrates, the similarity of K_i (see Fig. 5.6) and K_t values thus obtained indicate that all the sugars tested share a common transport system. Although this system is sensitive to changes in pH and temperature, it differs in two features from carbohydrate transport systems described in other animals. First, phloridzin, usually a potent inhibitor of sugar uptake, fails to affect the rate of uptake of 3-*O*-methylglucose, and second, the uptake of this monosaccharide is not influenced by a replacement of medium Na^+ by K^+. When the relative contributions of endocytosis and transport mechanisms are determined with reference to total glucose uptake, it is found that the former accounts for only 1/1000 of the total amount of glucose absorbed. These data do not permit conclusions to be drawn on the possible importance in *Entamoeba* of endocytosis in the acquisition of other classes of nutrient. Certain strains of *Entamoeba* apparently possess an unusual organelle called a surface lysosome, which is considered to release hydrolytic enzymes when a trigger mechanism is stimulated. There is good evidence for the presence of peripheral hydrolases in *Entamoeba*, but whether these are associated with a surface lysosome and, if so, what is the possible role of the trigger in their release, is less certain.

5.4   NUTRITION IN CESTODA AND ACANTHOCEPHALA

A cursory glance at bibliographies citing works on cestode nutrition will reveal many references on this topic. The vast majority of these, however, relate to a single species, *Hymenolepis diminuta*, and even then to *in vitro* studies on only a single stage of the life cycle—the pre-patent worm in the rat intestine. Illuminating though such information is, there are no grounds for assuming that it is universally applicable to other tapeworms.

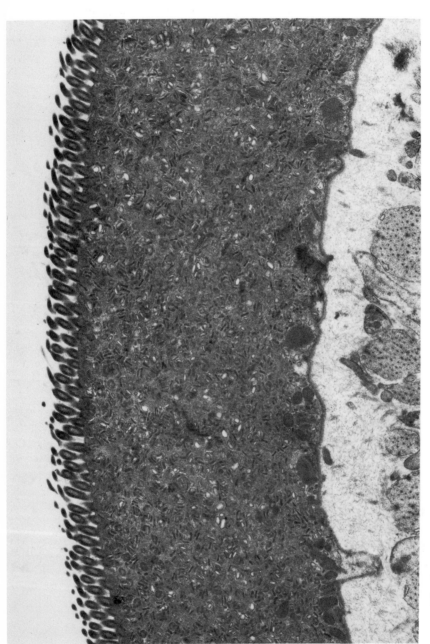

Fig. 5.7. Electron micrograph of tegument of *Hymenolepis diminuta*. ×25 000. (Original photograph by L.T. Threadgold.) This figure should be compared with Figs. 5.8, 5.10, 5.11 and 5.12. The traditional view that the surface of cestodes, monogeneans, digeneans and acanthocephalans is an inert cuticle is at variance with present concepts. The external layers of these parasites are limited by a plasma membrane under which is a syncytial cytoplasmic layer. The surface of the plasma membrane is covered by a glycocalyx. The tegument of *H. diminuta* and other cestodes is covered by numerous microvillus-like projections termed microtriches (sing. microthrix). They differ from microvilli mainly in their possession of a dense distal tip.

All tapeworms lack a mouth, gut and anus; the only route available for nutrient acquisition is therefore across the tegument. The tegument of *Hymenolepis diminuta* is selective in the types of molecules to which it is permeable. Thus proteins and other macromolecules are not absorbed in this species, although protein uptake into the bladders of certain larval taeniids has been claimed and endocytosis in a larval pseudophyllid *(Schistocephalus solidus)* has recently been demonstrated.

The tegument of *Hymenolepis* (Figs. 5.7, 5.8) is readily permeable to a variety of low molecular-weight organic nutrients. For amino acids at least six uptake sites

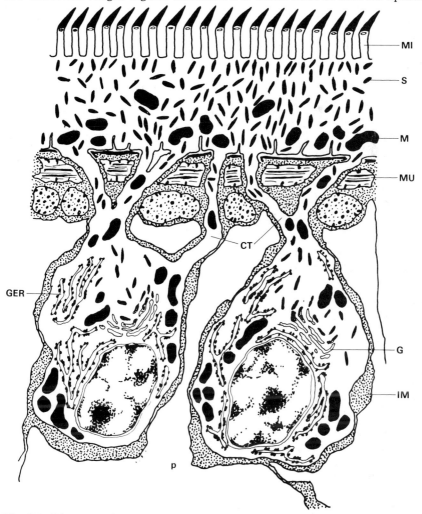

Fig. 5.8. Diagrammatic representation of the tegument of *Hymenolepis diminuta* (L.T. Threadgold). MI: microthrix; S: secretion; M: mitochondrion; MU: muscle; CT: connecting tubule; GER: granular endoplasmic reticulum; G: golgi complex; IM: interstitial material; P: parenchyma.

have been demonstrated: four for neutral, one for basic and one for acidic amino acids. These uptake systems are unusual in that the limited data available suggest that amino acid uptake may be insensitive to ion gradients. If this is so it would be of great interest to determine the 'driving force' of the transport system. Glucose uptake occurs via a single site, shared by galactose, and is sensitive to Na^+ and Cl^-. Transport systems for the absorption of glycerol, fatty acids, purines, pyrimidines, thiamine and riboflavin have also been characterized in *H. diminuta*, and, although most of the observations were made *in vitro*, the limited data available from *in vivo* studies suggest that similar uptake systems operate in the intact symbiosis. It must not be thought that the transport systems described above are unidirectional. There is some evidence of a mediated efflux of amino acids from *H. diminuta*, and a continuous and complex exchange of materials between host and parasite probably occurs *in vivo*. The possible significance of these exchanges has been discussed in detail elsewhere (Pappas and Read, 1975).

In addition to an absorptive role, the tegument of *H. diminuta* also has a digestive function, possessing intrinsic membrane-bound digestive enzymes, and also interacting with extrinsic host-pancreatic enzymes which become adsorbed onto the surface of the parasite. Although no intrinsic disaccharidases or aminopeptidases have been demonstrated in *H. diminuta*, there is evidence of intrinsic ribonuclease, monoglyceride hydrolase and phosphohydrolase activity. Most information is available on the surface phosphohydrolases, which appear to function in a digestive capacity by hydrolysing a variety of phosphate esters—to which the worm is impermeable—and releasing free phosphate and an organic component, both of which may then be absorbed. Glucose, liberated from glucose phosphates, is rapidly absorbed and does not appreciably diffuse into the medium. This implies that the glucose transport systems and sites of phosphohydrolase activity are in close spatial proximity. However, since each system may be inhibited independently, without effect on the other, it may be concluded that they are separate and that phosphohydrolases play no *direct* role in glucose transport in this species.

Extrinsic enzymes of host origin have also been shown to interact with the surface of *H. diminuta in vitro*. Thus, in the presence of the worm the activity of α-amylase is enhanced; Ugolev described an analogous effect, following the interaction of pancreatic amylase with mucosal cells of the intestine, which he termed 'contact' or 'membrane' digestion.

The degree of enhancement of enzyme activity appears to be a function of worm surface area and the effect cannot be demonstrated if parasites are first preincubated in polycations known to be adsorbed onto the worm surface. These two observations lead to the conclusion that amylase becomes adsorbed onto the worm surface and that this is accompanied by a change in its molecular configuration (possibly because of alterations in charge distribution in the molecule) which favours an enhancement of catalytic activity.

The overall effect of increased amylase activity in the gut lumen is to increase the supply of disaccharides. Because *H. diminuta* lacks any intrinsic disaccharidase activity these cannot be directly utilized by the parasite, although it is possible that host mucosal membrane-bound disaccharidase activity may increase the amounts of luminal glucose available to the worm. *Hymenolepis* interacts with pancreatic trypsin and α- and β-chymotrypsin, all of which are irreversibly inactivated *in vitro* in the presence of the worm. Lipase activity is also inhibited, but in this case the effect is reversible. The 'survival value' to the parasite of this mechanism for escaping the potentially destructive effect of host digestive enzymes is obvious.

The data summarized above clearly indicate that *Hymenolepis* interacts with its environment in a number of complex ways and that the morphological basis for these interactions is the tegument and associated structures (e.g. the glycocalyx). The parasite surface may be regarded as a functional mosaic serving absorptive, digestive and protective roles. The extent to which some of the above features of tegument function may become modified *in vivo* must remain speculative, in the absence of detailed studies. The reader may care to reflect upon the morphological and physiological similarities between the vertebrate intestinal mucosa and the tegument of *H. diminuta*.

The Acanthocephala also lack a gut. Membrane transport of amino acids and sugars has been demonstrated in this group but, in contrast to *Hymenolepis diminuta*, adsorption of amylase onto the surface of *Moniliformis dubius* does not result in an enhancement of its catalytic activity.

Protein uptake (horseradish peroxidase) has been reported in *Moniliformis dubius*. Absorption occurs via surface crypts, from which protein-containing vesicles are formed, which eventually fuse with lysosomes.

5.5   NUTRITION IN MONOGENEA

Whereas in the Cestoda and Acanthocephala the absence of a mouth and gut result in the tegument playing a dominant role in nutrition, in the remaining three major helminth groups—the Monogenea, Digenea and Nematoda—feeding is a more complex process. Members of these groups typically possess a differentiated gut and, in addition, the tegument of certain Monogenea and Digenea and the cuticle of a few Nematoda have been shown to be permeable to low molecular-weight organic nutrients.

The most detailed description of the role of the gut in monogenean nutrition has been derived from studies by Halton (1975) and co-workers on *Diclidophora merlangi*, a blood-feeding gill parasite from whiting. In the anterior gut, numerous gland cells are present: buccal glands may secrete anticoagulants, and enzymes from prepharyngeal and oesophageal glands predigest the blood meal (Fig. 5.9). By the time the blood has reached the intestinal caeca it is noncellular and homogeneous, and gastrodermal cells absorb haemoglobin and blood proteins. Studies with an electron microscope have demonstrated that uptake occurs by endocytosis and coated vesicles so formed discharge their contents into a lysosomal system of interconnecting channels. Here, digestion of absorbed protein occurs and the un-digestible residues of haematin are periodically extruded by exocytosis. These

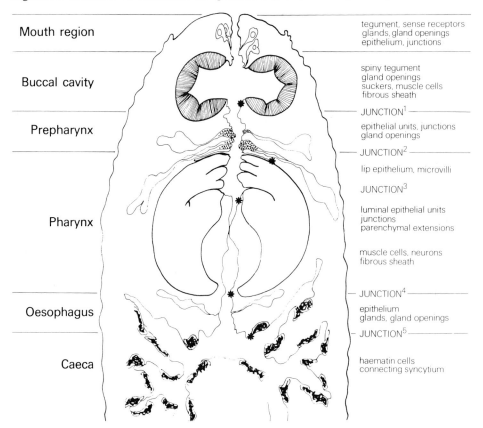

Mouth region	tegument, sense receptors glands, gland openings epithelium, junctions
Buccal cavity	spiny tegument gland openings suckers, muscle cells fibrous sheath
	JUNCTION[1]
Prepharynx	epithelial units, junctions gland openings
	JUNCTION[2]
	lip epithelium, microvilli
	JUNCTION[3]
Pharynx	luminal epithelial units junctions parenchymal extensions
	muscle cells, neurons fibrous sheath
	JUNCTION[4]
Oesophagus	epithelium glands, gland openings
	JUNCTION[5]
Caeca	haematin cells connecting syncytium

Fig. 5.9. *Diclidophora.* The foregut is lined by a complex series of morphologically distinct epithelia that characterize the regions listed on the left. The epithelia (whose features are described on the right) are interconnected by septate desmosomes at junctions 1–5 (marked by asterisks) and are penetrated by the openings of numerous unicellular glands. This complexity of structure reflects the function of the foregut in (1) locating and attaching to a suitable feeding site on the host, using the sense receptors and sticky secretions of the gland cells in the mouth region; (2) ingesting blood through the sucking action of the buccal suckers and pharynx, aided by anticoagulant secretions from the buccal glands; and (3) pre-digesting the blood meal by enzymes released from the prepharyngeal and oesophageal (?) glands. The semi-digested blood proteins are then taken up by the haematin cells in the caeca and further degraded intracellularly through a lysosomal system. Some absorption of the soluble components of the meal is thought to occur across the microvillous lining of the pharynx. (Original drawing by D.W. Halton.)

results illustrate how the applicaton of a new technique can throw light on an old problem. Prior to the ultrastructural studies described above, observations using the light microscope suggested that haematin residues accumulated in certain gastrodermal cells in sanguinivorous monogeneans, and were eliminated from the parasite by a process of cell sloughing.

The structure of the monogenean tegument (Figs. 5.10, 5.11) has been the subject of a number of investigations, although detailed studies on its possible role in nutrition are few. The principal difficulty encountered in designing experiments to assess the relative roles of gut and tegument in fluke nutrition is to eliminate the possibility of ingestion of the incubation medium via the mouth. The immediately obvious step of ligaturing the anterior end of the parasite has been shown to damage the tegument, allowing 'leakage' into the animal. For *Diclidophora*, two approaches to this problem have been employed. First, the fluke has been suspended with its mouth out of the incubation medium and amino acid uptake demonstrated, and second, incubation of unligatured *Diclidophora*, completely immersed in a medium containing an electron-dense tracer (ruthenium red) resulted in no dye being detected in the gut during subsequent ultrastructural investigation. Thus, *in vitro*, it is concluded that no uptake of medium occurs via the mouth.

Subsequent experiments demonstrated that the tegument of *Diclidophora* is permeable to glucose and certain neutral amino acids and that the latter are absorbed by a mediated process. Low concentrations of amino acids and other nutrients are present in sea-water (in the Irish sea, for example, levels are glycine $1.28\mu M$, leucine $0.49\mu M$, glucose $0.5\mu M$). The contribution of their tegumentary uptake to the overall nutrition of a parasite which has access to a diet of vertebrate blood is however not known—at most it may presumably be regarded as only a supplement. It is conceivable that the significance of tegumentary transport systems in *Diclidophora* may be revealed by considering their possible operation in an *outward* direction. In this way they may contribute to the regulation of the internal parasite metabolite pools.

5.6   NUTRITION IN DIGENEA

The vast majority of digeneans possess an oral sucker, pharynx and caeca which, together with the tegument, play a role in nutrition. Members of the group occupy a wide range of feeding niches and utilize blood, mucus, host tissue and host gut contents in their diet. Typically, food is drawn into the animal by the combined action of the oral sucker and a pumping action of a muscular pharynx and/or oesophagus. Digestion may be initiated in the anterior gut and completed in the gut caeca, predominantly by the action of extracellular enzymes. In many Digenea the gastrodermis has been depicted as static in structure although in *Fasciola hepatica* it

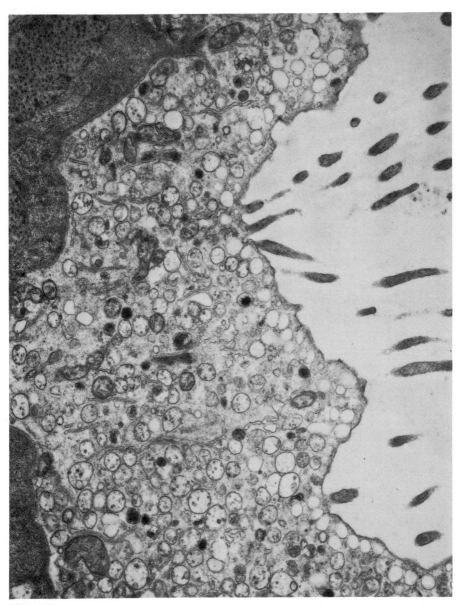

Fig. 5.10. Electron micrograph of the tegument of *Diclidophora merlangi* (original photograph by D.W. Halton). The general structure of the tegument resembles that of digeneans except that microvillus-like cytoplasmic projections are present.

has been suggested that a single gastrodermal cell may undergo sequential changes and assume a variety of roles. Three gastrodermal cell types have been described in this species: group I cells are tall and columnar in appearance and are considered to be secretory; group II are short columnar cells with an absorptive role; and group III cells are small and cuboid: their function is not clear.

Despite the wealth of information on the morphology, ultrastructure and enzyme histochemistry of the digenean gut, there are surprisingly few observations on the physiology of digestion and absorption in the group. Most information is available for two species, *Fasciola hepatica* and *Schistosoma mansoni*.

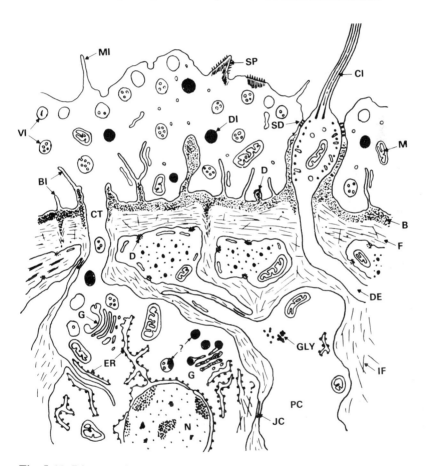

Fig. 5.11. Diagram of the tegument of *Diclidophora merlangi* (original drawing by D.W. Halton and G.P. Morris). MI: microvillus; SP: spiny bristles; CI: cilium; VI: vesicular inclusion; DI: dense inclusion; SD: septate desmosome; M: mitochondrion; BI: basal infolding; D: desmosome; CT: cytoplasmic connection; B: basal lamina; F & IF: fibrous interstitial material; DE: nerve ending; G: Golgi stack; ER: endoplasmic reticulum; JC: junctional complex; GLY: glycogen granules; PC: parenchymal cell.

The nature of the diet of *Fasciola* has been the subject of some debate, the point at issue being whether the animal is mainly a blood or tissue feeder. It is difficult to imagine how the parasite could exert a high degree of selectivity in its food, for example by feeding on tissue and avoiding blood or vice versa. Gut proteases in *Fasciola* are able to degrade globin to amino acids and peptides, but detailed

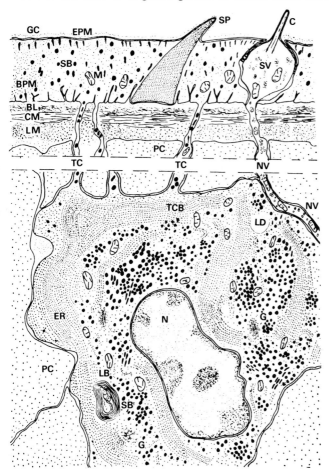

Fig. 5.12. Diagram of the ultrastructure of the tegument of the digenean *Cyathocotyle bushiensis*. BL: basement layer; BPM: basal plasma membrane; C: cilium of sense organ; CM: circular muscle; EPM: external plasma membrane; ER: endoplasmic reticulum; G: golgi complexes; GC: granular external coat; LD: lipid droplet; LM: longitudinal muscle; LB: lamellar body; M: mitochondrion; N: nucleus; PC: parenchymal cell; SB: secretory body; SP: spine; SV: vesicle of sense organ; NV: nerve process from sense organ; TC: cytoplasmic connection between external tegument and the tegumentary cell body; TCB: tegumentary cell body. (After D.A. Erasmus, 1972.)

The tegument of digeneans does not bear microtriches but is often thrown up into ridges. Distinctive spines are present.

experimental observations on the absorption of soluble nutrients by the gastro-dermal cells are lacking. In *Schistosoma*, gut proteases apparently release peptides from protein, rather than amino acids. There is no experimental evidence of endo-cytosis occurring in the schistosome gut and the question arises, How are these peptides absorbed? Three possibilities suggest themselves: that membrane-bound peptidases hydrolyse the peptides to amino acids which are then absorbed; that the gastrodermis is permeable to peptides; or that *in vivo* the presence of peptides in the gut induces endocytosis which did not occur *in vitro* in the presence of artificial markers like ferritin or thorotrast.

The importance of the tegument (Fig. 5.12) in digenean nutrition is well established in certain species. In *Fasciola*, glucose, galactose, fructose, mannose, ribose and glucosamine, are absorbed by facilitated diffusion via two systems. One—the glucose system—interacts with glucose, galactose 3-O-methylglucose, glucosamine and mannose; the other is a fructose system, to which several other monosaccharides have been found to bind nonproductively. Sugar uptake in *Schistosoma mansoni* also occurs via mediated tegumentary systems which transport glucose, galactose, fructose, 3-O-methylglucose, glucosamine and ribose. The rate of glucose metabolism is so high in this species that it is not possible to demonstrate its accumulation against a concentration gradient.

Interesting differences have been noted between the tegumentary absorption of amino acids in *Fasciola* and *Schistosoma*. In the former, uptake occurs by simple diffusion whereas, in contrast, uptake in *Schistosoma* involves two systems for mediated transport, both of which are dependent upon the presence of sodium ions. There is insufficient information available to permit a conclusion on the reason for these striking differences in amino acid uptake mechanisms in *Fasciola hepatica*. It is, however, tempting to speculate that the apparent inability of *Schistosoma* gut enzymes to completely digest protein might render the organism dependent on exogenous amino acids. A further possible line of enquiry might involve observa-tions on the distribution of γ-glutamyl cycle enzymes in helminths. Preliminary surveys indicate their presence in the cestode *Moniezia expansa* but their absence in *Fasciola* and *Ascaris*, neither of which transports amino acids across their body wall.

Acetate and other fatty acids are excreted by *Fasciola*, and mediated tegumentary transport systems for their absorption have also been demonstrated. Perhaps this is an example of a transport mechanism the main function of which is the selective *outward* movement of metabolites as part of the excretory process.

5.7   NUTRITION IN NEMATODA

The Nematoda is a large group made up of free-living forms occupying a wide variety of feeding niches, and parasites of animals and plants. In the majority of nematodes feeding occurs via the gut, and a wide range of feeding mechanisms have been developed by organisms inhabiting different habitats. The cuticle of most nematode species is impermeable to organic nutrients but there are a number of exceptions to this general rule and these are described below.

The presence of microvilli has been demonstrated on the surface of certain members of the Mermithidae and experimental studies of *Mermis nigrescens* have revealed transcuticular uptake systems for glucose and certain neutral amino acids. Glucose uptake occurs by a saturable system which is not inhibited by 2, 4-DNP or KCN, suggesting a process of facilitated diffusion. The neutral amino acids investigated are mutually competitive inhibitors and thus presumably share a common transport system. Studies on the infective larvae and adults of the filarial nematode *Brugia pahangi* have shown that leucine, D-glucose and adenosine are absorbed by a transcuticular route. L-glucose and sucrose are not absorbed, indicating that the mechanisms for sugar uptake might exhibit some specificity.

There are only limited data on the physiology of the alimentary canal in nematodes. A number of species possess pharyngeal glands which secrete enzymes and other substances, for example anticoagulants. In addition to initiating digestion in the gut, a number of species transfer enzymes from pharyngeal glands onto food where extracorporeal digestion occurs; other species which penetrate skin and other tissues produce a factor which resembles hyaluronidase in its action. A wide range of digestive enzymes is found in the intestine. Some, in particular disaccharidases, are intrinsic enzymes located in the brush-border of the intestine and, in *Ascaris*, these enzymes are specific for substrates containing only glucose and fructose. Mediated intestinal uptake systems for amino acids, glucose and fructose have also been demonstrated in the gut of *Ascaris*, although the same *in vitro* preparations are impermeable to galactose, indicating a degree of specificity unusual in monosaccharide transport systems.

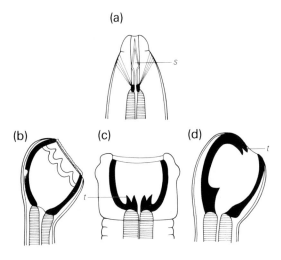

(a)

(b)   (c)   (d)

Fig. 5.13. Diagram of some nematode heads to show variations in the structure of the buccal cavity (a) *Tylenchus:* plant parasitic; (b) *Chabertia:* animal parasitic; (c) *Syngamus:* animal parasitic; (d) *Ancylostoma:* animal parasitic. *s:* stylet; *t:* tooth. (After Lee & Atkinson, 1976.)

Perhaps the greatest diversity in organs associated with feeding in the Nematoda is found in the stomodaeum. Variations in the buccal cavity are too diverse to discuss in detail in this work, but they range from a relatively simple tube found in liquid feeders like *Ascaris* to forms in which elaborate modifications are present, for example stylets and cutting plates or teeth (Fig. 5.13).

REFERENCES AND FURTHER READING

Aikawa M. (1971) *Plasmodium*—the fine structure of malarial parasites. *Expl. Parasit.* **30**, 284–320.

Arme C. (1975) Tapeworm–host interactions. In D. Jennings & D.L. Lee (eds.) Symbiosis. *Symp. Soc. exp. Biol.* **29**, 505–32.

Arme C. (1976) In C.R. Kennedy (ed.) *Ecological Aspects of Parasitology*, pp. 75–97. Amsterdam, North Holland Publishing Co.

Arme C. & Coates A. (1973) *Hymenolepis diminuta:* active transport of α-aminoisobutyric acid by cysticercoid larvae. *Int. J. Parasit.* **3**, 553–60.

Arme C. & Read C.P. (1968) Studies on membrane transport II. The absorption of acetate and butyrate by *Hymenolepis diminuta* (Cestoda). *Biol. Bull.* **135**, 80–90.

Befus A.D. & Podesta R.B. (1976) In C.R. Kennedy (ed.) *Ecological Aspects of Parasitology*, pp. 303–25. Amsterdam, North Holland Publishing Co.

Brooker B.E. (1971) The fine structure of *Crithidia fasciculata* with special reference to the organelles involved in the ingestion and digestion of protein. *Z. Zellforsch. mikrosk. Anat.* **116**, 532–63.

Chappell L.H. (1974) Methionine uptake by larval and adult *Schistosoma mansoni*. *Int. J. Parasit.* **4**, 361–9.

Chen S.H. & Howells R.E. (1979) The uptake *in vitro* of dyes, monosaccharides and amino acids by the filarial worm *Brugia pahangi*. *Parasitology* **78**, 343–54.

Dike S.C. & Read C.P. (1971) Relation of tegumentary phosphohydrolase and sugar transport in *Hymenolepis diminuta*. *J. Parasit.* **57**, 1251–5.

Erasmus D.A. (1972) *The Biology of Trematodes*, London, Edward Arnold.

Halton D.W. (1975) Intracellular digestion and cellular defecation in a monogenean, *Diclidophora merlangi*. *Parasitology* **70**, 331–40.

Hampton J.R. (1971) Arginine transport in the culture form of *Trypanosoma cruzi*. *J. Protozool.* **18**, 701–3.

Hopkins C.A., Law L.M. & Threadgold L.T. (1978) *Schistocephalus solidus:* pinocytosis by the plerocercoid tegument. *Expl. Parasit.* **44**, 161–72.

Langreth S.G. and Balber A.E. (1975) Protein uptake and digestion in bloodstream and culture forms of *Trypanosoma brucei*. *J. Protozool.* **22**, 40–53.

Lee D.L. & Atkinson H.J. (1976) *Physiology of Nematodes*, London, Macmillan.

Lumsden R.D. (1975) Surface ultrastructure and cytochemistry of parasitic helminths. *Expl. Parasit.* **37**, 267–339.

Pappas P.W. & Read C.P. (1975) Membrane transport in helminth parasites—a review. *Expl. Parasit.* **37**, 469–530.

Podesta R.B. (1977) *Hymenolepis diminuta*: unstirred layer thickness and effects on active and passive transport kinetics. *Expl. Parasit.* **43**, 12–24.

Read C.P., Rothman A.H. & Simmons J.E. Jr. (1963) Studies on membrane transport with special reference to host-parasite integration. *Ann. N.Y. Acad. Sci.* **113**, 154–205.

Ruff M.D. & Read C.P. (1974) Specificity of carbohydrate transport in *Trypanosoma equiperdum*. *Parasitology* **68,** 103–15.

Serrano R. & Reeves R.E. (1975) Physiological significance of glucose transport in *Entamoeba histolytica*. *Expl. Parasit.* **37,** 411–16.

Sherman I.W. & Tanigoshi L. (1972) Incorporation of ^{14}C-amino acids by malaria *(Plasmodium lophurae)*. V. Influence of antimalarials on the transport and incorporation of amino acids. *Proc. helminth. Soc. Wash.* **39,** 250–60.

Chapter 6
Immunology
F.E.G. Cox

6.1   INTRODUCTION

The immune system of any animal is concerned with defence against invading organisms and with the removal of potentially malignant cells. These two aspects of the immune system are interrelated and our understanding of immunity to microorganisms and parasites is largely dependent on our comprehension of the ways in which the cells of the immune system recognize and respond to tumour cells. Immunity to parasites can be considered at a broad descriptive level or at a detailed cellular level, and it is in the first area that our knowledge is most complete.

From the point of view of the immune response to parasites, it is important to distinguish between protozoa and helminths. Protozoa are microparasites, like viruses and bacteria, that multiply within the host, whereas helminths are macroparasites that normally do not do so. The host defence strategy must therefore be different in response to protozoa and to helminths, but there are several principles that apply to parasites of all kinds.

When an invading organism enters a host there are five possible outcomes.

1   *The parasite fails to become established.* This is usually called innate immmunity and occurs when the host does not provide the requisites for the existence of the parasite, when it is unable to utilize the requisites or if they are toxic.

2   *The parasite becomes established and kills the host.* This occurs when the host is invaded by a massive number of parasites, which either multiply rapidly and kill the host outright or feed on or block vital organs, or when the immune system of the host is inadequate to deal with the infection.

3   *The parasite becomes established and the host overcomes the infection.* This is classical acquired immunity and occurs when the parasite is recognized as foreign, elicits an effective immune response and is destroyed. In the case of most microparasites, this whole process is complete within 10–14 days and, thereafter, the host is resistant to infection with the same organism for a variable period.

4   *The parasite becomes established and the host begins to overcome the infection but instead of destroying the parasite becomes damaged itself.* This occurs when an immune response is mounted but the parasite, in some way, is able to avoid the consequences of the immune response which becomes misdirected towards, for example, parasite products in tissues which themselves become damaged. This is the basis of immunopathology which in some cases is more dangerous than the effects of the parasites themselves.

5   *The parasite becomes established and the host begins to ovecome the infection but not* *completely.* This occurs, as above, when the host mounts an immune response that keeps the infection under control but does not eliminate it completely. This is a compromise situation, commonly found among parasites, and is usually assumed to represent a balanced state. In fact, such compromise situations are unstable and often change to one of those listed as 2–4 above. Special forms of this situation are premunition (or non-sterile immunity) to protozoa, in which immunity to acute infection or reinfection exists only while the initial infection persists, and concomitant immunity in helminths, in which the established infection is unaffected while parasites arriving subsequently are destroyed.

Most infections with microorganisms, for example influenza or staphylococcal infections, are acute and there is a rapid immune response that quickly eliminates the infective organisms and renders the host resistant to reinfection. Such infections are of the type described as 3 above. In most parasitic infections, the immune response develops slowly and often fails to eliminate the organism although it may keep it under control. Parasitic infections, therefore, resemble fulminating infections of type 2 or chronic infections of types 4 and 5. Until comparatively recently, many people felt that there was no effective acquired immunity of type 3 in diseases caused by parasites and that seeking to develop vaccines against such diseases was a misplaced activity. It is now clear, however, that acquired immunity to parasitic infections is the rule. The evidence for this comes from two sources. Firstly, in endemic areas the prevalence of infection declines with age whereas the presence of antibodies in the serum increases and, second, in every experimental model investigated acquired immunity can be demonstrated under certain circumstances. It is clear then that acquired immunity does occur and parasite immunologists are now largely concerned with investigating the nature of the acquired immunity with the specific aims of developing vaccines and moderating, or eliminating, immunopathological side-effects. Such investigations have led to a fairly clear understanding of the ways in which parasites manage to evade the immune response but, before this can be discussed, it is necessary to consider the nature of acquired immunity.

6.2   THE IMMUNE RESPONSE

When a foreign protein or polysaccharide is injected into a mammal it acts as an antigen and elicits an immune response (Fig. 6.1). The main cells involved are monocytes and lymphocytes. The fully differentiated monocytes are macrophages and these take up the antigen and present it to the lymphocytes. There are two classes of lymphocytes—B cells and T cells. Both arise from undifferentiated stem cells but the T cells differentiate in the thymus while B cells differentiate in the fetal liver. Differentiation involves the acquisition of cell surface markers; in the case of B cells, these are immunoglobulins. The T and B cells migrate to appropriate T-dependent and B-dependent areas of the lymph nodes, spleen- and gut-associated lymphoid tissues, from which they enter the circulation. They are activated on stimulation by an antigen. Some T cells become cytotoxic while others produce a range of soluble substances, called lymphokines, which act on other cells. Macrophage migration inhibition factor, for example, inhibits the movement of macrophages. B cells, when stimulated, produce antibodies. T cells can act independently of B cells by inducing what is known as cell-mediated immunity (see section 6.2.2). B cells, on the other hand, require the cooperation of T cells (TH or helper cells) when producing antibodies to T-dependent antigens, which include the majority of antigens. This cooperation occurs at the stage of antigen presentation by the macrophages and thus most antibody production depends on three cells—a macrophage, T cell and B cell.

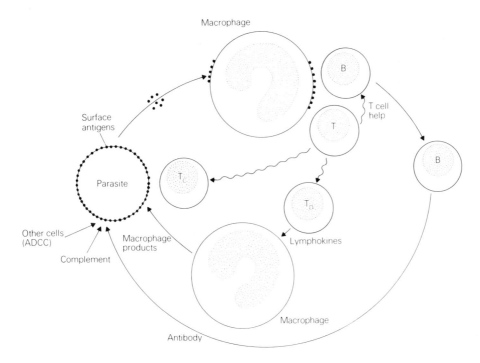

Fig. 6.1. The main events in the immune response. The response begins when the immune system is stimulated by an antigen that is taken up and processed by a macrophage. Most parasites are too large to be phagocytosed whole and the effective antigen is a part of the parasite such as a surface molecule. The processed antigen is presented to T and B lymphocytes. T lymphocytes respond by stimulating various clones of cells some of which are cytotoxic (Tc cells), others (TD) secrete lymphokines that in turn affect macrophages or other lymphocytes and others stimulate B lymphocytes to produce antibody (T cell help). The parasite bearing the antigens originally recognized as foreign now becomes a target cell and can be attacked in various ways described in the text.

The implication of T cells in an immune response does not necessarily mean that the response is a cell-mediated one. It could equally well mean that they are involved as helper cells.

6.2.1   Antibodies and complement

Antibodies are immunoglobulins which consist of basic units of four polypeptide chains, two heavy and two light (Fig. 6.2). The Fab, or antigen binding part, is formed from one heavy and one light chain, thus there are two on each basic unit. The opposite end of the molecule is the Fc portion and this is capable of binding to any cell with an appropriate Fc receptor. There are five classes of immunoglobulins—IgG, IgM, IgA, IgE and IgD—of which only the first four are involved in immune responses to parasites.

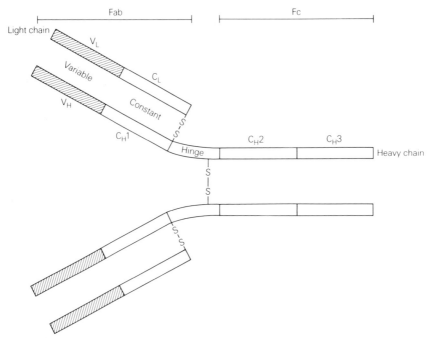

Fig. 6.2. Diagrammatic representation of an immunoglobulin molecule. Immunoglobulin molecules consist of four polypeptide chains, two heavy and two light. Each heavy chain consists of four domains, three constant in amino acid composition (C_H1, C_H2, C_H3) and one variable (V_H). Each light chain consists of two domains, one constant (C_L) and one variable (V_L). Within each of the variable domains there are three hypervariable regions or 'hot spots'. The amino acids of the variable regions, particularly the hypervariable parts of a heavy and a light chain, form a cup-like antigen binding site. Complement binds to domain C_H2 and immunoglobulin molecules bind to cells via domain C_H3. This diagram represents a molecule of IgG1. Other subclasses of IgG and other classes of imunoglobulin differ in detail.

Essentially, IgM is a pentameric form with 10 antigen binding sites, and is the immunoglobulin first produced phylogenetically, ontogenetically, and during an immune response. Its structure is ideally suited to binding with organisms with repeated antigenic sites as in many bacteria. IgG is a monomeric form and is the most abundant immunoglobulin. It is produced after IgM during a primary immune response and eventually replaces the larger molecule and persists after the disappearance of the antigen. IgA is a secretory immunoglobulin that occurs in the serum and in the secretions in the gut and similar sites. It is either a monomer or a dimer in which case it is combined with a secretory piece. IgE is also a monomer but does not occur free in the serum. IgE binds to cells, particularly mast cells, by its Fc portion and, having bound antigen molecules, causes the cell to release its contents.

IgG and IgM can act in various ways. They can cause microorganisms to agglutinate, in the same way as mismatched red blood cells, or cause them to be phagocytosed by binding to the antigens by the Fab portion and to the phagocytic cell by the Fc portion. They can also fix complement—a series of 11 factors in the blood which, when activated in order, result in the activation of cytolytic factors (Fig. 6.3). The first component of complement binds to receptor sites on an immunoglobulin molecule which has itself bound to an antigen. If this antigen is a microorganism, the final result is the activation of the cytolytic enzymes which destroy it. The activated enzymes, however, need not necessarily be in the immediate vicinity of the microorganism, in which case host cells may be

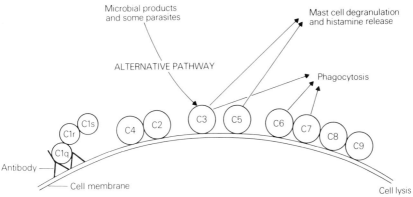

Fig. 6.3. Complement activation. Complement activation is initiated when immunoglobulin (IgG or IgM) combines with an antigen, in this case a cell membrane, revealing complement binding sites on two adjacent C_H2 domains. The first component of complement, C1q, binds and together with C1r and C1s, activates components C4 and C2 which stick to the cell surface as $\overline{C42}$. $\overline{C42}$ activates C3 which combines with $\overline{C42}$ to produce $\overline{C423}$. This activates C5, C6 and C7 and eventually the lytic components C8 and C9, which lyse the cell. Byproducts of complement activation enhance phagocytosis, cause cell adherence and stimulate mast cell degranulation leading to the release of histamine and pharmacologically active substances. The alternative pathway does not depend on antigen-antibody binding and can be initiated by a number of substances including microbial products.

destroyed—a process known as 'bystander lysis'. Complement components are also chemotactic for white blood cells, enhance phagocytosis, aggregate platelets, and cause increased vascular permeability. The complement system is therefore ideally suited for the destruction of microorganisms and is also potentially destructive for macroparasites, but can cause inflammation and damage to the host. Complement can also be activated in the absence of an antibody-antigen reaction by various substances, including bacterial lipopolysaccharides, through what is known as the alternative pathway (Fig. 6.3).

IgA is also able to bind to bacteria, causing them to lose the ability to adhere to mucosal surfaces, and to activate complement through the alternative pathway. These properties, and the fact that IgA is not destroyed by the enzymes in the gut, make it an ideal first line of defence against intestinal pathogens.

IgE is a cell-bound or homocytotropic antibody. It binds to cells, including mast cells and basophils, by its Fc portion and, if the Fab portion binds antigen, the cell degranulates causing a local release of histamine and other substances. This is the basis of anaphylaxis, asthma and hayfever, but it may also play an important role in the immune response to helminth infections.

6.2.2   Cell-mediated immunity

Cell-mediated immunity is independent of antibody and is brought about by cytotoxic T cells or by the secretion of lymphokines by T cells. The lymphokines cause other cells, usually lymphocytes and macrophages, to aggregate in the region of a T-cell-antigen interaction, causing a local reaction. This kind of response also leads to the formation of granulomas which are important in some parasitic infections. Cytotoxic T lymphocytes (Tc cells) can bring about the direct lysis of tumour cells or virally altered cells. They are, however, restricted in their activity and can only destroy cells bearing 'self' and 'foreign' antigens simultaneously. This means that they cannot destroy parasites directly but could possibly do so indirectly by destroying infected cells.

6.2.3   Cells involved in the immune response

The cells central to the immune response are the lymphocytes, but these are not the only cells involved as other kinds can come under the influence of activated lymphocytes and take part, directly or indirectly, in the destruction of invading organisms. Macrophages and polymorphonuclear cells can be involved in phagocytosis, usually through antibody bridges and Fc receptors, but also through complement receptors on these cells. Mast cells and basophils have already been mentioned in the context of IgE. Eosinophils have considerable phosphatase and peroxidase activity and can take part in the immune response to certain helminth worms. The most recently identified cell involved in the immune response is the natural killer or NK cell. This cell is a lymphocyte, with some of the characteristics of an immature T cell, that can destroy certain tumour cell lines, particularly those of lymphoid origin, without lengthy preactivation. There have been suggestions that such cells may be involved in the immune response to some parasites.

6.2.4   Hypersensitivity

'Hypersensitivity' is the term applied to an enhanced state of responsiveness following sensitization to a particular antigen. Hypersensitivity states are important in parasite immunology and the most widely accepted classification is that of Coombs and Gell in which four types are recognized.

● *Type I: Anaphylaxis.* This involves homocytotropic antibody, particularly IgE, on mast cells or basophils. When antigen is bound, configurational changes occur in the cell, resulting in the release of pharmacologically active substances such as histamine, serotonin and eosinophil chemotactic factor.

● *Type II: Antibody dependent cytotoxicity.* This involves antibodies binding to cell surface antigens by the Fab portion. The antibody may then activate complement, bringing about the lysis of the cell, or it may bind a phagocytic or cytotoxic cell, through the Fc portion, thus bringing about the phagocytosis or destruction of the antigen bearing cell. This direct cell killing is known as antibody-dependent cell-mediated cytotoxicity (ADCC).

● *Type III: Immune complex hypersensitivity.* This occurs when antibody and antigen are both in solution and bind to form complexes that lodge in various organs with or without activating complement.

● *Type IV: Delayed hypersensitivity.* This is the cell-mediated immunity involving lymphokines described above, and involves T cells and their products but not antibody.

Types I, II and III hypersensitivity reactions occur because of the presence of preformed antibody in a sensitized individual, and the allergic reactions occur immediately after another exposure to the same antigen. Delayed hypersensitivity is essentially local and takes several hours to develop.

Immunopathological changes represent the debit side of the immune response and often result from the hypersensitivity reactions listed above. Such changes are not caused directly by the parasite but by the host's attempts to destroy it; in other words, the host damages itself.

6.2.5   Regulation of the immune response

The very nature of the immune response, particularly its specificity and the dangers inherent in any malfunctioning, demands that it should be very carefully controlled and regulated. This regulation is mediated by T lymphocytes. Helper T cells (TH cells) initiate or enhance immune responses and suppressor T cells (Ts) switch them off. The importance of helper T cells is best understood in the induction of the immune response to T-dependent antigens. The antigen is processed by a macrophage and presented to a T and a B cell. The T cell acts as a helper cell and stimulates the B cell to give rise to a clone of cells that eventually secrete the appropriate antibody. This combination of macrophage, T cell and B cell, is central to most immune responses. Certain antigens are able to induce an immune response without involving T cells and these are known as T-independent antigens.

The actual regulation of the immune response is extremely complex and it is clear that helper and suppressor cells do not act directly as the effector cells, but take part in multicellular interactions that eventually culminate in enhancement or suppression. The interactions themselves are brought about by soluble factors and the overall modulation of the immune response results from the balance between these helper and suppressor factors. Suppressor cells are not only important in the normal regulation of the immune response but play a major role in controlling, or attempting to control, responses that have got out of hand, as is frequently the case in parasitic infections.

6.3   IMMUNITY TO MICROORGANISMS

Acquired immunity is the rule in viral, bacterial and rickettsial infections and such infections usually follow a characteristic pattern of an incubation period, a period of patent infection, a crisis and relatively rapid recovery. On subsequent exposure to the same pathogen, the resultant infection is usually either asymptomatic or mild. There are a number of exceptions to this general rule but in most cases the infection is rapidly overcome and the ensuing immunity lasts for a considerable time. The acquisition of immunity to viruses is relatively straightforward. The main defence mechanism is the production of nonspecific interferon and, if the viruses broach this barrier, they are vulnerable to attack from neutralizing antibodies, which are usually IgG in the plasma or IgA in secretions. Alternatively, if they appear on the surface of an infected cell, they are recognized and destroyed by cytotoxic T lymphocytes specifically mobilized for this purpose. The destruction of virus-infected cells seems to be analogous with the destruction of tumour cells and involves a similar dual recognition system in which the T cells recognize both 'self' and 'foreign' antigens simultaneously.

Bacteria are considerably larger than viruses and cannot be neutralized so easily. The first lines of defence are nonspecific barriers, such as the skin, gastric juices or lysozyme. If the bacteria succeed in entering the body they are immediately subject to passive phagocytosis by macrophages or neutrophils. This phagocytosis may be reinforced by antibodies which coat the bacteria and render them more likely to be ingested. Such antibodies are called opsonins and IgM is a particularly good opsonizing antibody. IgM is also important in bringing about the agglutination of bacteria; this stops them spreading and also renders them more likely to be taken up by phagocytic cells. A third function of IgM is that of inducing complement-mediated lysis, and the complement pathway also reinforces phagocytosis. IgG may be involved in opsonization, agglutination and complement activation as well. A number of bacteria can also activate complement through the alternative pathway. Finally, cell-mediated immunity may be involved particularly in infections such as leprosy and tuberculosis, in which the bacteria are intracellular and so do not normally succumb to antibody-mediated immune responses.

Although the general patterns of immunity to microorganisms are relatively straightforward, the actual mechanisms involved in each particular infection are still not fully understood. However, all seem to involve the complex interplay of several specific and nonspecific phenomena carefully modulated in space and time. It is microorganisms such as the mycobacteria that cause tuberculosis and leprosy and persist for long periods (sometimes the lifetime of the host) that present immunologists with their most intractable problems, and it is these that most resemble the infections caused by protozoa and helminths.

6.4   IMMUNITY TO PARASITES

Parasites possess three major characteristics that make them difficult for a host to control immunologically: their size, their elaborate life-cycles, and their antigenic complexity. These characteristics also make it difficult to interpret and understand the various immune responses that do occur and to identify what data are relevant. It is fair to say that we do not fully understand the actual mechanism of immunity in a single parasitic infection but, on the other hand, a number of general principles are gradually becoming clear.

Let us consider first the protozoa. Most have complex life cycles and the various stages are either antigenically distinct, as in the malaria parasites, or variable as in the African trypanosomes. Protozoa inhabit the gut, blood or other tissues, including macrophages, and the immune responses elicited are more appropriate to the site of infection than to the nature of the parasites themselves. In the helminth infections, the nature of the surface of the worm, which is the part available for immune stimulation and attack, is important. In digeneans and cestodes it is the tegument of the worm that is exposed while in nematodes the outer surface is a protective cuticle, the antigenic nature of which may vary during the life cycle. Like protozoa, different helminths occupy different sites: usually the gut, but sometimes the blood or other tissues and the immune response is, again, more appropriate to the site of infection than to the actual parasite.

A further complication in helminth infections is that during its life cycle a worm may not only change its form but may also change its site of infection several times. In *Ascaris lumbricoides* infections, for example, larvae pass through various internal organs before maturing in the gut. The net result of these variations in the expression of antigens and frequent changes in site of infection is that the immune responses elicited may be against antigens that are no longer present or in places where the parasites no longer live.

In spite of the various differences between parasites, there are a number of characteristics that parasitic infections have in common and that are of immunological importance. The immune responses tend to develop slowly and, although they often bring the infection under control, usually fail to eliminate the parasite completely. In humans, *Plasmodium malariae, Trypanosoma cruzi, Trypanosoma gambiense* and *Leishmania donovani*, for example, tend to persist for the lifetime of the host while *Schistosoma mansoni* persists for its lifetime as do some of the filarial worms. This long persistence is due in part to the ability of many parasites to evade the immune response (see section 6.7), and in part to the various ways in which parasites are able to influence the immune response but which may or may not be associated with evasion.

All parasites elicit immune responses. Wherever they have been sought, specific antibodies belonging to IgM, IgG and IgA classes have been detected, and where appropriate, so has IgE. The presence of these antibodies, however, only signals the recognition of parasite antigens and there is little or no correlation between much of the antibody produced and protection, either in the form of recovery or resistance to reinfection. Similarly, cell-mediated immune responses are almost invariably detected but seldom correlated, even loosely, with protection.

As well as stimulating specific immune responses, parasites often stimulate B cells to produce what is effectively nonspecific antibody (polyclonal activation), and may also nonspecifically activate macrophages. Both of these phenomena will be discussed below (see sections 6.4.1 and 6.4.2). In contrast to the specific and nonspecific stimulation that occurs during parasitic infections there is almost invariably a depression of the immune response to superimposed antigens and this will also be discussed below (see section 6.4.3). Polyclonal activation, macrophage activation and immunodepression seem to be characteristic of many parasitic infections and are important not only because they may play roles in the evasion of the immune response, but also because of the consequences for concomitant infections, vaccination procedures and pathology.

6.4.1   Polyclonal activation of B lymphocytes

Bacterial lipopolysaccharide and a number of other substances, mainly of microbial origin, are able to stimulate B lymphocytes to give rise to a large number of clones, each secreting antibody of a different specificity and each unrelated to the original stimulating substance. Such activating substances are called B cell mitogens and the immunoglobulins produced are usually IgM. A number of parasites, or their extracts, are capable of acting as B cell mitogens, and these include the blood parasitic protozoa *Trypanosoma brucei* (in which this phenomenon has been most thoroughly studied). *T.b. gambiense*, *T. congolense*, *Plasmodium falciparum*, *P. berghei*, *P. yoelii* and *Babesia microti* and also *Entamoeba histolytica* and *Trichinella spiralis*. The immunoglobulins produced contribute to the high background levels characteristic of trypanosome and malaria infections. Polyclonal stimulation soon leads to the depletion of antigen-sensitive B cells and may contribute to the immunodepression associated with these infections. This phenomenon seems to have no protective function.

6.4.2   Macrophage activation

During many infections, monocytes and macrophages become non-specifically stimulated and exhibit enhanced phagocytosis, spreading on glass, killing of bacteria and inhibition of tumour cell growth.

Macrophage activation is characteristic of infections caused by certain bacteria, such as *Salmonella typhimurium*, *Brucella abortus* and *Mycobacterium bovis*; intracellular parasites, such as *Leishmania enriettii*, *Toxoplasma gondii* and *Besnoitia jellisoni*; and also occurs in experimental malaria and babesiosis. Macrophage activation is also associated with *Trichinella spiralis*, *Nippostrongylus brasiliensis* and schistosome eggs. Cytostatic effects on tumour cells have been observed in mice infected with *Giardia muris* or *Spironucleus muris*. It is probable that macrophage activation occurs in a number of parasitic infections but it is difficult to ascribe a protective role to it.

6.4.3   Immunodepression

During the course of many infections the response to a wide variety of superimposed antigens is depressed. This is true of viral, bacterial and most parasitic infections investigated. In the laboratory, immunodepression has been recorded during infections with a range of parasites including *Trypanosoma brucei*, *T. congolense*, *T. musculi*, *T. cruzi*, *Leishmania* spp., *Giardia muris*, *Entamoeba histolytica*, *Toxoplasma gondii*, *Plasmodium* spp., *Babesia microti*, *Schistosoma mansoni*, *Fasciola hepatica*, *Trichinella spiralis*, *Nippostrongylus brasiliensis* and *Dipetalonema viteae*. There is also evidence that immunodepression occurs during infections with Chagas' disease, kala azar, African trypanosomiasis and malaria in man, and during trypanosomiasis in cattle. It is probable that immunodepression occurs in most parasitic infections but apparently not in coccidiosis in chickens where it has been looked for but not found. Whether or not this has anything to do with the fact that the immune response to coccidiosis is relatively effective remains to be seen.

A number of mechanisms have been suggested to account for immunodepression and these include: polyclonal B cell stimulation leading to the exhaustion of antigen sensitive cells; the production of lymphocytotoxic factors by the parasites themselves; antigenic competition during the induction of the immune response; macrophage activation resulting in antigen destruction instead of processing; total immunological commitment to the parasitic infection; alteration of lymphoid cell traffic; and the stimulation of suppressor macrophages or T suppressor cells. The fact that immunodepression occurs in athymic mice makes the last suggestion unlikely. Extracts of trypanosomes cause both polyclonal stimulation and immunodepression, suggesting that these two phenomena are closely associated, but it may be that in different infections different mechanisms operate.

The reasons for immunodepression are also unclear. It may possibly be directed by the parasite to ensure that it itself is not destroyed, with the induced depression coincidentally extending to other antigens, or the host may attempt to switch off an unproductive immune response. Whatever the cause, the effects have important consequences for both the evasion of the immune response by the parasite and for the immunopathology produced during parasitic infections. A final consequence relates to vaccination procedures which are impaired during parasitic infections.

6.5   IMMUNITY TO PROTOZOA

There is evidence for the existence of acquired immunity in the majority of protozoan infections although in many cases it is not fully effective. Protozoa, being microparasites, multiply within their hosts and, unless this multiplication is contained, the host will inevitably and quickly die. The fact that not all hosts infected with protozoa actually die indicates that some kind of immunity has intervened. It is convenient to consider the immune responses in relation to three separate functions, bringing the initial infection under control, eliminating residual parasites and protecting the host from subsequent reinfection. There is evidence that suggests that the actual immune mechanisms involved in each phase may be quite different from one another. It is also clear that each of the separate immune responses is multifactorial and involves different effector mechanisms probably operating in a predetermined temporal sequence. Each infection probably evokes a unique combination of immunological mechanisms, and there may be several alternative mechanisms operating at any one time. All protozoa seem to have ways of evading the host's immune response and all generate a myriad of immunological reactions quite unrelated to protection. All these factors, coupled with the fact that different strains or species of hosts may react in quite distinct ways to the same protozoan infections, have combined to make it difficult for any investigator to actually identify *the* immune mechanism in any particular infection. Nevertheless, considerable progress has been made and it is possible to recognize a number of the protective mechanisms involved and to unravel them from the irrelevant ones.

6.5.1   Intestinal protozoa

The majority of the amoebae and flagellates that inhabit the lumen of the gut are harmless commensals and elicit no immune response. *Entamoeba histolytica* falls into this category until it invades the intestinal wall and, possibly later, the liver and other organs. This invasion is accompanied by the production of complement activating antibodies capable of lysing the trophozoites. However, there is no correlation between antibody production and protection, and repeated reinfections involving the invasion of the gut wall are relatively common even in the face of high levels of antibody. In hepatic amoebiasis, reinfections are rare. In experimental animals, spontaneous recovery and resistance to reinfection have been demonstrated and it has been shown that trophozoites coated with antibody are resistant to complement lysis. Thus the balance between antibody and complement may be crucial to the outcome of this infection.

Human giardiasis is accompanied by antibodies in the serum but the protective effect of these is not known. In mice, *Giardia muris* infections elicit immune responses that bring the infection under control, eliminate residual parasites and protect the host from subsequent reinfection. The actual mechanisms involved are unclear. The immune response varies greatly between strains of mice and in young animals brings the infection under control but fails to eliminate residual parasites which tend to persist for the life time of the host. Results similar to those described for *G. muris* have been obtained with *Spironucleus muris*.

6.5.2   Leishmaniasis

Leishmaniasis exists as a complex of diseases that, from an immunological point of view, fall into two major categories, the self-healing dermal forms such as *Leishmania tropica* and *L. mexicana* and the effectively non-healing visceral forms caused by *L. donovani*, but even this simple classification is confused by the existence of a spectrum of many forms intermediate between these extremes. In the case of *L. tropica*, the lesions heal spontaneously but the immune response is slow to develop and recovery takes from a few months to over a year. After recovery, there is strong immunity to reinfection with the homologous strain, although there is very little antibody produced. At the other extreme, visceral infections with *L. donovani* frequently progress to fatal conclusions over a number of years but during this time vast amounts of antibody are produced. About a quarter of the patients with visceral leishmaniasis do recover, however. The various forms of American leishmaniasis are characterized by recovery, although this is usually very slow and in some cases too slow to save the patient. After recovery, there is strong immunity to reinfection with the homologous parasite.

In laboratory animals, there is excellent evidence for acquired immunity to *Leishmania* spp., especially *L. enriettii* in guinea pigs and *L tropica* and *L. donovani* in mice. In the cases of *L. tropica* and *L. donovani*, resistance is genetically determined and is controlled by alleles at single loci unrelated to the major histocompatibility complex. The use of laboratory models has thrown considerable light on the mechanism of immunity to leishmaniasis. *Leishmania* spp. live in macrophages where they are able to avoid the immune response and also resist lysosomal cytolysis. They may, however, be destroyed by activated macrophages. This suggests that the immune response is a cell-mediated one in which the target cell is the infected macrophage. Parasite killing is intracellular and involves the generation of toxic metabolites by the host cell. There is no apparent role for antibody or complement.

6.5.3   African trypanosomiasis

African trypanosomiasis in man, cattle and laboratory animals is characterized by successive waves of parasitaemia in which the antigens present during each wave differ from those of preceding waves (Fig. 6.4). This is due to changes in the surface coat of the trypanosomes, resulting in antigenic variation. The trypanosomes in the blood are completely enveloped in a thick glycoprotein coat (Fig. 6.5) which, in the case of *Trypanosoma brucei*, is produced while in the salivary glands of the tsetse fly. Most trypanosomes injected by a fly possess glycoprotein

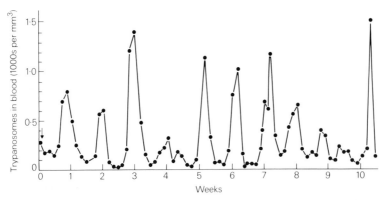

Fig. 6.4. Antigenic variation in trypanosomiasis. This graph shows the fluctuations in parasitaemia in a patient with trypanosomiasis. Such fluctuations are characteristics of human and bovine trypanosomiasis and are also seen in laboratory infections. The trypanosome population of each peak is antigenically different from those of preceding or succeeding peaks. (After Ross & Thomson, 1910.)

coats of a single kind (the homotype), but a few display variations in the polypeptide structure, giving rise to antigenically different coats (heterotypes). An immune response to the homotype is quickly mounted and the parasites are destroyed, but the heterotypes survive to produce successive parasitaemias in which they become the homotypes. New heterotypes are continually being produced and, as their range seems to be almost limitless, the parasite is always one step ahead of the immune response of the host. When the trypanosomes are taken up by a tsetse fly they lose the coat and acquire it again in the salivary glands but there is no reversion to a single basic antigenic type. Antigenic variation occurs in *T. congolense* and *T. vivax* infections, as well as those caused by the subspecies of *T. brucei*, but in the case of *T. vivax* the surface coat is apparently acquired while in the blood of the mammalian host.

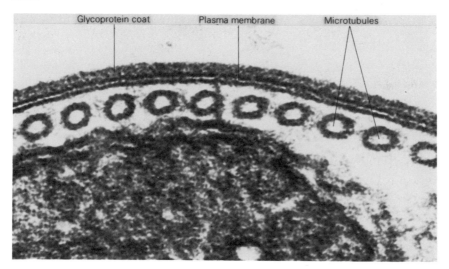

Fig. 6.5. Electronmicrograph of bloodstream *Trypanosoma brucei*, showing the thick glycoprotein coat which consists mainly of the variant antigen. (Photograph supplied by Professor K. Vickerman.)

The immune response to trypanosomes actually recognized by the host is extremely rapid and efficient and involves agglutination and complement-mediated lysis. Cell-mediated responses are not involved.

Most laboratory animals are unable to overcome trypanosome infections but in humans some infections become chronic. Cattle occasionally recover and some breeds are more resistant than others. Cattle that have been repeatedly exposed to trypanosomiasis, and drug-treated when ill, eventually acquire a considerable degree of immunity to reinfection. This indicates that, in the field, a host is eventually able to build up an immunity to all the important variant antigens in a particular area, and this might also apply to man.

6.5.4   American trypanosomiasis

American trypanosomiasis, caused by *Trypanosoma cruzi*, progresses in a series of well-defined stages. There is an incubation period of 2–3 weeks followed by an acute phase lasting 4–5 weeks, which is common in children but rare in adults. This is followed either by a chronic phase which may persist for 20 years or more before again becoming acute or, alternatively, by a latent phase which is a chronic one without any recurrence of symptoms. Some individuals die early in the infection but most are able to keep it under control at least for a while. Spontaneous recovery, however, is rare or nonexistent and the infection, once acquired, is lifelong. The parasites are unable to undergo antigenic variation but are able to avoid immune attack by entering muscle and other cells where they divide in the amastigote stage, although antibody is produced. Laboratory animals, particularly mice, can be infected with *T. cruzi* but are unable to contain the early acute phase of the infection unless they are treated in some way or immunized against the worst of the infection. Transfer of antibody to other animals is sometimes, but not always, protective. The available evidence suggests that antibody is involved in whatever immunity does exist but this does not necessarily exclude the involvement of macrophages. The most important aspect of the immune response in Chagas' disease relates to the immunopathology caused and this will be discussed later (see section 6.8).

6.5.5   Coccidiosis

Coccidiosis is intrinsically self-limiting and the duration of infection is governed by the genetically controlled number of asexual schizogonies, culminating in the production of sexual stages. The immune response is generated during the asexual stages but plays little part in the control of the initial infection. It is, however, extremely effective against reinfection with the homologous parasite, although it does not affect the sporozoites which enter the host cells normally and survive there for about 48 hours without development. Immunity seems to be antibody-mediated and agglutinating, and lytic antibodies have been demonstrated. The antibodies involved may include secretory IgA.

6.5.6   Toxoplasmosis

Toxoplasma gondii, in hosts other than the cat, multiplies indefinitely in cells of various kinds including macrophages, in which the parasites are able to survive by preventing phagosome-lysosome fusion. Antibodies—both IgM and IgG—are produced during the early stages of the infection and the IgG persists for the lifetime of the infected individual. The immune response brings the infection under control but is incapable of eliminating residual parasites, which persist at relatively low levels. Nor can it protect against reinfection although the potential severity is considerably reduced. The importance of the immune response can be appreciated from the fact that immunodepressed patients suffer from fulminating infections. There are numerous laboratory models for toxoplasmosis and in these the outcome of the infection is markedly influenced by the strain of both the parasite and the host. From all the evidence available, it seems that activated macrophages are able to either kill or inhibit the growth of intracellular parasites and this is associated with the products of cellular oxidative metabolism. Antibody-coated parasites are also destroyed by such cells, suggesting that the major immune mechanism is macrophage activation reinforced by antibody.

6.5.7   Malaria

More effort has been put into the investigation of immunity to malaria than any other protozoan disease, but this infection steadfastly refuses to yield up its secrets. Malaria infections are long and chronic, lasting about 2–4 years in the cases of *Plasmodium vivax*, *P. ovale* and *P. falciparum*, and probably lifelong in *P. malariae*. How these parasites survive is unclear and the evidence for antigenic variation, long suggested as a mechanism, is controversial. It may be that the dormant stages of *P. vivax* and *P. ovale* (see section 1.8.1) are able to evade the immune response by remaining in the liver but this cannot be true for the recrudescing forms *P. falciparum* and *P. malariae*. Nevertheless, immunity to malaria does occur and the evidence for this is that many people do recover and are resistant to reinfection with the homologous parasite and that, in endemic areas, mothers pass on protective antibodies in the milk to their offspring. Experimentally, people can be protected by the passive transfer to immune serum.

All this evidence suggests antibody involvement and there is a strong correlation between antibody levels, measured in various ways, and the disappearance of parasites from the blood. The malaria parasites are host-specific and cannot therefore be studied in the more usual laboratory animals, so much of the experimental work has involved laboratory models of human malaria. The most intensively studied have been *P. knowlesi* and *P. cynomolgi* in monkeys and *P. berghei*, *P. yoelii* and, less intensively, *P. chabaudi*, in rodents. A vast amount of data has accumulated and it is apparent that major differences in the immune response occur in different strains of hosts and parasites and it is not at all clear how these various findings relate to human malaria.

One universal finding is that the antigens and protection elicited are stage-specific. The sporozoites, exoerythrocytic schizonts, erythrocytic stages, merozoites and gametocytes, all possess different antigens but immunity to one of these stages does not extend to the others. Antibodies to sporozoites that cause precipitation, the shedding of surface antigens or blocking of liver cell penetration, have been identified and there is some evidence available to suggest that these are protective in the field. There seems to be no immune response at all to the exoerythrocytic stages under normal circumstances. A number of antibodies against the erythrocytic forms, particularly the late schizonts, have been identified and these include lysins, agglutinins and opsonins. These are the most specific of all the antibodies to malaria parasites and are specific not only to the strain of parasite but also, in many cases, to individual variants. The antibodies to merozoites include agglutinins, erythrocyte invasion-blocking and metabolic inhibitors, but these are not as specific as those against the intracellular stages and they cross-react between variants and even strains. Finally, the gametocyte antigens are only apparent within the mosquito, when the parasite has left the red cell, so are irrelevant to protection.

There is also evidence for cellular involvement in the immune response to malaria but the protective aspects are restricted to enhanced phagocytosis of parasite material, which could well be brought about by opsonins, and there is no apparent role for cell-mediated immunity proper. One last aspect of immunity to malaria is the possible involvement of nonspecific factors (see section 6.9).

From all the evidence available, it appears that antibodies are the effector arms of immunity to malaria. Those against erythrocytic forms or merozoites bring the infection under control, possibly in cooperation with nonspecific factors, and the same or other antibodies eventually eliminate the residual forms from the blood. Resistance to reinfection in immune individuals probably involves anti-sporozoite antibodies generated after numerous exposures to infected mosquitoes.

6.5.8   Piroplasmosis

Piroplasmosis embraces two quite distinct forms of cattle disease: babesiosis, caused by *Babesia* spp. which multiply in red blood cells; and theileriosis, caused by *Theileria* spp. which multiply in lymphoid cells. *Babesia* infections are characteristically long-lasting and persist even after clinical recovery. There is some evidence of antigenic variation but this is unlikely to be important as there is no predominant antigenic type as in trypanosomiasis. In laboratory mice, *B. rodhaini* infections are almost invariably fatal while recovery from *B. microti* is the rule. Immunity, either natural or induced, in laboratory animals and cattle can sometimes be transferred with serum or from the mother to a new-born animal. Immunity is species- and strain-specific and presumably involves antibodies which act on the merozoites while outside the red cells. Laboratory experiments also suggest that nonspecific factors may be involved but not cell-mediated immunity.

Theileriosis is a much more virulent disease than babesiosis, presumably because rapid division of parasites takes place in lymphoid cells and outpaces the immune response of the host. Some animals do recover, however, and these are resistant to reinfection with the homologous strain. Immunity cannot usually be transferred with serum and seems to involve a cell-mediated response in which the infected lymphocytes are the target cells.

6.6   IMMUNITY TO HELMINTHS

With the exception of larval cestodes, helminths do not multiply within their vertebrate hosts, so the immune response is not concerned with the immediate problem of bringing a life-threatening infection under control, as happens in microbial and protozoan infections, but with curtailing the lives of established worms, and in the case of the filarial worms their larvae, and preventing reinfection. Some kind of immunity to reinfection is the general rule but existing worms are not always destroyed. Most helminths have life cycles in which larval stages migrate through the body of the host before the adults settle in their final sites, and immunity is elicited by these stages and is effective against subsequent invading larvae. This often gives rise to a situation in which the host harbours a population of adult worms but is immune to reinfection—a state called concomitant immunity.

Adult, and even larval worms, are too large to be destroyed by antibody, with or without complement, or by phagocytic cells. The universal effector mechanism, therefore, seems to be some form of antibody-dependent cell-mediated cytotoxicity (ADCC) in which the worms become coated with IgG or IgE antibody which binds eosinophils, and other cells that actually destroy the parasite. As in protozoan infections, the actual immune responses are multifactorial and differ according to the stage of development of the invading worm and the phase and site of the infestation, so there is no single mechanism of immunity to any helminth infection. Similarly, helminths are all capable of evading the immune responses of the host and thus these responses may be misdirected and contribute to the pathology of the infection.

6.6.1   Schistosomiasis

In human schistosomiasis, there is no evidence of spontaneous recovery although infected individuals are able to resist reinfection while harbouring adult worms (concomitant immunity). The most intensively studied species is *Schistosoma mansoni* in which the immune response is stimulated by schistosomula burrowing through the skin. This response is ineffective against the primary invasion or against adult worms, which have evolved a number of ways of evading the immune response, including coating themselves with host antigens. It is, however, very effective against subsequent reinfection in which the young schistosomula are the targets for attack.

Because of the difficulties inherent in investigating human schistomiasis, most of the experimental work has involved the use of rhesus monkeys, mice and rats. The immune response of the rat is unusual in that immunity to the adult worms does occur and the worms are eliminated between 4 and 8 weeks after infection and immunity to reinfection then rapidly declines. In the monkey and mouse, on the other hand, the adult worms are not eliminated and the infections are more comparable with the human ones.

Much of what is known about the mechanisms of immunity to reinfection has been derived from *in vitro* studies and these have revealed at least six possible methods of schistosomulum killing involving ADCC. These are:

1 IgG + neutrophils;
2 IgG + eosinophils;
3 IgG + macrophages;
4 IgG + eosinophils + mast cells;
5 IgE + macrophages; and
6 IgE + eosinophils + mast cells.

Schistosome killing by eosinophils involves the attachment of the eosinophil to the outer surface membrane of the schistosomulum by way of an antibody bridge, the parasite binding by the Fab portion and the eosinophil by the Fc, or by complement receptors. The eosinophils flatten out and extrude granules containing hydrolytic enzymes onto the surface of the worm. These disrupt the membrane and allow the eosinophils to enter the body and detach the tegument. Mast cells may be involved and these attach to the schistosomulum, again by Fab and Fc receptors, and a signal passes from the mast cell to the eosinophil to initiate the destruction. In neutrophil killing, the cells cannot damage the tegument alone and require the presence of antibody and complement. Macrophages only become involved after the damage by eosinophils and neutrophils has been done. It is not entirely clear what relevance these mechanisms of schistosome killing have to the human disease but there is considerable evidence to suggest that eosinophils are involved and therefore the mechanisms are probably comparable.

6.6.2   Fascioliasis

Fasciola hepatica causes infections of long duration, probably lifelong in sheep and about a year in calves which, however, do recover and show some resistance to reinfection. How these flukes evade the immune response is not known, but they seem to be unable to take up host antigens as do schistosomes. Immunity is stimulated by migrating juvenile worms and the killing of juvenile flukes *in vitro* involves eosinophil attachment and tegument destruction; this also applies to adult worms and presumably requires antibody. The laboratory models of fascioliasis include *F. hepatica* in rabbits, mice and rats, particularly the latter, in which strong concomitant immunity develops.

6.6.3   Cestodiasis

There is no evidence of any acquired immunity to the adult stages of the three important tapeworms of man—*Diphyllobothrium latum*, *Taenia saginata* and *T. solium*. Immunity does develop to the larval stages of the last two in cattle and pigs respectively, but this is slow to develop, suggesting that these parasites are able to evade the immune response in some way. The larval stages of *Echinococcus granulosus*, which form hydatid cysts in man, also seem to be able to evade the immune response. Much of what we know about immunity to larval cestodiasis is derived from laboratory studies on *Taenia crassiceps* in mice, in which eosinophils and mast cells have been implicated in damage to the microthrix border of the tegument, and this is followed by the encapsulation of the damaged worm by cells of various kinds including macrophages. It may be that the early part of this immune response is similar to that described for *S. mansoni* in which case antibody would be an essential component.

6.6.4   Intestinal nematodes

Many intestinal nematodes have life cycles with larval stages that migrate through the body of the host until the adult finally settles in the intestine. There is evidence of strong immune responses to all intestinal nematodes and these are elicited by the migrating larvae, the best studied examples being *Dictyocaulus viviparus* and *Ancylostoma caninum*, against which effective vaccines have been developed using irradiated larvae. Many nematode infections are also characterized by 'self-cure reactions' in which the adults in the intestine are spontaneously eliminated, as in *Nippostrongylus brasiliensis* in rats (Fig. 6.6), or after infection with a new batch of larvae as in *Haemonchus contortus* in sheep. Even in long chronic infections, such as in human hookworm disease, there is some evidence of acquired

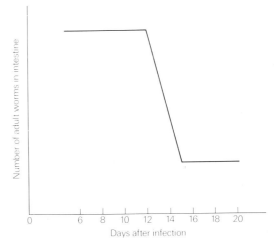

Fig. 6.6. The 'self-cure' reaction to *Nippostrongylus brasiliensis* in rats. After infection with 2000–6000 larvae, adult worms appear in the blood four days later and the numbers remain constant for about eight days, when there is a sudden drop to low levels but worms are not eliminated altogether. (After Ogilvie, 1969.)

immunity. Hosts that have recovered from infections with intestinal nematodes are frequently resistant to reinfection.

The immune responses to nematodes are therefore capable of reducing or terminating existing infections and preventing reinfection. The mechanisms of the two processes are probably different as, in one, the target is the adult and, in the other, it is a larval stage and the immune responses seem to be stage-specific. The immune mechanisms involved include the attachment of antibody, and possibly complement, followed by the adherence of eosinophils which damage the cuticle and permit attack by these cells and neurophils, and finally phagocytosis by macrophages. These processes are similar to those seen in digenean and cestode infections and differ only in the time taken to broach the more resistant cuticle.

Raised IgE levels are frequently encountered in nematode infections and it has been suggested that this immunoglobulin may take part in type I hypersensitivity, or anaphylactic, reactions resulting in the release of vasoactive substances that affect mucosal permeability and bring about the expulsion of worms from the gut. Such an effector mechanism would be nonspecific and there is evidence to suggest that this may occur during the elimination of established adult worm infections. Alternatively, the mediators released may enhance eosinophil and neutrophil activity. In some infections, for example, *N. brasiliensis* in rats, antibody damage precedes worm expulsion. A further mechanism of immunity may be complement activation via the alternative pathway, and the cuticle of a number of nematodes is capable of activating complement in this way although not all stages in the life cycle necessarily do so.

6.6.5   Filariasis

The filarial worms that infect man mature slowly from the infective larval stage for about 3–12 months before the adults eventually settle in the lymphatic system or subcutaneous tissues. The microfilariae produced then circulate in the blood or remain in the skin for a considerable time. This suggests that both the tissue forms and the microfilariae can evade the immune response, but immunity does eventually develop and, at the time the parasites are eliminated from the blood, antibody can be detected on the surface of the microfilariae. In all the species investigated, antibody initiates attack by cells of various kinds. The classes of antibody involved vary, as do the types of cells, but IgG and IgE, eosinophils and neutrophils, have been implicated in various infections suggesting that immunity to filariasis involves mechanisms similar to those described for other helminths. There is also evidence of strong immune responses against the adult worms, especially those damaged by drugs, and this may be responsible not for protection but for the pathology associated with filariasis.

6.7   EVASION OF THE IMMUNE RESPONSE

From the moment a parasite enters its host it is recognized as foreign and is subjected to a wide range of immune responses which transform the host into a totally hostile environment. Microorganisms are able to counteract the immune response, to some extent, by rapid multiplication, which allows them to build up large numbers and infect new hosts before being brought under control. Parasites, because of their complex life cycles, require a considerable period during which to complete their development and have evolved numerous ways of evading the immune response. So successful have these evasive methods been, that many parasites can survive in what ought to be an immune host for its lifetime. A number of examples of evasion have been given in sections 6.5 and 6.6 and, of these, the best known are the African trypanosomes, which undergo antigenic variation, and the schistosomes, which disguise themselves by taking up host antigens. There are, however, many more examples and it is probably true to say that every parasite has a unique method of evasion and that most employ several methods.

There are three essentially different aspects of evasion and these relate to the site of infection, specific methods of avoiding the consequences of the immune response, and general interference with the response as a whole. Parasites within cells are effectively out of the range of immune attack and the simplest method of avoiding the immune response is by not stimulating it. Thus parasites that enter host cells immediately are safe as long as they remain there. However, few parasites can stay hidden for long; protozoa have to invade new cells and helminths have to grow, and most parasites cannot avoid eliciting an immune response. These have had to evolve specific ways of evading the consequences of the immune response they themselves have stimulated, and there are many ways in which this is done. If, however, a parasite is not able to avoid the specific immune response, it has one other escape mechanism: it can interfere with the immune response as a whole, for example by suppressing it or activating it nonspecifically, which not only protects the parasite but also leaves the host open to attack from other organisms.

The various methods of evasion available to parasites are shown diagrammatically in Fig. 6.7. Initially, a parasite can evade the immune response by becoming intracellular or entering an immunologically privileged site before being recognized as foreign. This probably applies to malaria parasites when they enter liver cells and, in related forms such as *Hepatocystis* and *Haemoproteus* which have no schizogonic stages in the blood, this is a completely adequate way of avoiding eliciting an immune response. This method is also suitable for helminths, such as metacercariae, that do not grow within their hosts and is even more efficient if the site selected is one out of contact with the cells of the immune system (an immunologically privileged site), for example the brain or eye.

The immune response may also be avoided if the parasite becomes disguised with host antigens soon after it enters the host. This is what happens with schistosomes

Fig. 6.7. Methods by which parasites can evade the immune responses of their hosts. Parasites can evade the immune response by (1) becoming intracellular or entering an immunologically privileged site soon after infection; (2) becoming disguised with host antigens; (3) surviving in macrophages; (4) living in lymphocytes; (5) inactivating host lymphocytes, (6) causing polyclonal stimulation of lymphocytes; (7) moving away from an established immune response; (8) shedding antigens; (9) undergoing antigenic variation or (10) inhibiting cell or antibody binding. For further details see the text.

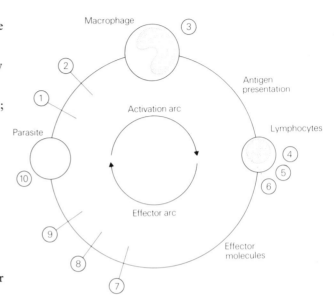

which exhibit on their surface glycoproteins or glycolipids identical with those of the host. These are acquired by the schistosomulum after it has penetrated the skin and their most likely source is blood cell antigens, although the possibility that they are parasite antigens which mimic those of the host cannot be ignored. Whatever the source, these antigens disguise the adult worms, which live in a vulnerable site within blood vessels, and protect them from immune attack. Antigenic stimulation does occur, however, and this is directed against the indisguised schistosomula of subsequent infections, thus providing some degree of protection, and against schistosome eggs lodged elsewhere in the body, giving rise to the pathology associated with schistosomiasis. Although disguise of this kind is obviously simple and efficient, it does not appear to be widely utilized and has not been incontrovertibly demonstrated in other helminth infections.

Some parasites are able to evade the immune response by invading cells of the immune system itself. Probably the most successful at doing this are *Theileria* spp., which enter lymphoblasts and transform these into continuously dividing cell lines, in which each daughter cell receives some the dividing parasites. *Leishmania* spp., *Trypanosoma cruzi* and *Toxoplasma gondii* all live within phagocytic cells and circumvent the lytic activities of these cells in different ways. Normally such cells take in particulate material by endocytosis and form a phagosome with which lysosomes fuse to produce a phagolysosome. Within the phagolysosome, digestion occurs. However, *Leishmania* spp. are somehow able to survive in the phagolysosome, *T. gondii* prevents lysosome–phagosome fusion and *T. cruzi* is able to lyse the phagosome before it fuses with the lysosome and lives in the cytoplasm of the cell.

Parasites have also evolved ways of evading immune responses they themselves have elicited. The simplest examples are the intestinal nematodes, such as *Ascaris lumbricoides* and the hookworms, which migrate around the body stimulating various immune responses in the tissues, but escaping their consequences by entering the gut. This is similar to what happens in schistosomiasis but the nematode worms do not need to disguise themselves, although some of them change their antigens during their life cycles. The immune response is effective against reinfection and this pattern of migration presumably evolved to prevent overcrowding in the gut.

The best known example of evasion involving escape from an active immune response is the antigenic variation shown by the African trypanosomes particularly *Trypanosoma brucei* and its subspecies and *T. congolense*. In these infections, the trypanosomes injected into the mammalian host represent a heterogeneous population with different glycoprotein surface coats, each representing a variable antigen type (VAT). An effective immune response is mounted against the predominating VAT and the parasitaemia declines to recur with a different collection of VATs. This process is repeated indefinitely until the host dies or is able to bring the infection under control (see Fig. 6.4). In *T. vivax*, the trypanosomes injected by the tsetse fly do not have a glycoprotein surface coat and acquire it later, and it may be that not all salivarian trypanosomes evade the immune response in the same way as *T. brucei*.

Antigenic variation has been assiduously looked for in many other parasitic infections and a distinction must be made between the different antigens specific to particular stages of a life cycle, which probably remain constant for each stage, and true variant antigens, like those of the trypanosomes, in which variation occurs within a single stage. Different antigens specific to different stages are now known to be commonplace and are best exemplified by the malaria parasites and the nematode *Trichinella spiralis*. These should not be confused with variant antigens proper. Antigenic variation has been reported for various malaria parasites and piroplasms, but the observations have been indirect ones and, except in the case of *Plasmodium knowlesi* in monkeys, not absolutely convincing.

A third way of evading an established immune response is by shedding antigens. This occurs in the African trypanosomes, *Entamoeba histolytica*, *Ancyclostoma caninum* and probably many other species, and may lead to the production of antigen–antibody complexes which direct the response away from the invader.

The nonspecific way of evading the immune response is by interfering with the operation and control of its delicate balance. All parasites seem to be able to do this to some extent and the mechanisms involved include immunodepression (see section

6.4.3); polyclonal B lymphocyte activation, leading to the exhaustion of clones of antibody producing cells (see section 6.4.1); macrophage activation, leading to the disruption of antigen handling by macrophages (see section 6.4.2); lymphocytotoxicity; and the production of anti-complement factor. It is not at all clear whether all these mechanisms are evasive ones or whether they are indications of attempts by the host to switch off an immune response that has got out of control as a consequence of some other evasive mechanism. Trypanosome products are capable of inducing both immunodepression and polyclonal stimulation, suggesting that these parasites directly interfere with the immune response as part of an evasive mechanism, but the situation may be different in other infections.

The mechanisms for evading the immune response are many and, in most infections, several different ones probably operate either sequentially or concurrently. In the case of *Schistosoma mansoni*, for example, as well as masking with host antigens, schistosomula are able to cleave specific antibody and inactivate macrophages, while the adults can inhibit eosinophil attachment and killing. There is probably no single evasion mechanism for any one parasite.

6.8   IMMUNOPATHOLOGY

The pathology of parasitic infections is poorly understood, even in well-studied diseases such as malaria and trypanosomiasis, largely because it is multifactorial. One factor is the parasite which causes physical damage either directly or by way of its various byproducts. Migrating nematode larvae, for example, damage tissues during their boring activities, while haemolytic fatty acids produced by trypanosomes cause anaemia. The main factor responsible for pathological changes, however, is the immune response itself. Immunopathological processes result from the characteristic long duration of parasitic infections coupled with a variety of immune responses that are unable to eliminate the source of the antigen. The net result is a hyperactive immune response that does not switch off as normally happens when the source of stimulation is removed. Instead, circulating antigens either coat cells or lodge in vessels or tissues, causing hypersensitivity reactions of the immediate type II (complement activation and tissue lysis), type III (immune complex formation), and delayed type IV kinds. These reactions may also be accompanied by macrophage activation, polyclonal B lymphocyte stimulation and various other nonspecific immune processes, operating alone or in concert.

Immunopathological changes are such important characteristics of parasitic infections that in many cases one can say that the disease begins with the immune response. Schistosomiasis is an excellent example of this. The adult worms, coated with host antigens, and therefore immunologically invisible, live relatively harmlessly in blood vessels, but produce eggs which become trapped in tissues of various kinds, including those of the liver. There they produce enzymes that are antigenic and stimulate local cell-mediated delayed hypersensitivity reactions, leading to the formation of granulomas. In laboratory animals, these granulomas eventually shut off the portal blood flow, giving rise to portal hypertension. In man, the evidence also suggests that reactions to schistosome eggs are responsible for much of the pathology of the disease.

Filariasis also has a large immunopathological component. In the most important species, *Wuchereria bancrofti* and *Brugia malayi*, the adult worms in the lymphatic vessels cause disease, particularly when they die and initiate local cell-mediated responses leading to inflammation and blockage of the lymphatics. It is not clear what component of the adult worm is responsible for initiating the immunopathological reactions but it may be the moulting fluid. The microfilariae themselves cause immediate hypersensitivity reactions associated with raised levels of IgE and eosinophils.

Among the protozoa, immunopathology is particularly obvious in African trypanosomiasis, as the host attempts first to rid itself of successive waves of parasites with different antigens and then tries to switch off the futile immune response. The surface coat of the trypanosome is the main source of antigenic stimulation and some of these antigens lodge in various tissues activating complement and initiating autoimmune reactions. Some antigens circulate and combine with the abundant antibody to form immune complexes which, in their turn, activate complement and macrophages and stimulate the production of pharmacologically active substances. The disease is a complicated one involving anaemia, wasting, fever, intravascular coagulation and many other destructive processes, most of which can be traced back to immunological origins.

Chagas' disease is another immunological disease in which the damage occurs some time after the acute stage. This damage is, to large extent, autoimmune and initiated by parasite antigens on the surface of infected and uninfected cells, particularly those of the endocardium. Cutaneous leishmaniasis is a spectral disease, like leprosy, with strong immunological responses at one pole and weak or nonexistent ones at the other. Where the immune responses are weak, the parasites cause the damage, and where they are strong they eliminate the parasites. In between these extremes, the pathology is dominated by the immune response and involves the formation of granulomas, consisting of macrophages and lymphocytes, an essentially cell-mediated response. In kala azar, on the other hand, antibody is involved in antigen–antibody complexes which give rise to a range of immunopathological reactions. Circulating antigen–antibody complexes are also found in malaria and, although it has been difficult to implicate these in the pathology of the disease, they are thought to be involved in the glomerular nephritis associated with quartan malaria. Also, in malaria, B lymphocyte activation results in splenomegaly, and autoantibodies contribute to the anaemia associated with the disease.

6.9   IMMUNIZATION AGAINST PARASITIC INFECTIONS

Immunization has many advantages over chemotherapy or the prevention of transmission as a method of control or eradication of any disease, and spectacular successes have been achieved against a number of viral and bacterial diseases of man and animals. A considerable amount of attention has been paid to the possibilities of developing vaccines against parasitic diseases but the practical results have been limited. This is partly because parasite antigens are complex and difficult to define, immune responses are multifactorial, parasites have evolved ways of evading the immune response and, even if an immune response is generated, it is seldom completely efficient. Nevertheless, in laboratory models, immunization against most of the commonly used parasites has been achieved, using attenuated or irradiated parasites, killed parasites, homogenates or extracts; the protection being best with the first two and least with the last. In addition, some successes have been achieved using or stimulating various mediators of nonspecific immunity. However, most of these immunological procedures have only limited application to human and veterinary medicine and, at the present time, merely indicate possible lines of approach.

Despite all the problems, a number of successful vaccines have been developed. The best known of these is that against the cattle lungworm, *Dictyocaulus viviparus*, which consists of irradiated larvae that live sufficiently long to stimulate an immune response but not so long as to cause an infection. This vaccine is commercially available and has been used successfully for over 20 years. A similar irradiated larval vaccine against canine hookworm, caused by *Ancylostoma caninum*, has also been developed and marketed, but is no longer commercially available. Another has been used against gapeworm of poultry caused by *Syngamus trachea*. The next most likely candidate for an irradiated larval vaccine is *Haemonchus contortus* in adult sheep in which considerable success has been achieved but not, unfortunately, in lambs. Irradiated ceracriae and schistosomula have been successfully used as vaccines against *Schistosoma bovis* and *S. mattheei* in cattle but these are still at the trial stage. The use of similar vaccines against experimental fascioliasis has been extremely disappointing. There is some hope of vaccine against *Taenia saginata* (*Cysticercus bovis*) in cattle and a suitable antigen has been obtained from the culture fluid in which oncospheres have been grown.

Among the protozoa, a simple vaccine consisting of whole blood containing parasites with reduced virulence, has been successfully used against *Babesia bovis* and encouraging results have been obtained using irradiated parasite vaccines against *B. bovis*, *B. bigemina* and *B. major*. Protection against *Theileria annulata* has been obtained using attenuated strains in lymphoid cell culture. In coccidiosis in chickens, protection can be achieved by allowing the birds to become infected with small numbers of oocysts which do not cause serious disease but do protect against subsequent infection. Cocktails of small numbers of commonly occurring oocysts have been produced commercially.

The prospects of any conventional vaccine against the parasitic diseases of man are remote, partly because the results of experiments using laboratory models have either not been wholly sucessful or have produced undesirable side-effects, and partly because of the difficulties inherent in developing any vaccine against a human disease. Among the potential vaccines now being considered are two against malaria, one against the sporozoites and one against the merozoites, but these are still at the early experimental stage. Vaccines against African trypanosomiasis or Chagas' disease are unlikely because of the antigenic variation in the former and the pathology resulting from the immune response to parasite antigens in the latter. Vaccines against leishmaniasis are also being considered but these will be difficult to develop because of the spectral nature of the disease.

A vaccine against human hookworm is a theoretical possibility in view of the success achieved with canine hookworm disease. Similarly, a vaccine against human schistosomiasis, like that against the cattle disease, is a possibility. However, in both cases, the use of irradiated, but living, larval vaccines is unlikely to be easily acceptable in man.

Immunostimulants are substances that either elicit a nonspecific immune response or boost a weak one and have been used successfully in connection with a number of tumours, particularly in laboratory animals. This has encouraged parasitologists to use similar substances, and immunostimulants such as *Mycobacterium bovis* (BCG) and *Corynebacterium parvum* have been used with considerable success to protect laboratory animals against *Leishmania* spp., *Trypanosoma cruzi*, *Babesia* spp., *Plasmodium* spp., *Toxoplasma gondii*, *Schistosoma mansoni* and *Echinococcus* spp. However, these successes have not been emulated in primates or cattle but, in due course, new immunostimulants may well be used to boost or reinforce an immune response induced by a more conventional vaccine.

REFERENCES AND FURTHER READING

Allison A.C. (1980) Effector and escape mechanisms in host-parasite relationship. In M. Fougereau & J. Dausset (eds.) *Progress in Immunology IV*, pp. 809–12. London, Academic Press.

Barriga O.O. (1981) *The Immunology of Parasitic Infections*, Lancaster, M.T.P. Press.

Bloom B.R. (1979) Games parasites play: how parasites evade immune surveillance. *Nature* **279**, 21–6.

Brener Z. (1980) Immunity to *Trypanosoma cruzi*. In W.H.R. Lumsden, R. Muller & J.R. Baker (eds.) *Advances in Parasitology*, vol.18, pp. 247–92. London, Academic Press.

Capron A., Capron M. & Dessaint J.P. (1980) ADCC as primary mechanisms of defence against metazoan parasites. In M. Fougereau & J. Dausset (eds.) *Progress in Immunology IV*, pp. 782–93. London, Academic Press.

Capron A., Lambert P.H., Ogilvie B. & Pery P. (eds.) (1978) Immunity in Parasitic Diseases. *Colloque INSERM* 72. Paris, INSERM.

CIBA Foundation (1974) *Parasites in the Immunized Host: Mechanisms of Survival*. CIBA Foundation Symposium No. 25. Amsterdam, Elsevier/Excerpta Medica/North Holland Publishing Co.

Clegg J.A. & Smith M.A. (1978) Prospects for the development of dead vaccines against helminths. In W.H.R. Lumsden, R. Muller & J.R. Baker, *Advances in Parasitology*, vol. 16, pp. 165–218. London, Academic Press.

Cohen S. (1980) Humoral responses to protozoal infections. In. M. Fougereau & J. Dausset (eds.) *Progress in Immunology IV*, pp. 763–81. London, Academic Press.

Cohen S. & Warren K.S. (eds.) (1982) *Immunology of Parasitic Infections*. 2nd ed. Oxford, Blackwell Scientific Publications.

Cox F.E.G. (1978) Specific and nonspecific immunisation against parasitic infections. *Nature*, **273**, 623–6.

Davies J.S., Hall J.G., Targett G.A.T. & Murray M. (1980) The biological significance of the immune response with special reference to parasites and cancer. *J. Parasit.* **66**, 705–21.

Flisser A., Perez-Montfort R. & Larralde C. (1979) The Immunology of human and animal cysticercosis: a review. *Bull. Wld Hlth Org.* **57**, 839–56.

Greenwood B.M. & Whittle H.C. (1981) *Immunology of Medicine In The Tropics*, London, Edward Arnold.

Holmes P.H. (1980) Vaccination against trypanosomes. In A.E.R. Taylor & R. Muller (eds.) *Vaccines against Parasites*, pp. 75–105. Oxford, Blackwell Scientific Publications.

Krause R. (ed.) (1980) Immunopathology of Parasitic Diseases. *Springer Seminars in Immunopathology* vol.2 (No. 4), pp. 355–442. Berlin, Springer-Verlag.

Kreier J.P. & Green T.J. (1980) The vertebrate host's immune response to plasmodia. In Kreier, J.P. (ed.) *Malaria*, vol.3, pp. 111–62. New York, Academic Press.

Miller T.A. (1978) Industrial development and field use of the canine hookworm vaccine. In W.H.R. Lumsden, R. Muller & J.R. Baker (eds.) *Advances in Parasitology*, vol.16, pp. 333–42. London, Academic Press.

Mitchell G.F. (1979) Responses to infection with metazoan and protozoan parasites in mice. In F.J. Dixon & H.G. Kunkel (eds.) *Advances in Immunology*, vol.28, pp. 451–511. New York, Academic Press.

Mitchell G.F. (1980) T-cell-dependent effects in parasitic infection and disease. In M. Fougereau & J. Dausset (eds.) *Progress in Immunology IV*, pp. 794–808. London, Academic Press.

Ogilvie B.M. (1969) Immunity to *Nippostrongylus brasiliensis*. In A.E.R. Taylor (ed.) *Nippostrongylus and Toxoplasma*, pp. 31–40. Oxford, Blackwell Scientific Publications.

Playfair, J.H.L. (1980) Vaccines against malaria. In A.E.R. Taylor & R. Muller (eds.) *Vaccines against Parasites*, pp. 1–23. Oxford, Blackwell Scientific Publications.

Purnell R.E. (1980) Vaccines against piroplasms. In A.E.R. Taylor & R. Muller (eds.) *Vaccines against Parasites*, pp. 25–55. Oxford, Blackwell Scientific Publications.

Rose M.E. & Long P.L. (1980) Vaccination against coccidiosis in chickens. In A.E.R. Taylor & R. Muller, *Vaccines against Parasites*, pp. 57–74. Oxford, Blackwell Scientific Publications.

Ross R. & Thomson D. (1910) A case of sleeping sickness studied by precise enumerative methods: Regular periodical increase of the parasite described. *Proceedings of the Royal Society of London*, B, **82**, 411–15.

Taylor A.E.R. & Muller R. (eds.) (1980) *Vaccines against Parasites. Symposia of the British Society for Parasitology*, vol.18. Oxford, Blackwell Scientific Publications.

Taylor M.G. (1980) Vaccination against trematodes. In A.E.R. Taylor & R. Muller (eds.) *Vaccines against Parasites*, pp. 115–40. Oxford, Blackwell Scientific Publications.

Teixeira A.R.L. (1979) Chagas' disease: trends in immunological research and prospects for immunoprophylaxis. *Bull. Wld Hlth Org.* **57**, 697–710.

Van den Bossche H. (ed.) (1980) *The Host-Invader Interplay. 3rd International Symposium on the Biochemistry of Parasites and Host-Parasite Relationships*. Amsterdam, Elsevier/North Holland.

Vickerman K. (1978) Antigenic variation in trypanosomes. *Nature* **273**, 613–17.

Wakelin D. (1978) Immunity to intestinal parasites. *Nature* **273**, 617–20.

Wakelin D. (1978) Genetic control of susceptibility and resistance to parasitic infection. In W.H.R. Lumsden, R. Muller & J.R. Baker (eds.) *Advances in Parasitology*, vol.16, pp. 219–308. London, Academic Press.

W H O (1979) Immunology of Malaria. *Bull. Wld Hlth Org.* **57**, (Supplement No. 1), 1–290.

Zwart D. & Brocklesby D.W. (1979) Babesiosis: Non-specific resistance, immunological factors and pathogenesis. In W.H.R. Lumsden, R. Muller & J.R. Baker (eds.) *Advances in Parasitology*, vol.17, pp. 49–113. London, Academic Press.

Chapter 7
Epidemiology
R.M. Anderson

7.1   INTRODUCTION

Epidemiology is the study of disease behaviour within populations of hosts, and as such it is a discipline with many links to a broader area of scientific investigation—namely, that of ecology.

Our knowledge of the epidemiology of infectious disease agents has expanded rapidly in the past few decades, drawing on research from many separate areas of scientific study. It is a subject of great significance in the world today with respect to man's own diseases and those of his crops and livestock.

Epidemiology is a quantitative science which relies on statistical methods for the accurate measurement of disease parameters, and mathematical techniques for the provision of a theoretical framework to aid in the interpretation and integration of field and experimental observations. A sound and detailed knowledge of the biology of the organisms under study, however, is an essential prerequisite for the successful application of these methods.

This chapter concentrates on outlining general principles, in the belief that these may be applied successfully to the epidemiological study of disease agents as diverse as the measles virus and the schistosome fluke. Before proceeding to describe these, however, some brief comments on epidemiological measures and units of study are necessary. Among the many possible measures of disease behaviour we must clearly aim to choose the most objective, the clearest and least ambiguous, and the most practically useful. What this measure will be depends on many factors, including the type of disease agent, but care must be devoted to its choice.

7.2   UNITS OF STUDY

7.2.1   The population as a unit of study

The definition and description of the host and parasite populations is clearly important in the study of disease epidemiology. A population is an assemblage of organisms (hosts or parasites) of the same species which occupy a defined point in the plane created by the dimensions of space and time. The basic unit of such populations is the individual organism.

Populations may be divided into a series of categories or classes, the members of which possess a unifying character (or characters) such as age, sex or their stage of development (egg, larvae or adult). Such subdivisions may be made on spatial criteria where distinctions are made between local populations within a larger assemblage of organisms.

Host–parasite associations are often characterized by the existence of a number of host populations (final and intermediate hosts) and several distinct parasite populations formed by the various developmental stages within the parasite life cycle (eggs, larvae and adults). We will use the term *subpopulation* to describe the number of parasites of a defined developmental stage within an individual host. The host here provides a convenient sampling unit. The total population of a given parasite stage is formed from the sum of all the subpopulations within the total host population. In the case of parasite transmission stages, their population is defined as the total number of organisms in the habitat of the host population.

The boundaries in space and time between these various host and parasite populations are often vague, but it is important to define them as clearly as possible.

7.2.2   Parasitic infection as a unit of study

The basic unit of study for the parasite population varies according to the type of infectious disease agent. *Microparasites* (the viruses, bacteria and protozoa) are small in size and possess the ability to multiply directly and rapidly within the host population. The measurement of the number of parasites within an individual host is usually difficult, if not impossible, and as a direct consequence, the *infected host* provides the most convenient unit for the study of these parasites. The choice of this unit leads to the division of the host population into a series of classes such as susceptibles, infecteds and immunes, categories which are based on the current or past infection status of the host. *Macroparasites* (helminths and arthropods) are much larger than microparasites and in general do not multiply directly within their hosts. The *individual parasite*, therefore provides the basic unit of study for these infections. The number of parasites harboured by an individual host may be measured in many cases (sometimes by indirect methods) and this quantity is invariably directly related to the pathology of the disease. In certain helminth life cycles, such as those of the schistosome flukes, the parasite multiplies directly within the intermediate host. In these cases, the infected host forms the unit of study for the intermediate host segment of the life cycle and the parasite acts as the basic unit for the phase involving man.

The duration of viral and bacterial infections in vertebrate hosts is typically short in relation to the expected lifespan of the host, and therefore is of a *transient* nature. This is a direct consequence of the ability of such directly multiplying parasites to elicit a strong immunological response from the host which tends to confer immunity to reinfection in those hosts that overcome the initial onslaught. There are of course some exceptions of which the slow viruses are particularly remarkable examples.

The immune responses elicited by macroparasites and many protozoan micro-parasites generally depend on the number of parasites present in a given host, and tend to be of relatively short duration. Such infections therefore tend to be of a *persistent* nature with hosts being continually reinfected.

7.2.3   Measurement of infection within the host population

The most widely used epidemiological statistic is the *prevalence of infection* which records the proportion or percentage of the host population that is infected with a specific parasite (Fig. 7.1a–d). This measure is particularly convenient for the study of microparasitic infections where the infected host forms the basic unit of study but it is also widely used for helminth diseases.

Prevalence may be measured in different ways: by direct observation of parasites within or on the host—the examination of blood films for malarial parasites; on the basis of serological evidence—the detection of *Trichinella* infections; and by the emission of infective stages—the examination of host faeces for helminth eggs. Immunological evidence provides the basis for a further epidemiological measure, namely the proportion of serologically positive individuals within the host population. This approach is widely adopted for human viral diseases, such as measles and yellow fever, which induce lifelong immunity to reinfection. In such circumstances, the measure records the proportion of the population that have experienced infection at some time in their life (Fig. 7.1e & f).

The severity of disease symptoms shown by a host is often related to the number of parasites harboured. This number is referred to as the *intensity of infection* while the mean number of parasites per host is denoted as the *mean intensity of infection* (note that this mean should be calculated for the total host population including the uninfected individuals) (Fig. 7.1d).

The measurement of disease intensity is rarely straightforward. It may be estimated by direct counting (e.g. ectoparasites such as ticks and lice), from samples of host tissues or fluids (e.g. the use of blood films to count malaria parasites), or by the use of chemotherapeutic agents to expel gut helminths in the faeces of the host (e.g. *Ascaris* and hookworms). Indirect measures may often be necessary, such as the recording of helminth egg and protozoan cyst numbers in the faeces of the host, or the measurement of the levels of host immunological responses to parasite antigens. It is usually difficult, however, to relate these indirect measures to parasite numbers.

The prevalence and intensity of infection are often recorded within different age classes of human populations in order to ascertain the sections of the community most at risk. Data of this form are often plotted as *age-prevalence* or *age-intensity* curves (Fig. 7.1). The examination of alternative and finer stratifications of the population may be necessary for certain infections. Sex, religion, age and occu-pation, for example, are important factors in the epidemiology of many directly transmitted helminths of man.

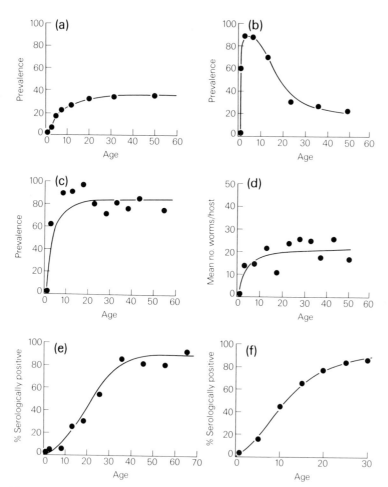

Fig. 7.1. Some examples of horizontal cross-sectional surveys of the prevalence and intensity of parasitic infection in human communities (age prevalence and age intensity curves). (a) *Entamoeba histolytica* in West Africa. (After Bray & Harris, 1977.) (b) Malaria in Nigeria. (After Fleming *et al.*, 1979.) (c) & (d) *Ascaris* in Iran. (After Arfaa & Ghadivian, 1977). (e) Yellow fever in Brazil. (After Muench, 1959.) (f) Measles in New York. (After Muench, 1959.)

The examination of various classes within a community at one point in time, or over a short time interval, is referred to as a *horizontal cross-sectional epidemiological survey* (Fig. 7.1). The monitoring of these classes over successive points in time is described as a *longitudinal cross-sectional study* (Fig. 7.2). Horizontal surveys of prevalence and intensity within different age classes of a community can provide valuable information on the rate at which hosts acquire infection through time, provided that the host and parasite populations have remained approximately stable for a period of time (stable endemic disease).

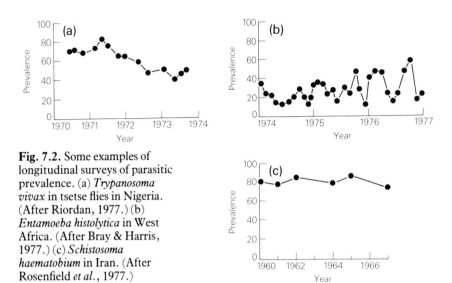

Fig. 7.2. Some examples of longitudinal surveys of parasitic prevalence. (a) *Trypanosoma vivax* in tsetse flies in Nigeria. (After Riordan, 1977.) (b) *Entamoeba histolytica* in West Africa. (After Bray & Harris, 1977.) (c) *Schistosoma haematobium* in Iran. (After Rosenfield *et al.*, 1977.)

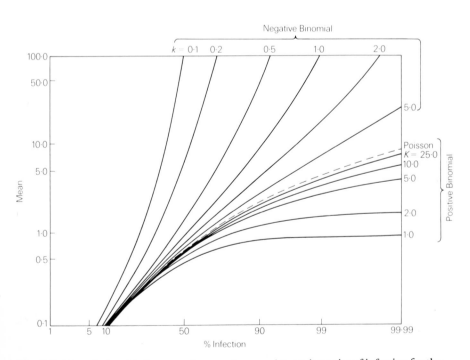

Fig. 7.3. The relationship between the prevalence and mean intensity of infection for the positive binomial (K), Poisson and negative binomial distributions (k) of parasite numbers per host.

7.3   FREQUENCY DISTRIBUTION OF PARASITE NUMBERS PER HOST

Measures such as parasite prevalence and mean intensity are statistics of the probability or frequency distribution of parasite numbers per host. The form of this distribution determines the relationship between prevalence and intensity (Fig. 7.3). Dispersion or distribution patterns of parasites within the host population can be broadly divided into three categories: underdispersion (regular, homogeneous; variance < mean), random (variance = mean) and overdispersion (contagious,

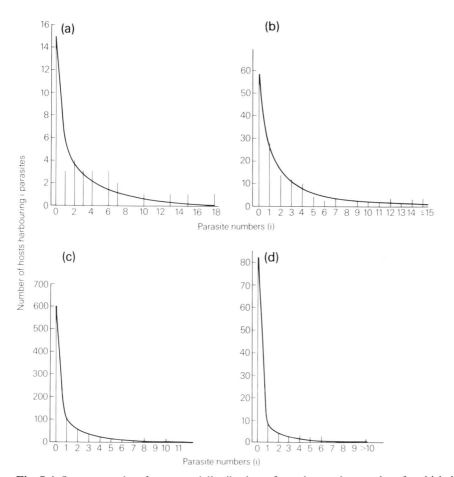

Fig. 7.4. Some examples of aggregated distributions of parasite numbers per host for which the negative binomial is a good empirical model (vertical bars: observed frequencies; solid line: fit of negative binomial. (a) A gut nematode *(Toxocara canis)* of foxes (Watkins & Harvey, 1942). (b) Nematode microfilariae *(Chandlerella quiscoli)* in mosquitos *(Culicoides crepuscularis)*. (After Schmid & Robinson, 1972.) (c) Lice *(Pediculus humanis capitis)* on man. (After Williams,

aggregated, heterogeneous; variance > mean). These patterns are well-described empirically by three well-known probability distributions: the positive binomial (underdispersion), Poisson (random), and negative binomial (overdispersion).

Parasites are almost invariably overdispersed or aggregated within their host populations, where many hosts harbour a few parasites and a few hosts harbour large numbers of parasites (Fig. 7.4). The causes of such heterogeneity are many and varied but they are usually associated with variability in 'susceptibility' to infection within the host population. Such variability may be due to differences in host behaviour, spatial aggregation of infective stages, or differences in the ability of individual hosts to mount effective immunological responses to parasitic invasion (due either to past experiences of infection, other parasitic species within the host or genetic constitution) (Table 7.1).

Table 7.1. Parasite dispersion in host populations.

Dispersion Spectrum

————→

All hosts harbour the same number of parasites	Parasites randomly (independently) distributed (variance = mean)	All parasites in one host, all other hosts uninfected

←————

Underdispersion (variance < mean) (Regularity, homogeneity)	Overdispersion (variance > mean) (Aggregtion, heterogeneity)
Some factors which generate underdispersion	Some factors which generate overdispersion
Parasite mortality	Heterogeneity in host behaviour
Host immunological processes	Heterogeneity in effective immunity within the host population
Density-dependent processes	Direct reproduction within the host
Parasite induced host mortality when the death rate of the host is positively correlated with parasite burden	Spatial heterogeneity in the distribution of infective stages

The aggregation of parasites within the host population has many implications for epidemiological study. The most important concerns the sampling of the host population to measure disease intensity. A high degree of variability in parasite numbers per host necessitates the examination of large numbers of hosts (large sample size) if an accurate picture is to be obtained of parasite abundance within the host population. Very misleading results may be obtained from small samples.

Parasite aggregation also has important implications for the regulation of parasite numbers within the host population and these are discussed in a latter section.

7.4   TRANSMISSION BETWEEN HOSTS

Parasites may complete their life cycles by passing from one host to the next either directly or indirectly via one or more intermediate host species (see Chapter 4). *Direct transmission* may be by contact between hosts (for example venereal diseases) or by specialized or unspecialized transmission stages of the parasite that are picked up by inhalation (respiratory viruses), ingestion (such as pinworm) or penetration of the skin (such as hookworm). *Indirect transmission* can involve biting by vectors (flies, mosquitos, ticks and others) that serve as inter- mediate hosts (the parasite undergoing obligatory development within the vector). In other cases, the parasite is ingested when an infected intermediate host is eaten by the predatory or scavenging final host. A special case of direct transmission arises when the infection is conveyed by a parent to its unborn offspring (egg or embryo), as can occur in rubella (german measles). This process has been termed *vertical transmission* in contrast to the variety of *horizontal transmission* processes discussed above and in Chapter 4.

The prevalence and intensity of a parasitic infection within the host population is *in part* determined by the *rate* of transmission between hosts. Many factors influence this rate including climatic conditions, host and parasite behaviour, and the densities of both host and infective stage, plus their respective spatial distributions. The rate of transmission (sometimes referred to as the rate or force of infection) is measured in a variety of ways, the method depending on the type of parasite and its mode of transmission.

7.4.1   Transmission by contact between hosts

For many directly transmitted viral and protozoan diseases, where in- fection results either from physical contact between hosts or by means of a *very* short- lived infective agent, the net rate of transmission is *directly proportional* to the frequency of encounters between susceptible (uninfected) and infected hosts. In these cases no attempt is made to measure the number of parasites transmitted between hosts (due to their small size and ability to multiply rapidly within the host); attention is simply focused on the rate at which hosts become infected.

If we define the parameter β as the rate of contact between hosts which result in transmission (where $1/\beta$ is directly proportional to the average time interval between contacts), then during an interval of time Δt, in a population of N hosts consisting of X susceptibles and Y infecteds ($N = X + Y$), the number of new cases of an infection is often approximated by the quantity $\beta X Y \Delta t$. The parameter β is called the *per capita* rate of infection and is the product of two components, namely the average frequency of contact between hosts, times the probability that an encounter between susceptible and infected will result in the transference of infection.

If the time interval Δt becomes very small we arrive at a differential equation representing the rate of change of the number of infected hosts through time:

$$dY/dt = \beta XY = \beta(N-Y)Y. \tag{1}$$

This equation has the solution

$$Y_t = NY_0/[Y_0 + (N-Y_0)\exp(-\beta Nt)], \tag{2}$$

where Y_0 represents the number of infecteds introduced into the population at time $t=0$. In practice we are often more interested in the rate at which new cases of infection arise (or are reported) (i.e. dY/dt). Calling this rate ω and substituting equation (2) into equation (1) we find that

$$w = \beta Y_0 (N-Y_0)N^2 \exp(\beta Nt)/[(N-Y_0)+Y_0\exp(\beta Nt)]^2 \tag{3}$$

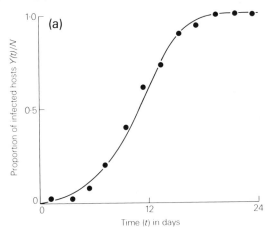

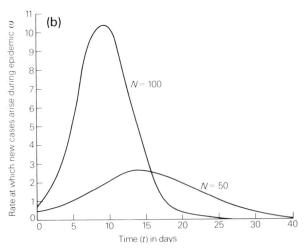

Fig. 7.5. (a) An epidemic of the protozoan *Hydramoeba hydroxena* in a population of the coelenterate *Chlorohydra viridissima*. (Stiven, 1965.) (b) Two examples of epidemic curves for populations of different sizes ($N = 100$ and $N = 50$, see text).

Equation (3) describes an epidemic curve which is roughly bell shaped in form (Fig. 7.5b). Note that as the density of the host population (N) increases, the development of the epidemic occurs more rapidly. The net rate of parasite transmission is always greater in dense populations than sparse ones.

Equations (2) and (3) accurately mirror the growth and decay of various types of disease epidemics, including infections within laboratory populations of animals and viral diseases within human communities (Fig. 7.5a). The agreement between observation and theory supports the assumption that transmission of many direct life-cycle microparasites is directly proportional to the rate of encounter between hosts. It is important to note, however, that within certain human communities the rate of transmission of some viral and bacterial diseases appears to be non-linearly related to population density (see Anderson & May, 1982). This is thought to arise as a consequence of non-homogeneous mixing within such communities.

The value of the transmission rate β in equation (1) often varies seasonally, due to the influence of climatic factors on either the frequency of host contact or the life expectancy of the infective stages which determines the probability of parasite transference during host encounters. Seasonal contact rates are important in the epidemiology of many common viral infections of man such as measles, mumps and chickenpox.

Within large communities where there exists a continual inflow of new susceptibles (births), a disease may exhibit recurrent epidemic behaviour or may even persist in a stable endemic manner through time. In the case of human viral infections such as measles, where children who have recovered from infection are immune from further attack, the persistence of the parasite is very dependent on the rate of inflow of susceptibles. The number of new births per unit of time is related to community size and thus such infections are more likely to persist from year to year

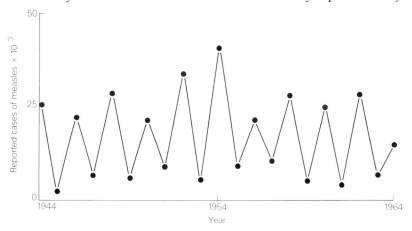

Fig. 7.6. Reported cases of measles in New York city from 1944 to 1964. (After Yorke & London, 1973.)

in large communities. Interestingly, seasonal contact rates can, in conjunction with other factors (such as the rate of input of susceptibles and incubation periods during which hosts are infected but not infectious), produce complicated nonseasonal cycles in the prevalence of viral infections. For example, Fig. 7.6 shows a biannual cycle of measles incidence in New York City from 1944 to 1964. The two–year cycle is superimposed over a regular seasonal cycle induced by changes in the infection rate β.

Aside from the influence of climatic factors on β, it is important to note that human *behaviour patterns* have a major effect on disease transmission. They will determine both the frequency and intimacy of contact between individuals.

7.4.2   Transmission by an infective agent

Many directly and indirectly transmitted parasites produce transmission stages with a not insignificant lifespan outside of the host. Examples are the miracidia and cercariae of the schistosome flukes, the infective larvae of hookworms and the eggs of *Ascaris*. In the case of helminth parasites, we are usually interested in the number of parasites a host acquires, since parasite burden is invariably related to the severity of disease symptoms induced by parasitic infection. The measurement of transmission must therefore be based on the rate of acquisition of *individual parasites* rather than simply the rate at which hosts become infected (as in equations 1, 2 and 3).

The rate of acquisition is often directly proportional to the frequency of contact between hosts and infective stages. If we define the parameter $\hat{\beta}$ as the rate of contact between hosts (N) and infective stages (I) which results in successful infection, the number of infections that occur in a small interval of time Δt is $\beta I N \, \Delta t$ (the mean number per host is $\hat{\beta} I \, \Delta t$). The parameter $\hat{\beta}$ again represents the product of two components; namely, the rate of contact times the probability that a contact results in the establishment of the infective stage within the host.

The properties of this form of transmission are well illustrated by the following simple example. If N uninfected hosts are introduced into a habitat with I_0 infective stages, whose life expectancy in the free-living habitat is $1/\mu$, the rates of change through time of I_t and the mean number of parasites acquired by each host, M_t, are described by the following differential equations:

$$dI/dt = -(\hat{\beta}N + \mu)I \tag{4}$$

$$dM/dt = \hat{\beta}I. \tag{5}$$

These equations have the following solutions:

$$I_t = I_0 \exp[-(\hat{\beta}N + \mu)t] \tag{6}$$

$$M_t = \left[\hat{\beta}I_o/(\hat{\beta}N+\mu) \right] \left[1-\exp[-(\hat{\beta}N+\mu)t] \right].$$

In an interval of time $\bar{t}$ the relationship between the mean number of successful infections per host (M) and the initial exposure density of infective stages (I_o) is linear where

$$M = I_o A. \tag{8}$$

The constant A is defined for notational convenience as

$$A = \hat{\beta} \left[1-\exp[-(\hat{\beta}N+\mu)\bar{t}] \right] /[\hat{\beta}N+\mu]. \tag{9}$$

The linear relationship predicted by equation (8) is observed in many experimental situations, various examples of which are shown in Fig. 7.7. Such experiments enable the parameters $\hat{\beta}$ and $1/\mu$ to be estimated under defined laboratory conditions.

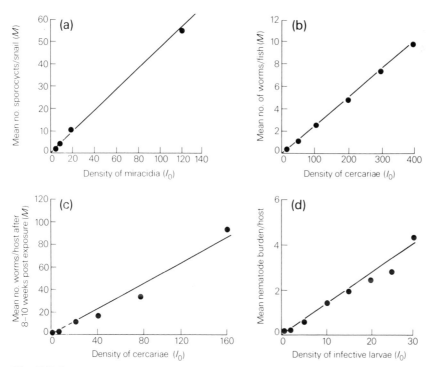

Fig. 7.7. Some examples of the linear relationship between the number of parasites that establish on or in a host when exposed to varying numbers of infective stages. (a) *Biomphalaria* exposed to miracidia of *Echinostoma lindoense*. (After Lie *et al.*, 1975.) (b) Fish exposed to cercariae of *Transversotrema patialense*. (After Anderson *et al.*, 1978.) (c) Hamsters exposed to cercariae of *Schistosoma mansoni*. (After Grove & Warren, 1976.) (d) Mosquitos exposed to infective larvae of the nematode *Romanomermis culicovorax*. (Tingley, unpublished data.)

This simple model (equations 4 and 5) illustrates a number of important general points concerning the dynamics of parasite transmission.

1   The existence of a *linear* relationship between infective stage density and the average number of parasites acquired per host (Fig. 7.7) indicates that the net rate of infection is *directly* proportional to the density of infective stages times the density of hosts.

2   The number of parasites acquired during an interval of time ($\bar{t}$) is very dependent on the expected lifespan of the infective stage ($1/\mu$) (Fig. 7.8b). Very high infection rates ($\hat{\beta}$) may not necessarily lead to the rapid accumulation of parasites within the host population if the expected lifespan of the infective stage is short (e.g. the infection of molluscs by the miracidia of digeneans). Conversely, high parasite burdens may accumulate even when the contact rate is low, provided that the infective stage is long-lived (e.g. *Ascaris* eggs and the acquisition of infection by man). Overall transmission success (measured by the accumulation of parasites within the host population) is therefore dependent on a number of rate determining processes (influencing various developmental stages in the parasite life cycle), and not simply on infection or contact rates ($\hat{\beta}$).

3   The total number of parasites that manage to establish within the host population (MN) during a fixed time interval ($\bar{t}$) increases as host density (N) rises (Fig. 7.8a). This relationship is non-linear, the total approaching an asymptote whose size is determined by both the number of infective stages available within the habitat (I_o) and their expected life span ($1/\mu$).

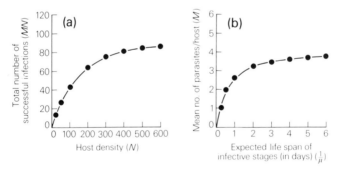

Fig. 7.8. (a) The relationship between the total number of parasites that establish within the host population and host density, N (see text). (b) The relationship between the mean number of parasites established per host and the expected lifespan of the infective stage, $1/\mu$ (see text).

4   A relationship exists between the mean number of parasites acquired (M) and the prevalence of infection (the proportion of the population infected, p) within the exposed host population. The precise form of the relationship depends on the statistical distribution of parasite numbers per host (Fig. 7.3). If the parasites are

randomly distributed (Poisson distribution), this relationship is defined by

$$p = [1 - e^{-M}]. \tag{10}$$

The prevalence rapidly rises to unity, where all hosts carry infection, as the exposure density of infective stages (I_o) increases (Fig. 7.9). Random patterns are, however, rarely observed even under laboratory conditions. More usually, the distribution is aggregated or contagious, where a high degree of variability exists between the worm burdens of individual hosts (the statistical variance is greater than the average burden). This variability is, as discussed earlier, principally due to heterogeneity in susceptibility to infection within the host population.

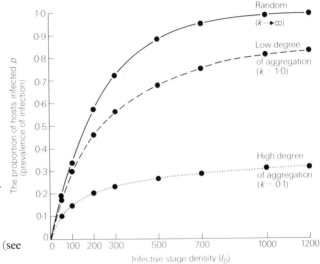

Fig. 7.9. The relationship between the prevalence of infection and infective stage density for varying distribution patterns of parasite numbers per host (see text).

The negative binomial distribution is a good empirical model of aggregated patterns of parasite numbers per host. It is defined by two parameters, the mean (M) and a parameter k, which varies inversely with the degree of parasite aggregation. The relationship between prevalence and mean parasite burden predicted by this distribution is given by

$$p = 1 - [1 + M/k]^{-k}. \tag{11}$$

If the host population is highly heterogeneous with respect to susceptibility (k small), the prevalence of infection will not rise rapidly to unity as the density of infective stages rises. A few hosts will acquire the majority of parasites, always leaving a proportion of the host population uninfected (Fig. 7.9). The results of an experimental investigation of the relationship between infective stage density, host density and the resultant prevalence of infection are recorded in Fig. 7.10.

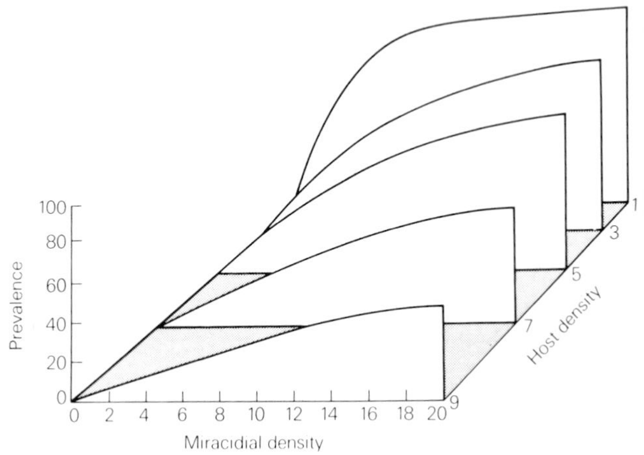

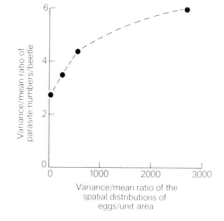

Fig. 7.10. Experimental determination of the relationships between the prevalence of snail infection (*Biomphalaria*) with *Schistosoma mansoni* and snail density plus miracidia density. (After Carter, Anderson & Wilson, 1982.)

A good illustration of the type of mechanism that generates heterogenity in the distribution of parasite numbers per host, is provided by the influence of various spatial patterns of infective stages on the acquistion of *Hymenolepis diminuta* infections by the beetle intermediate host *Tribolium confusum*. For a fixed density of eggs in experimental infection arenas, increasing degrees of aggregation in the spatial distribution of these infective stages resulted in a concomitant increase in the level of aggregation of worm numbers per beetle (Fig. 7.11). Interestingly, the spatial pattern of eggs does not affect the *average* rate of parasite acquisition, it simply acts to determine the distribution of the number of parasites acquired by each individual host (Fig. 7.11).

The duration of exposure to infection ($\bar{t}$) and infective stage density (I_0) also influence the distribution of successful infections per host *if* the host population is heterogeneous with respect to susceptibility to infection. A *constant* degree of variability in susceptibility (caused by either, behavioural, immunological or genetic

Fig. 7.11. The influence of the spatial distribution of *Hymenolepis* eggs on the distribution of infections within the beetle (*Tribolium*) intermediate host. (After Keymer & Anderson, 1979.)

differences) generates an *increasing* degree of aggregation of successful infections per host, as both the density of infective stages and the duration of exposure to infection increase.

7.4.3 Transmission by ingestion

The rate of transmission of a parasite which gains entry to the host by ingestion is influenced by the feeding behaviour of the host. Ingestion may occur as a result of the host actively preying on infective stages (fish predating digenean cercaria), consuming food contaminated with infective agents (human consumption of vegetables contaminated with *Ascaris* eggs), or consuming an intermediate host which is infected with larval parasites (human consumption of fish infected with *Diphyllobothrium*)—a predator-prey association existing between final and inter- mediate hosts.

In such cases the relationship between the number of parasites acquired and infective stages density, or the density of infected intermediate hosts, *may no longer be linear*. The net rate of infection is determined by the feeding rate of the host which is non-linearly related to food or prey density. This is a consequence of either sati- ation effects or the amount of time taken to capture and consume a prey item. Host satiation results in a decrease in the rate of food consumption, and hence the rate of ingestion of parasites, irrespective of the density of infective stages or infected intermediate hosts. A predator will also only be able to consume a finite number of prey items during an interval of time due to the amount of time taken to hunt, capture and consume a prey item (commonly called the 'handling time').

The net effect of both influences is to limit the rate of parasite acquisition, some examples of which are shown in Fig. 7.12.

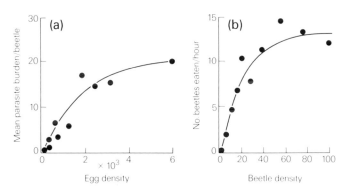

Fig. 7.12. Non-linear relationships between infective stage, (or infected host) density and the rate of parasite (or intermediate host) acquisition. (After Keymer & Anderson, 1979; Keymer, unpublished results.) (a) The acquisition of *Hymenolepis* by *Tribolium* beetles. (b) The rate of eating beetles by rats.

7.4.4   Transmission by a biting arthropod

Many microparasites and macroparasites have indirect life cycles where transmission between hosts is achieved by a biting arthropod, for example yellow fever, malaria, sleeping sickness and filariasis. The intermediate arthropod host, or vector, tends to make a fixed number of bites per unit of time, independent of the number of final hosts available to feed on. The transmission rate from infected arthropods to people (and from infected people back to susceptible arthropods) is therefore proportional to the 'man biting rate' ($\bar{\beta}$ times the probability that a given human is susceptible (or infected) and not simply proportional to the number of susceptibles (or infected) people (see equation 1). If the number of susceptible and infectious final hosts and vectors are represented by X, Y, and X' and Y' respectively, the net rate at which susceptible people acquire infection is $\bar{\beta}(X/N)Y')$. The quantity N represents the total number of people and the 'man biting rate' $\bar{\beta}$ consists of two components; the biting rate times the probability that an infectious bite leads to infection. Similarly, the net rate at which susceptible vectors acquire infection is $\bar{\beta}X'(Y/N)$.

If N uninfected final hosts are exposed to Y' infectious vectors, the number of hosts that acquire infection, Y, in a period of time, t, is approximately given by

$$Y = N\left[\,1 - \exp\ (-\bar{\beta}(Y'/N)t)\,\right].\tag{12}$$

The degree of transmission measured by Y is critically dependent on the biting rate $\bar{\beta}$, irrespective of the density of hosts, N, which are susceptible to infection (Fig. 7.13).

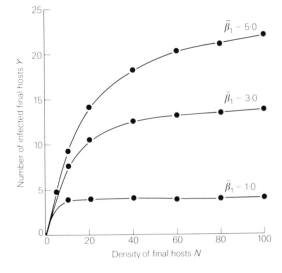

Fig. 7.13. The relationship between the number of final hosts that acquire infection (Y) when exposed to five infectious vectors for 10 units of time, and final host density (N) for different vector biting rates ($\bar{\beta}$) (see text).

The prevalence of infection of many parasitic diseases within their vector populations is characteristically low, even when the level of infection within the vertebrate host population is high. In regions of endemic malaria, for example, where more than 50% of the human population is infected, the prevalence of infection within the mosquito vector is typically 1–2%. In bancroftian filariasis it is 5–8% and in blackfly infected with *Onchocerca volvulus* it is 1–5%. This is basically a consequence of the inverse relation between standing crop (the number of infected hosts) and population turnover rates (the rates of loss of infected hosts) that arises in many biological systems.

There is often a substantial difference in the life expectancy of infection within the vertebrate host and vector, sometimes as a consequence of differences in host life-expectancy. For a fixed transmission rate (as is the case for vector borne diseases where the biting rate determines transmission both from vertebrate to vector and vice versa), infections of long duration will give rise to higher prevalences than those of short duration. A single infection of malaria in man, for example, may last from a few months to many years (depending on the species of *Plasmodium* and the immunological status of the host), while the duration of infection in the vector is limited by the short life expectancy of the mosquito which is typically of the order of one week. This type of pattern is common amongst vector borne protozoan and helminth diseases of man. Viral infections, however, often have different characteristics, exemplified by yellow fever where the duration of infection in man is roughly 10 days.

Transmission of a vector borne disease is also influenced by the developmental period of the parasite in the vector; a period during which the host is infected but not infectious. This developmental delay is called the *incubation* or *latent* period and may often be not insignificant in relation to the expected lifespan of the intermediate host. In malaria, for example, the incubation period in the mosquito is 10–12 days, whereas the life expectancy is between 2–15 days, according to the species. The precise manner in which all these various factors (the biting rate $\bar{\beta}$, the expected lifespan of the vector $1/b$, and the incubation period τ) influence the rate of transmission is clearly not easy to determine.

However, in areas where the prevalence of infection in the human population (y) remains roughly constant through time (endemic regions) the prevalence of infectious vectors y') is given by

$$y' = \frac{[\bar{\beta} y \exp(-b\tau)]}{(b + \bar{\beta} y)}. \tag{13}$$

The insertion of a range of parameter values into this expression (Fig. 7.14) illustrates how important vector life expectancy ($1/b$) and the duration of the incubation period (τ) are as determinants of transmission success (measured by y').

Short vector life expectancy and long incubation periods result in very low prevalences of infectious vectors even in areas of stable endemic disease where the disease is very prevalent within the human population.

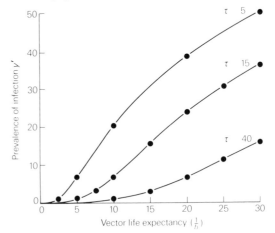

Fig. 7.14 The relationship between the prevalence of infectious vectors (y') and vector life expectancy $1/b$ for varying disease incubation periods (τ) (see text).

7.5   REGULATION OF PARASITE ABUNDANCE WITHIN THE HOST POPULATION

The *perpetuation* of a parasite within its host population is distinct from the survival or *persistence* of an infection within an individual host. The mechanisms which control parasite population size within an individual host, however, are central to our understanding of perpetuation and stability within the host population as a whole. It is convenient to consider these issues under two headings.

7.5.1   The host as the basic unit of study

As noted earlier, the epidemiological study of many human infections, particularly viral, bacterial and protozoan diseases, is based on the division of the host population into a series of categories. Hosts are allocated to these categories on the basis of their infection status which, for example, may be either susceptible, infected or immune. The basic unit of study is therefore an individual host and the perpetuation of an infection is judged on whether or not infected hosts are present.

Vertebrate hosts mount responses to parasitic invasion which may be immunological in nature. If successful, these responses will either eliminate the parasite or constrain its population size within the host to a low level (see Chapter 6). Acquired immunity can cause second and later infections to be eliminated with no overt signs of disease (and without the host becoming infectious to others), so that hosts with acquired immunity in effect join an immune category that is protected from infection. In short, there are two main points relevant to our considerations of the regulation of the number of infected hosts. First, hosts may recover from infection and, second, hosts that recover may possess a degree of protection, either transient or longer term, to future infection.

Host immunity is clearly an important regulatory constraint on the spread and perpetuation of infection within the host community. The greater the proportion of immunes within the population (commonly referred to as the degree of herd immunity), the lower will be the potential for disease transmission. Host immunity essentially acts as a form of delayed regulation or negative feedback on the number of infected hosts. The prevalence of infection at one point in time is related to the proportion of hosts that will become immune at some future point in time, the length of the time interval being dependent on the average duration of infection within an individual host. A large number of infecteds, which eventually become immune, leads in due course to a reduction in the number of susceptibles. This reduction acts to decrease transmission success and thus limits the number of infecteds arising in the next generation. In other words, the number of infecteds at one point in time is inversely related to the number at some future point in time, host immunity acting as a regulatory constraint on the prevalence of infection (see Fig. 7.15).

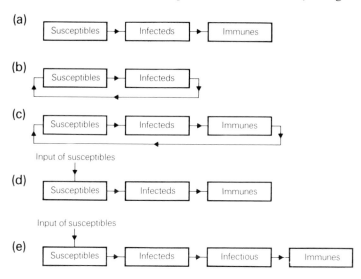

Fig. 7.15. Diagrammatic representations of the division of the host population into various compartments and the flow of hosts between these compartments (see text). (a) Host population of constant size consisting of susceptibles, infecteds (all assumed to be infectious) and immunes. Immunity is lifelong). (b) As (a) but no immune class, recovered infecteds passing back into the susceptible class. (c) As (a) but loss of immunity such that hosts pass back from the immune to the susceptible class. (d) As (a) but input of susceptibles due to new births or the arrival of immigrants. (e) As (d) but the infected class divided into two categories: those infected but not infectious and those infectious.

The mechanisms of host immunity are dealt with in Chapter 6; our interest here centres on the population consequences and regulatory potential of acquired immunity.

Whether or not an infection spreads and perpetuates once it is introduced into a host population is dependent on a variety of factors. Initial spread is determined by (a) the density of susceptibles; (b) the frequency of host contact; (c) the infectiousness of the disease (the probability that a contact between susceptible and infected results in transmission); and (d) the average time period during which an infected host is infectious. To illustrate these points consider the following example. If a few infecteds are introduced into a population of hosts consisting of X susceptibles, Y infecteds, and Z immunes, the initial spread of infection is described by the following differential equations:

$$dX/dt = -\beta XY \tag{14}$$

$$dY/dt = \beta XY - \gamma Y \tag{15}$$

$$dZ/dt = \gamma Y. \tag{16}$$

For simplicity it is assumed that all infecteds are infectious. The parameter β represents the transmission rate (see equation 1), its magnitude being determined by the product of two components, namely the frequency of contact between hosts, times the probability that a contact results in infection. The parameter γ denotes the rate of recovery from infection where $1/\gamma$ is the average duration of infectiousness.

The introduction of a few infecteds (numbering Y_0) into a population of N susceptibles will only result in an epidemic (representing the spread of the disease) provided that

$$N > \beta/\gamma \quad \text{(Fig. 7.16a \& b)}. \tag{17}$$

This condition is a direct consequence of the fact that equation (1) must initially be positive if the number of infecteds is to increase above its introduction level Y_0. In other words, for an epidemic to occur, the density of susceptibles must be greater than a *critical threshold level*, N_T, which is determined by the product of the transmission rate (β) times the average duration of infectiousness of an individual host $1/\gamma$. A diagrammatic flow chart of the model described by equations (14) to (16) is displayed in Fig. 7.15a and the temporal changes of the number of infected hosts (Y) when equation (17) is, and is not, satisfied, are shown in Fig. 7.17a and b.

In our simple model we have assumed that once hosts recover from infection they are then immune for life, as is the case for certain human viral infections such as measles. In a closed community therefore, provided that equation (17) is satisfied, the disease will initially spread (leading to an epidemic) but will eventually die out once the supply of susceptibles is exhausted (Fig. 7.15a). The infection could perpetuate if some loss of immunity occurred, such that hosts passed back from the immune to the susceptible category (Fig. 7.15b & c; Fig. 7.16c).

More generally, however, disease perpetuation within the host population over a period of years will be dependent on the net inflow of susceptibles into the community either as a consequence of new births or immigration (Fig. 7.16d). Thus in addition to the threshold density of susceptibles necessary for the occurrence of an epidemic, long-term endemic perpetuation will also depend on community size, larger communities tending to produce more offspring (susceptibles) than smaller ones. Epidemics of measles, for example, occur in school communities of a few hundred susceptible children, but the virus only becomes endemic on a continuous month-to-month and year-to-year basis in urban populations greater than 500 000

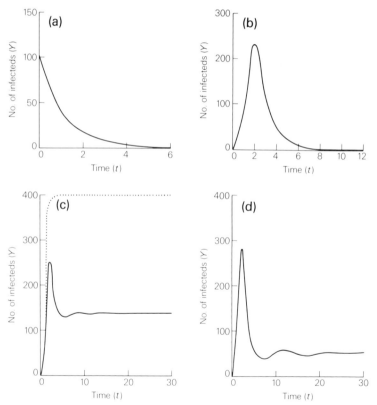

Fig. 7.16. (a) Host density below the threshold level for the occurrence of an epidemic ($X_0 = 500$, $Y_0 = 100$, $\beta = 0.0001$, $\gamma = 1.0$) (Flow chart (a) in Fig. 7.15). (b) Host density above the threshold level ($X_0 = 500$, $Y_0 = 2$, $\beta = 0.01$, $\gamma = 1.0$) (Flow chart (a) in Fig. 7.15). (c) The maintenance of endemic disease in a host population of fixed size where immunity is either absent (dotted line) (Flow chart (b) in Fig. 7.15), or not lifelong (solid line) (Flow chart (c) in Fig. 7.15). (d) Maintenance of endemic disease when immunity is lifelong by the input of new susceptibles (Flow chart (d) in Fig. 7.15).

people. Even in very large communities the epidemiology of measles is characterized by cyclic, recurrent epidemic behaviour (Fig. 7.6). Infections of this kind are probably diseases of modern societies; in primitive societies the net inflow of susceptibles into small communities was probably too low to maintain the diseases.

In brief, the perpetuation and stability of infectious diseases within their host populations revolves around a series of factors, some of which are interrelated. These factors are; (i) the ability of the parasite to persist within an individual host; (ii) the length of the period during which an infected host is infectious; (iii) the duration of acquired immunity to reinfection; (iv) the infectiousness of the disease agents (transmissibility being dependent on both host and parasite characteristics);(v) the degree of herd immunity; and (vi) the net rate of inflow of susceptibles into the host community.

Many viral and bacterial infections of man are *transient* in nature and tend to induce lasting immunity to reinfection. These diseases only occur endemically, without periodic disappearance, in large communities with high inputs of susceptibles. Such infections characteristically exhibit wide fluctuations in prevalence through time, recurrent epidemic behaviour being a feature of their epidemiology.

Conversely, most protozoan diseases are able to *persist* within individual hosts for long periods of time and do not tend to induce lasting immunity to reinfection. These infections are able to survive endemically in small host communities with low inputs of susceptibles. The prevalence of protozoan infections is characteristically more stable through time than viral and bacterial diseases.

7.5.2   The parasite as the basic unit of study

The individual parasite forms the basic unit of study for helminth and arthropod infections (macroparasites), the pathology of these diseases being related to the number or burden of parasites harboured by the host.

In contrast to microparasites, the majority of helminths do not multiply directly within their vertebrate hosts (*direct reproduction*) but produce transmission stages (such as eggs or larvae) which pass out of the host as a developmental necessity (*transmission reproduction*). The number of parasites within an individual host (a *subpopulation* of parasites) is therefore controlled by the rate at which new infections arrive and the rate at which established parasites die. This is an immigration–death process in contrast to the birth–death one which governs the growth of microparasites within their hosts.

Macroparasites tend to produce *lasting* infections, with the host harbouring populations of parasites for long periods due to continual reinfections. Among many examples are the hookworm species of man *Ancylostoma duodenale* and *Necator americanus*. For such diseases the rate of production of transmission stages, and any resistance of the host to further infection, both typically depend on the number of parasites present in a given host. Most importantly, helminths tend to be long-lived in their vertebrate hosts and do not usually induce lasting immunity to reinfection (Table 7.2).

Table 7.2. Life expectancies of various helminth parasites in man and the time taken to reach reproductive maturity.

Parasite	Life expectancy (years)	Development to maturity (days)
Ascaris lumbricoides	1–1½	60–70
Ancylostoma duodenale	1–1½	45–55
Necator americanus	3–5	28–49
Schistosoma mansoni	2–5	25–28

Vertebrates are able to mount immunological responses to helminth invasion but these often act to restrict rather than eliminate parasite establishment, reproduction, and survival within the host. As such, an immune category of hosts, totally protected from infection, rarely exists for helminth diseases. The important characteristic of host responses to helminth infections is the *density-dependent* manner in which they act. The proportional reduction in establishment, survival, and reproduction is greater in dense subpopulations of parasites than sparse ones (Fig. 7.17). These processes act as negative feedback mechanisms to constrain parasite population growth within individual hosts. Although immunological responses normally induce such effects, competition between parasites for finite resources, within or on the host, may also be important. This is particularly so within invertebrate intermediate hosts, where competition between larval parasites for limited space and food resources is often severe (e.g. the production of cercariae within the molluscan hosts of digeneans).

Negative feedback or density-dependent mechanisms also occur in segments of helminth life cycles not involving the vertebrate host. For example, the rate of parasite-induced intermediate host mortality is often proportional to the burden of parasites harboured, hosts with high worm burdens dying more rapidly than those with light burdens (Fig. 7.18). Host death invariably results in the death of the parasites contained within and hence such responses cause density-dependent parasite mortality. Density-dependent constraints also act on the rate of acquisition of parasites, particularly if the parasite gains entry to the host by ingestion, either as an infective stage, or within the body of an intermediate host. As we saw earlier, the rate of parasite acquisition in these cases is determined to a large extent by host feeding behaviour and is therefore much less dependent on the density of infective stages or infected intermediate hosts. Limitations on the rate at which hosts consume

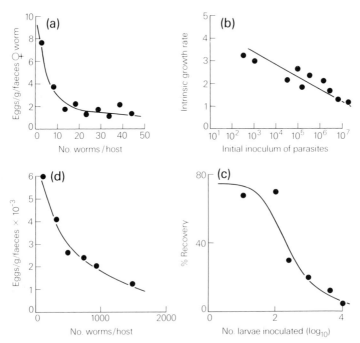

Fig. 7.17. Density-dependent survival and reproduction within parasite subpopulations. (a) Egg production by *Ascaris* in man. (After Croll, Anderson, Gyorkos & Ghadirian, 1982.) (b) The intrinsic population growth rate of *Trypanosoma musculi* in mice. (Brett, unpublished data.) (c) Egg production by *Ancyclostoma* in man. (After Hill, 1926.) (d) The survival of the hookworm *Ancyclostoma canium* in dogs. (After Krupp, 1961.)

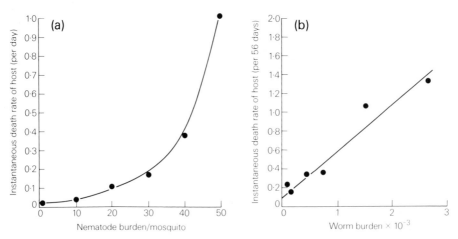

Fig. 7.18. The influence of parasite burden on host survival. (a) Mosquitos (*Aedes trivittatus*) and the nematode *Dirofilaria immitis*. (After Christensen, 1978.) (b) Sheep and *Fasciola hepatica*. (After Boray, 1969.)

food items, due to satiation and handling time, act to regulate the intake of parasites at high densities of infective stages (and infected intermediate hosts) (see Fig. 7.12).

Any given parasite life cycle may contain more than one density-dependent process, particularly if the life cycle involves two or more hosts. The human schistosomes are good examples: adult worm survival and egg production are influenced in a density-dependent manner in the human host and cercarial production in the mollusc is virtually independent of the number of miracidia that penetrate the snail.

Despite many such examples it is relevant to note that a single density-dependent process, in any segment of the parasite's life cycle, will act to restrict the population growth of all the various developmental stages throughout the entire cycle. A useful physical analogy is provided by water flow through a circular system made up of a series of interconnecting pipes of differing diameters. The rate of water flow through the entire system is determined by the segment of pipe with the narrowest diameter.

Regulation of parasite abundance by density-dependent processes within individual hosts acts to constrain the growth of the total parasite population within the community of hosts. The severity of such processes and the number that occur in the various segments of a parasite's life cycle determines the endemic level of helminth infection within the host population. This level is often measured by the average worm burden (average intensity) per host.

The average intensity, however, is a statistic of the frequency distribution of parasite numbers per host. The precise form of this distribution plays a major role in determining the net force of density-dependent regulation acting on the total parasite population. These distributions are invariably highly aggregated in form, where the majority of hosts harbour few parasites and a few hosts harbour most of the parasites. It is precisely in these few hosts that density-dependent effects will be most severe and they will thus influence the majority of the total parasite population. As the distribution of parasites becomes more aggregated, so the regulatory impact of density-dependent processes will be more pronounced.

In summary, macroparasite abundance is regulated by density-dependent processes acting on parasite subpopulations within individual hosts. The severity of these processes is a major determinant of the observed stability of many helminth infections (such as hookworms, roundworms and schistosomes) within human communities, even in the face of severe perturbations induced by climatic change or man's intervention. In contrast to many microparasites, since a truly immune category of hosts rarely exists, threshold densities of susceptibles, the degree of herd immunity, and the rate of input of susceptibles do not in general act to regulate the abundance of helminth and arthropod parasites.

7.6   POPULATION DYNAMICS

In the preceding section we considered the factors which exert a regulatory influence on the transmission of infection (or parasites) between hosts and the flow of parasites through their life cycles. These factors determine the ability of a parasite population to withstand perturbations and are particularly relevant to the interpretation of endemic patterns of disease. We now consider the broader question of how all the various rate-determining processes, which govern the population size of the many developmental stages involved in parasite life cycles, influence the overall population behaviour of a disease and its ability to perpetuate within the host population. These topics are considered in more detail by Anderson & May, 1979a and May & Anderson, 1979.

7.6.1   Transmission thresholds

The flow of parasites between hosts must exceed a certain overall rate if the infection is to perpetuate within the host population, in order to compensate for parasite losses throughout the life cycle. There exists a set of parasite transmission, reproduction, and mortality rates, below which the infection will die out, and above which it will perpetuate. This level is defined as the *transmission threshold* and its determination is of great importance to the design and implementation of disease control policies (see Macdonald, 1965 and Anderson, 1980).

The determination of this threshold and its biological interpretation are dependent on the basic unit of epidemiological study (i.e. either the infected host or the individual parasite).

7.6.2   Microparasites: direct transmission

In the case of microparasites, where the unit of study is the infected host, an infection will only perpetuate provided that one infected host, throughout its infectious lifespan, gives rise to at least one new infection when introduced into a population of susceptibles. The average *number* of new cases that arise from one infectious host, if introduced into a population of N susceptibles, is called the *basic reproductive rate* of an infection and is denoted by the symbol R. [Note that although called a rate, R is in fact a dimensionless quantity defined in terms of the generation time of an infection]. The *transmission threshold* is therefore given by the condition $R = 1$.

The determination of R in terms of the rate parameters which control disease transmission is straight forward. In the case of a directly transmitted viral infection such as measles (which induces lifelong immunity in recovered hosts) R is defined as

$$R = \beta N/(b+\gamma). \tag{18}$$

Here β is the disease transmission rate (see equation 1), N is the population density of susceptibles, $1/b$ is the life expectancy of the host and $1/\gamma$ is the average period during which an infected host is infectious (see equations 14–16). R is simply the transmission or reproductive potential of the infection (βN), times the expected lifespan of the infectious host $(1/(b+\gamma))$. The concept of a basic reproductive rate gives rise to the following important epidemiological principles.

1   The *actual* reproductive rate of a disease, $\hat{R}$, within a population of N hosts of which only a proportion q are susceptible, as opposed to its *basic* reproductive rate R (which measures its potential for reproduction or transmission in a population totally susceptible to infection), is

$$\hat{R} = Rq. \tag{19}$$

2   When the prevalence of infection $y(y = Y/N)$ remains fairly constant through time, the disease is at equilibrium within the host population and $\hat{R} = 1$.

3   The threshold host density, N_T, necessary for the successful introduction and initial spread of an infection (defined in equation 17) is related to the quantity $\hat{R}$, where in a population of N hosts,

$$\hat{R} = N/N_T. \tag{20}$$

4   The basic reproductive rate R is related to the average age at which hosts acquire infection, A, where

$$R = 1 + L/A, \tag{21}$$

and L is the life expectancy, $1/b$, of the host. This relationship often facilitates the estimation of R from epidemiological data. For example, in England and Wales during the period 1956–69, the average age at which children experienced an attack of measles varied between 4.5 and 6 years. With a human life expectancy of roughly 70 years equation (21) yields R estimates of between 16.5 and 12.7.

5   If a vaccine is available for disease control, the proportion of the population, p, that must be protected at any one time for disease eradication is simply

$$p > 1 - 1/R. \tag{23}$$

In the case of measles, this would require the vaccination of roughly 92–94% of children. The magnitude of this figure provides an explanation of why measles and similar viral diseases are still endemic in western Europe.

6   On a different scale, the proportion of susceptibles, s, left after an epidemic has passed through a small community, can be used to estimate R, since

$$R = [1/(1-s)][\ln(1/s)]. \tag{24}$$

Thus if an epidemic of (say) chickenpox in a school leaves 30% of the children susceptible after its termination, R is 1.7. In order to have prevented this epidemic, 41% of the children would have had to have been vaccinated (equation 23).

7   Increased levels of vaccination will lead to a rise in the average age at which individuals experience their first attack of infection. Where the proportion of the population vaccinated is p, the mean age at first attack A is

$$A = L/[R(1-p)-1],\tag{25}$$

where L is host life-expectancy.

8   Disease incubation periods, during which a host is infected but not infectious, will only significantly reduce the basic reproductive rate R if the incubation period is long with respect to host life-expectancy. If the incubation period is of length $1/v$, then equation (18) becomes

$$R = \beta N f/(b+\gamma),\tag{26}$$

where f is the fraction of infected hosts that survive to become infectious, namely $v/(b+v)$.

9   The value of R determines both the relationship between the age of the host and the proportion of individuals who have experienced infection (the proportion serologically positive), and the equilibrium prevalence of infection $y^\star$ within the population (Fig. 7.19). The relationship between $y^\star$ and R is given by

$$y^\star = [1-(1/R)][b/(b+\gamma)].\tag{27}$$

Highly infectious diseases (large β's) which persist in the host and give rise to long periods of infectiousness (small γ's), have high R values. Conversely, diseases of low infectivity with short periods of infectiousness have small R values.

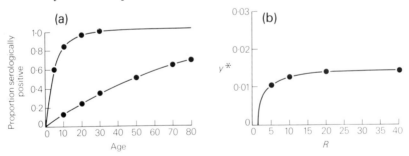

Fig. 7.19. (a) The relationship between the proportion of hosts serologically positive and the age of the host for various values of R (see text). (b) The relationship between the prevalence of infection and the basic reproductive rate R ($\gamma = 1$, $b = 0.014$). The level of the plateau is set by the duration of infectiousness ($1/\gamma$) and the life expectancy of the host ($1/b$) when the disease induces lifelong immunity.

7.6.3   Microparasites: vector-borne diseases

So far our attention has been restricted to directly transmitted microparasites. The concepts outlined above can be extended to encompass indirectly transmitted vector-borne diseases such as yellow fever and malaria. Without going into detail concerning derivations (see Anderson (1980c) for fuller discussion), and ignoring for the moment disease incubation periods, the basic reproductive rate of a vector-borne infection is

$$R = \frac{\bar{\beta}^2 N_2/N_1}{(b_1+\gamma_1)(b_2+\gamma_2)}. \tag{28}$$

Here $\bar{\beta}$ represents the effective man-biting rate of the vector (effective in the sense of the proportion of bites that lead to infection). This parameter is squared since the action of biting is responsible for transmission from man to vector and vector to man. N_1 and N_2 represent the densities of man and vector respectively, $1/b_1$ and $1/b_2$ denote the respective life expectancies of man and vector, while $1/\gamma_1$ and $1/\gamma_2$ represent the duration of infectiousness in man and vector. R is again defined by the net transmission success both from man to vector and back again ($\bar{\beta}^2 N_2/N_1$) times the product of the expected lifespans of infectious men and vectors ($1/(b_1+\gamma_1)$ and $1/(b_2+\gamma_2)$). If we explicitly take into account incubation periods in the vector and man, of length $1/v_2$ and $1/v_1$ respectively, then R becomes

$$R = \frac{\bar{\beta}^2 f_1 f_2 N_2/N_1}{(b_1+\gamma_1)(b_2+\gamma_2)}. \tag{29}$$

Here f_1 and f_2 represent the fraction of infected men and vectors that survive to become infectious (namely, $v_1/(b_1+v_1)$ and $v_2/(b_2+v_2)$). As noted earlier, the fraction f_2 may be small due to the short life expectancy of certain vectors and the comparatively long incubation periods of many viral and protozoan vector-borne diseases. In the human host, as in the case of directly transmitted infections such as measles, f_1 is normally close to unity in value.

Many of the epidemiological principles listed earlier for directly transmitted infections apply to vector-borne diseases. One important addition, however, concerns the threshold host density (or density of susceptibles) necessary for disease perpetuation. Note that this threshold condition now becomes

$$N_2/N_1 = (b_1+\gamma_1)(b_2+\gamma_2)/(\bar{\beta}^2 f_1 f_2). \tag{30}$$

In other words for the maintenance of a vector-borne parasite, the *ratio* of vectors to human hosts must exceed a critical level to maintain R greater than unity. This concept has been widely used in the design of control programmes for diseases such as malaria, where the aim of control has been to reduce vector density below this critical level (see Macdonald, 1957). The success or failure of such approaches, however depends on the level of accuracy achieved in estimating the many parameters which determine the value of R. Many problems surround the estimation of these parameters and, in addition, the biology of certain vector-borne diseases of man is poorly understood at present.

The epidemiology of human malaria, for example, has received considerable attention over the past three decades, but many issues concerning both its biology and the approach to be adopted for disease control remain unresolved at present. The rapidity with which the prevalence of infection rises in areas of stable endemic malaria within the younger age classes of children, and its decline thereafter (Fig. 7.1b) suggest (a) that the value of the basic reproductive rate R is very high in such areas, and (b) that the duration of acquired immunity to reinfection is relatively short. It is not clear as yet how immunity is related to the number of infections experienced by an individual. The marked decline in prevalence in the adult age classes (Fig. 7.1b) suggests the existence of a degree of herd immunity. The maintenance of this, however, is dependent on the frequency with which humans are exposed to infectious bites. Vector control programmes reduce the frequency with which an individual experiences infection, thus lowering the degree of herd immunity. As a direct consequence, the resurgence of malaria is often very severe when control ceases.

In certain areas, malaria appears to be much less stable as a consequence of low R values (caused by low vector densities; see Fig. 7.20) which fall below unity during certain periods of the year. In these areas the degree of herd immunity is comparatively low.

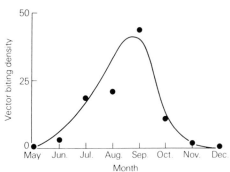

Fig. 7.20. Seasonal changes in the biting density of *Anopheles gambiae* in northern Nigeria. (After Garrett-Jones & Shidrawi, 1969.)

7.6.4   Macroparasites: direct transmission

The unit of epidemiological study for macroparasites is the individual parasite, and the definition of the basic reproductive rate outlined in the preceeding section therefore requires modification. Macroparasites will only survive from generation to generation provided that a reproductively mature female (or in the case of a hermaphroditic species, a mature parasite), on average, gives rise to sufficient offspring to at least replace herself in the next generation. The basic reproductive rate R now becomes the number of female offspring produced by an adult female worm throughout her reproductive lifespan, which survive to reach sexual maturity in a population of N uninfected hosts. The transmission threshold is again defined by the condition $R = 1$.

Ignoring for the moment, developmental delays, such as the time taken by a helminth to reach sexual maturity in the host, the basic reproductive rate of a directly transmitted hermaphroditic worm which is able to self-fertilize (e.g. the human tapeworm *Hymenolepis nana*) is

$$R = \hat{\beta} N \lambda / [(\mu_1 + b)(\mu_2 + \hat{\beta} N)] \tag{31}$$

In this expression, $\hat{\beta}$ is the transmission rate (see equations 4 and 5), λ is the rate of egg production per worm, while μ_1, b and μ_2 represent the death rates of the adult parasite, host and infective stage respectively. R is simply the net rate of reproduction of the parasite, $\hat{\beta} N \lambda$, (where the transmission component, $\hat{\beta} N$, is essentially a form of reproduction since it places the parasite in a location where it is able to reproduce), times the product of the expected lifespans of the adult parasite within the host, $1/(\mu_1 + b)$, (responsible for the production of transmission stages) and the infective stage outside the host, $1/(\mu_2 + \hat{\beta} N)$ (responsible for transmission between hosts). Viewed in another light, R is simply the reproductive contribution of the adult parasite, $\lambda/(\mu_1 + b)$, times the reproductive contribution of the infective stage, $\beta N/(\mu_2 + \hat{\beta} N)$. Note the basic similarity of equation (31) with that derived for microparasitic infections (equation 18). The differences which arise are a direct result of the basic unit chosen for the epidemiological study of the disease (either an infected host or an individual parasite).

Many of the epidemiological principles, outlined earlier for microparasites, apply equally to macroparasites. Some important differences occur, however, and these are as follows.

1   The *actual* reproductive rate of a parasite, $\hat{R}$, within a population which harbours a population of parasites, distributed between the individual hosts, will depend on the net force of density-dependent constraints on parasite reproduction and/or survival exerted by the established parasites. As mentioned previously, this net force will depend on the frequency distribution of parasite numbers per host.

2   If the mean parasite burden per host and the frequency distribution of parasites remain approximately constant through time, the parasite population is at equilibrium and $\hat{R} = 1$.

3   When significant developmental delays are present in the parasite's life cycle, either between the arrival of an infective stage in the host and its attainment of sexual maturity (see Table 7.2), or between the production of a transmission stage and its development to the infective state, R is reduced by a factor $f_1 f_2$, where f_1 is the proportion of worms that attain sexual maturity in the host and f_2 is the proportion of transmission stages that survive to become infective.

4   Many helminth parasites of man, such as hookworms and the schistosomes, have separate sexes. The production of transmission stages is therefore only achieved by female worms who have mated and R is reduced by a factor $r\phi$, where r is the proportion of female worms within a total parasite population (many helminths of

man appear to have sex ratios of approximately 1:1) and ϕ is the probability that a mature female worm is mated. The mating probability is dependent on a variety of factors, in particular whether the parasite is monogamous or polygamous (hookworms are thought to be polygamous while schistosomes appear to be monogamous), and the frequency distribution of parasite numbers per host (Fig. 7.21). The mating probability is of some significance to the dynamics of helminth infections and will be discussed further in connection with breakpoints in disease transmission.

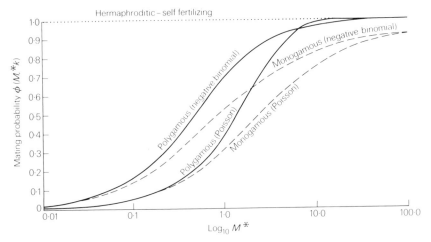

Fig. 7.21. The relationship between the probability that a female worm is mated (ϕ) and the mean parasite burden per host ($M^\star$) for various sexual habits and distributed patterns of worm numbers per host (Poisson and negative binomial with parameter $k = 0.34$). (After May, 1977.)

5   The mean worm burden per host (the intensity of infection) is linearly related to the value of R, while the prevalence of infection is determined by the mean and the frequency distribution of parasite numbers per host (Fig. 7.22). High mean burdens (resulting from high R values) may result in low prevalences if the distribution of parasites is highly aggregated within the host population (see Figs. 7.22 and 7.23). The negative binomial probability distribution is a good empirical model of aggregated distributions of parasite numbers per host (Fig. 7.4), and a rough guide to the degree of worm clumping within the host population may be obtained from the following equation

$$p = 1 - [k/(k+M)]^k. \tag{32}$$

This expression equates the mean parasite burden per host, M, and the prevalence of infection, p, with the parameter k of the negative binomial model which varies inversely with the degree of parasite aggregation (values of k in excess of 10 imply

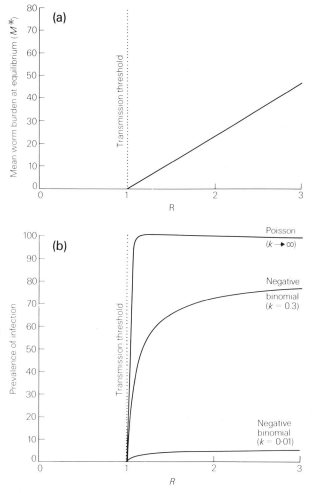

Fig. 7.22. (a) The relationship between R and the mean parasite burden per host at equilibrium ($M^\star$). (b) The relationship between the equilibrium prevalence of infection and R for various distribution patterns of worm numbers per host (Poisson $k \to \infty$, negative binomial $k = 0.34$, negative binomial $k = 0.01$).

that the worms are effectively randomly distributed within the host population; values close to zero imply a high degree of aggregation, with the majority of parasites being haboured by a few hosts). The degree of clumping often varies in different age-classes of hosts, due to variability in their susceptibility to infection (usually caused by differences in host behaviour within the various age-classes of the host population). Fig. 7.23 records estimates of k for the hookworm *Necator americanus* and the round worm *Ascaris lumbricoides* in different age-classes of two human populations.

6   The value of R determines the shape of age-prevalence and age-intensity curves, high values resulting in a rapid increase in these two epidemiological measures as host age increases. The intensity of infection of many direct life cycle helminths appears to reach a plateau or equilibrium level as host age increases (Fig. 7.1). The

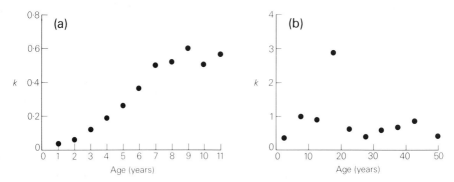

Fig. 7.23. The degree of parasite aggregation, measured inversely by the negative binomial parameter k, and host age. (a) *Necator* infections in an Indian community. (After Anderson, 1980a.) (b) *Ascaris* infections in Iran. (After Croll, Anderson, Gyorkos & Ghadirian, 1982.)

mean worm burden at this plateau, $M^\star$, is determined by the value of R and the force of density-dependent constraints on the survival and reproduction of parasite subpopulations within individual hosts. The relationship between these parameters for cases where density-dependence acts principally on parasite survival within the host is approximately given by

$$M^\star = (R - 1)/(ld). \tag{33}$$

Here l denotes the expected lifespan of the adult parasites within the host (in the absence of density-dependent mortality), while d measures the severity of density-dependent constraints on worm survival. The value of d is related to the degree of worm clumping within the host population (see Anderson, 1980a).

7 Control measures (see Chapter 8), such as chemotherapy, increase the mortality rate of the adult parasites (the term μ_1 in equation 31), and therefore reduce the average worm burden by their action in reducing the value of R (see equation 33). If chemotherapy ceases, the value of R is inversely related to the time taken by the parasite population to return to its precontrol level. Fig. 7.24 for example, portrays the rapid rise in the prevalence of *Ascaris* infections in a human community to its precontrol level, subsequent to the cessation of control. The time taken to return to the precontrol level is roughly one year, reflecting the high basic reproductive rate of infection in this community. Infections of this kind, which include human hookworms, will always be difficult to control by chemotherapy unless such measures are applied extensively within the population over many years. The precise number of years over which control must be applied should be in excess of the maximum lifespan of the longest lived stage in the parasite's life cycle (i.e. the adult worm in the case of the human hookworms and the egg in the case of *Ascaris*). The mean worm burden per host may be rapidly reduced by selectively treating the most heavily infected individuals (identified by means of faecal egg counts). High R values

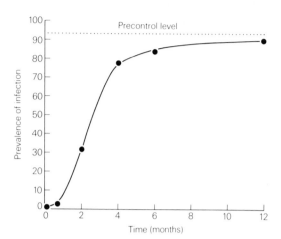

Fig. 7.24. The rise in the prevalence of infection of *Ascaris* after the cessation of chemotherapy in a human community in Iran. (After Arfaa & Ghadirian, 1977.)

and tight regulatory constraints on worm populations growth, however, generate a high degree of population resilience to perturbation. The cessation of chemotherapy will, therefore, invariably result in the parasite population returning to its precontrol level.

8   The critical threshold density of uninfected hosts N_T, for the initial establishment and spread of directly transmitted helminths, may be derived from equation (31), where

$$N_T = (\mu_1 + b)\mu_2/[\hat{\beta}(\lambda - \mu_2 - b)]. \tag{34}$$

For most directly transmitted helminths, the density of hosts is *not* a limiting factor in parasite transmission, due to the enormous reproductive capabilities of these parasites (λ is very large). The female of the human hookworm *Necator*, for example,

Table 7.3. Population parameter values for the human hookworm *Necator americanus* (Anderson, 1980a).

Parameter	Value
Human life expectancy ($1/b$)	50–70 years
Mature worm life expectancy ($1/\mu$)	3–4 years
Adult worm prepatent period	28–49 days
Proportion of L_3 larvae which gain entry to the host that survive to reach maturity	<0.1
Rate of egg production/female worm	15000/day
Average male to female sex ratio	1:1
Maturation time from release of egg to the development of the L_3 larvae	5+ days
Life expectancy of L_3 larvae	5+ days
The degree of worm aggregation within the host population (measured inversely by the negative binomial parameter k)	0.01–0.6

produces approximately 15 000 eggs/worm/day, while that of *Ascaris* is capable of producing in excess of 200 000 eggs/worm/day. These two helminths occur endemically in low density human communities.

9   Many rate parameters act to determine the value of R. The estimation of some of these is straightforward but certain parameters such as the rate of infection, $\hat{\beta}$, are more difficult to determine. Age-prevalence and age-intensity data, both from longitudinal and horizontal studies, often provide a basis for the determination of transmission or infection rates. Table 7.3, provides a rough guide to the parameters which determine the value of R for the human hookworm *Necator*.

7.6.5   Macroparasites: indirect transmission

Many helminths of importance to man have indirect life cycles involving two or more hosts. The principles outlined above for directly transmitted helminths apply equally to those with indirect transmission. Additional complexities arise, however, and some of these are well illustrated by reference to the epidemiology of human schistosomiasis caused by *Schistosoma mansoni*, *S. japonicum* and *S. haematobium* (see Chapter 2). These have two host life cycles, various species of snails acting as intermediate hosts. Transmission between man and snail, and snail and man, is achieved by means of two free-living aquatic larvae—the miracidium and cercaria, respectively. Both larvae gain entry to their respective hosts by direct penetration. The parasites have a phase of sexual transmission reproduction in man and one of asexual direct reproduction in the snail. In contrast to earlier examples the basic unit of epidemiological study differs in the two segments of the life cycle. The parasite acts as the unit in man, while, because of the phase of direct asexual reproduction, the infected host is the unit of study for the segment involving the snail.

Ignoring for the moment the problem of worm pairing, the basic reproductive rate R of a parasite with this type of indirect cycle is

$$R = \frac{\lambda_1 \lambda_2 \hat{\beta}_1 \hat{\beta}_2 N_1 N_2}{(\mu_1 + b_1)(\mu_2 + \hat{\beta}_2 N_2)(b_2)(\mu_3 + \hat{\beta}_1 N_1)}. \tag{35}$$

Although involving a large number of parameters (determined by the number of distinct developmental stages in the parasite's life cycle), this rather fearful expression has a very simple interpretation which is directly comparable to those discussed earlier for other types of disease agent. The parameters λ_1 and λ_2 represent the rate of egg production per female adult worm and the rate of cercarial production per infected snail; N_1 and N_2 denote human and snail density, while $\hat{\beta}_1$ and $\hat{\beta}_2$ represent the transmission rates from cercariae to man and from miracidia to snail respectively (see Fig. 7.7c). The rates b_1, b_2, μ_1, μ_2 and μ_3 represent mortality rates of human hosts, infected snails, adult worms, miracidia and cercariae, respectively.

R may therefore be interpreted as the product of the net rates of reproduction in man $(\lambda_1 \hat{\beta}_1 N_1)$ and the snail $(\lambda_2 \hat{\beta}_2 N_2)$, times the product of the expected lifespans of the parasite $(1/(b_1 + \mu_1))$, the miracidium $(1/(\mu_2 + \hat{\beta}_2 N_2))$, the infected snail $(1/b_2)$ and the cercaria $(1/(\mu_3 + \hat{\beta}_1 N_1))$. Viewed in another light we may express this statement as

> $R =$ The total number of eggs produced per female worm $(\lambda_1/(\mu_1 + b_1)) \times$ the proportion of those eggs that produced miracidia which infect a susceptible snail $(\hat{\beta}_2 N_2/(\mu_2 + \hat{\beta} N_2)) \times$ the total number of cercariae produced by an infected snail $(\lambda_2/b_2) \times$ the proportion of those cercariae which establish as adult worms $(\hat{\beta}_1 N_1/(\mu_3 + \hat{\beta}_1 N_1))$.

The influence of R on the prevalence and intensity of infection, within both the snail and human populations, is identical to that discussed in connection with directly transmitted helminths. Additional points of epidemiological significance are as follows.

1   In the case of human schistosomes only a proportion, v, of the eggs produced will gain exit from the host and enter a habitat in which they are able to hatch to produce miracidia. R is therefore reduced by a fraction v. Similarly, developmental delays occur as a consequence of both the maturation of the parasites in the human host prior to egg production (roughly 25–28 days for *S. mansoni*) and the development of the parasite in the snail before cercarial release (roughly 28–30 days for *S. mansoni* in *Biomphalaria glabrata*). These developmental delays are termed *prepatent, incubation* or *latent* periods. The expression for R is therefore multiplied by a term $f_1 f_2$, where f_1 represents the fraction of parasites that penetrate the human host which survive to reach sexual maturity, and f_2 denotes the fraction of infected snails which survive the prepatent period to release cercariae. The fraction f_2 is often small since the snail host has a short lifespan (roughly of the order of 14–54 days) in relation to the prepatent period within the mollusc. Note the similarities of these patterns with arthropod transmitted viral and protozoan diseases such as malaria and yellow fever (see 7.4.4).

2   Schistosomes are dioecious and are thought to pair for life (monogamy). The uncertainties associated with worm pairing act to reduce the value of R in the manner described for directly transmitted helminths.

3   The threshold host density necessary for the spread of infection is now determined by the product $N_1 N_2$, of the human and snail densities (equation 34). The product term, in contrast to the ratio N_2/N_1 for vector-borne infections, arises as a consequence of the fact that transmission between both man and snail, and snail and man is achieved by means of free-living infective stages. Host densities are thought to be a limiting factor in the transmission of schistosome parasites; snail densities often dropping to very low levels during certain seasons of the year (see Anderson & May, 1979b). The comparatively long lifespan of the parasites in man, however, to some extent offsets these seasonal fluctuations. Molluscicides are widely used for the control of schistosomiasis, the aim being to reduce snail density such

that the product N_1N_2 drops below the level required to maintain R above the transmission threshold ($R = 1$). A major problem in this approach, however, is the enormous reproductive capabilities of the snail which enables it to rapidly recolonize aquatic habitats once molluscicide treatment ceases (see Chapter 8).

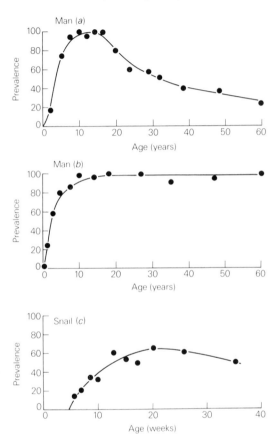

Fig. 7.25. The prevalence of schistosome infections in different age-classes of human (a) and (b), and snail (c) populations. (a) *Schistosoma haematobium* in Gambia. (After Wilkins, 1977.) (b) *Schistosoma mansoni* in Uganda. (After Ongom & Bradley, 1972.) (c) *S. haematobium* in *Bulinus nasutus productus* in West Aftica. (After Sturrock & Webbe, 1971.)

4   The prevalence of schistosome infection in endemic areas, within both the human and snail populations, has a tendency to decline (although not always; Fig. 7.25b) in older age-classes of hosts (Fig. 7.25a). It is unclear at present whether the decline within the human population is due to an increasing degree of acquired immunity (the phenomenon of concomitant immunity) or to age-related changes in host behaviour (older people having less frequent contact with water contaminated with cercariae). The latter factor is probably the more important. The decline in prevalence in older age-classes of snails may be due to either a decrease in susceptibility to infection (Fig. 7.25c) or to age-related changes in the mortality rate of snails, perhaps induced by varying degrees of parasite pathogenicity within the

different snail age-classes. Schistosome parasites are highly pathogenic to their molluscan hosts, decreasing snail reproduction and survival (Fig. 7.26b and c).

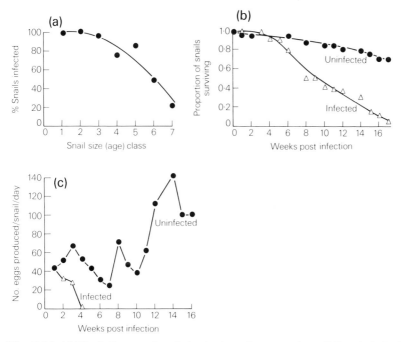

Fig. 7.26. (a) The influence of snail size (age) on the proportion of *Biomphalaria* that become infected by *Schistosoma mansoni* when exposed to a constant number of miracidia (Anderson, Mercer, Wilson & Carter, 1982) (size class 1 = diameter of 2–4 mm; size class 7 = diameter of 14–16 mm). (b) The influence of *S. mansoni* on the survival of *Biomphalaria*. (After Pan, 1965.) (c) The influence of *S. mansoni* on the rate of egg production by *Biomphalaria*. (After Pan, 1965.)

5   The numerical value of the basic reproductive rate R in any given area of endemic schistosomiasis, is clearly dependent on the many rate determining processes which govern the population sizes of the numerous developmental stages in the life cycles (equation 34). Certain of these rates are relatively easy to measure but others are more difficult, particularly the lifespan of the adult worms in man (μ_1) and the two transmission parameters $\hat{\beta}_1$ and $\hat{\beta}_2$. Transmission rates may, under certain circumstances, be estimated from age-prevalence data (see Muench, 1959).

7.6.6   Breakpoints in parasite transmission

The problems associated with finding a partner to mate with create additional complexities in the population dynamics of many helminth parasites.

This is particularly true for dioecious species such as hookworms and schistosomes, but is also important for hermaphroditic species which are unable to self-fertilize.

When cross-fertilization is necessary, the fall of the mean parasite burden per host below a critical level results in mating becoming too infrequent to maintain sufficient production of parasite transmission stages for the perpetuation of the infection. This critical worm burden therefore defines a *breakpoint* in parasite transmission which is *distinct* from the transmission *threshold* ($R = 1$) discussed earlier (see Macdonald, 1965).

The precise level of this breakpoint is set by a variety of factors; in particular, the sexual habits of the parasite (whether the parasite is monogamous or polygamous, or whether an adult female worm requires mating more than once to maintain egg production throughout her lifespan) and the frequency distribution of parasite numbers per host.

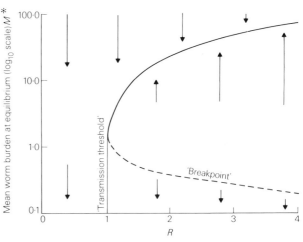

Fig. 7.27. The relationship between the equilibrium worm burden and R for a dioecious helminth. The graph illustrates the concepts of a transmission threshold ($R = 1$) and a breakpoint by reference to the population biology of the human hookworm *Necator*. (After Anderson, 1980a.)

The breakpoint and transmission threshold concepts are illustrated graphically in Fig. 7.27 by reference to the population biology of the human hookworm *Necator*. This species is polygamous and is invariably highly aggregated in its distribution within the host population (see Fig. 7.23). Below the point $R = 1$, the infection cannot maintain itself. Above this level, however, three equilibrium states exist: two are stable reflecting endemic disease (the solid line) and parasite extinction (the horizontal axis of the graph), while the third is the breakpoint which is unstable (the dotted line). If the worm burden falls below this point the parasite will become extinct, while above it the parasite population settles to the stable endemic disease level. This concept has obvious significance to parasite control and leads to the suggestion that the depression of helminth abundance below the breakpoint (say, by chemotherapy) would result in parasite eradication (see Macdonald, 1965). Un-

Fig. 7.28. The relationship between the equilibrium mean parasite burden and a transmission coefficient T which depicts the rate of transmission from man to snail $[\{\lambda_1 \hat{\beta}_2 N_2\}/\{(\mu_1 + b_1)(\mu_2 + \hat{\beta}_2 N_2)\}$ in eq. 34] for varying degrees of worm aggregation within the human population. The graph illustrates the breakpoint concept (dashed lines) by reference to schistosome infections in man (May, 1977). a, Random; b–d, Negative binomial with k values: b, 1; c, 0.2; d, 0.05.

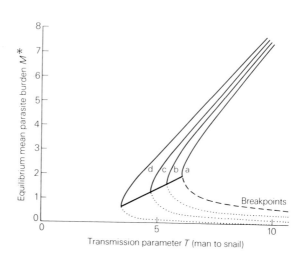

fortunately, however, recent studies indicate that the location of the breakpoint is critically dependent on the degree of worm clumping within the host population (Fig. 7.28). Highly aggregated parasite distributions, which are the rule for helminth infections (see Fig. 7.4), result in the breakpoint lying very close to zero worms per host (for example in Fig. 7.27 an R value of 3.0 gives a breakpoint of 0.3 worms per host). The intuitive explanation of this observation is that highly clumped worm distributions increase the frequency with which adult parasites encounter each other. The breakpoint concept is thus unfortunately of limited practical significance to disease control. This subject is discussed further by May, 1977 and Anderson, 1980a.

7.7   CLIMATIC FACTORS

Climatic changes have an important influence on the epidemiology of most infectious diseases of man. Environmental factor such as temperature and rainfall vary seasonally in the majority of habitats, tending to induce regular cyclic fluctuations in the prevalence and intensity of parasitic infection. The action of climate on host and parasite, however, is independent of population abundance. Thus although it may be the cause of conspicuous changes in density, its action is nonregulatory in nature. Climatic parameters are therefore referred to as *density-independent* factors.

Climatic factors influence the population biology of human disease agents in the following principal ways.

●*Host behaviour.* Seasonal changes in host behaviour, induced by the prevailing climatic conditions, often generate cyclic fluctuations in disease incidence. Such changes may be the result of differing work patterns associated with agricultural practices (the planting and harvesting of crops at different times of the year), or may result from social patterns influencing the behaviour of children (the vacation periods and school terms in Western societies). Agricultural practices are important to the transmission of helminth infections such as *Ascaris* and schistosomiasis, while the behaviour of children influences the epidemiology of many directly transmitted viral infections such as measles, mumps and chickenpox.

● *Intermediate host abundance.* Seasonal changes in the prevalence of many indirectly transmitted parasites are in part determined by the influence of climatic factors on the abundance of intermediate host populations. Seasonal fluctuations in the transmission of malaria and schistosomiasis, for example, are to a large extent the result of changes in the abundance of mosquitos and snails respectively (see Fig. 7.20, Anderson, 1980c and Anderson & May, 1979b).

● *Infective stage longevity.* Climate has an important influence on the longevity of parasite transmission stages such as helminth eggs and larvae, the cysts of protozoa and free viral particles. Temperature, for example, is a major determinant of the survival of the miracidia and cercariae of schistosome flukes and the L_3 infective larvae of hookworms (Fig. 7.29a). The longevity of transmission stages which live in

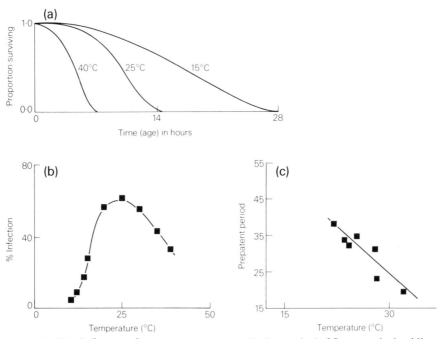

Fig. 7.29. The influence of water temperature on (a) the survival of *S. mansoni* miracidia (Anderson, Mercer, Wilson & Carter, 1982); (b) the infectivity of *S. mansoni* miracidia to *Biomphalaria* (Chu *et al.*, 1966); and (c) the prepatent period prior to cercarial release of *S. mansoni* in *Biomphalaria*. (After Anderson & May, 1979b.)

terrestrial habitats, such as the eggs of *Ascaris* and larvae of hookworms are also markedly influenced by soil moisture content.

•*Infectivity.* In addition to their influence on infective-stage longevity, factors such as temperature and humidity have an impact on the infectivity of both transmission stages and infectious intermediate hosts. Temperature, for instance, controls the activity of schistosome miracidia and thus influences their ability to contact and penetrate the molluscan host (Fig. 7.29b). In addition, this factor also affects the rate at which infected snails produce cercariae.

Climate may play a role in determining the activity and infectiousness of arthropod vectors. Christensen (1978), for example, demonstrated that the optimum air temperature for the transmission of a filarial worm *(Dirofilaria immitis)* from dog to mosquito *(Aedes trivittatus)* was roughly 23°C; the biting efficiency of the vector decreased at lower or higher temperatures (Fig. 7.30).

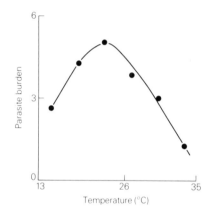

Fig. 7.30. The influence of air temperature on the rate of acquisition of larvae of the nematode *Dirofilaria immitis* by the mosquito *Aedes trivattatus* feeding on infected dogs. (After Christensen, 1978.)

•*Parasite development.* Temperature is an important determinant of the rate of parasite development either in the external habitat or within poikilothermic intermediate hosts such as snails or mosquitoes. The rate of development of human hookworms, from egg to infective larvae is most rapid at around 25–30°C in moist conditions (roughly 5 days). If temperatures are below 17–20°C, the ova and larvae of *Necator* cease development and death rapidly follows. *Ancylostoma* is able to develop at slightly lower temperatures than *Necator* and is thus found in certain temperate regions of the world.

Temperature also has a marked influence on the prepatent or incubation period of malaria in the mosquito vector and schistosome parasites in the molluscan host (Fig. 7.29c). The action of climatic factors on the rate of parasite development is a major determinant of the geographical distribution of many human diseases.

The influence of climate, whether acting on one or more of the parameters discussed above, is to alter a parasite's transmission success. If climatic change reduces the basic reproductive rate (R) it will result in a reduction in the prevalence of infection. Conversely, if it induces an increase in the value of R, disease prevalence will rise. Such changes often occur on a regular seasonal basis and sometimes result in the value of R falling below the tranmission threshold ($R = 1$) during certain periods of the year (Fig. 7.31). In these instances the parasite will only perpetuate within the host population, on a year to year basis, provided that the period during which R is less than unity, is shorter than the maximum lifespan of the longest lived developmental stage in the disease agent's life cycle. The human hookworm, *Necator*, for example, has an expected lifespan in man of approximately 3½ years and a maximum lifespan in excess of 5 years. For this parasite, therefore, seasonal changes in transmission success which result in R falling below unity during hot dry seasons are of little consequence to the long term stability of the infection. They do, however, induce observable seasonal fluctuations in the prevalence and intensity of infection.

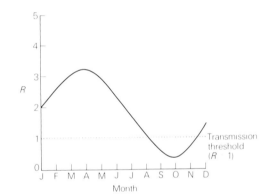

Fig. 7.31. A diagrammatic representation of seasonal changes in R, where the value of this parameter falls below unity at certain times of the year.

In contrast, the longest-lived stage in the life cycle of the measles virus is in an infectious host which remains infective for approximately 5–7 days. Seasonal changes in host behaviour which result in R falling below unity for long periods of time do not allow this disease to persist endemically. Such patterns are frequently observed on islands which support small human communities (see Black, 1966).

The important conclusions to be drawn from the above examples are twofold. First, dramatic seasonal changes in climate will result in conspicuous fluctuations in disease prevalence. These will be most marked if R falls below unity during certain periods of the year and when the longest lived stage in the parasites life cycle has a life span of less than one year. Secondly, and most importantly, disease control measures will be most successful if applied intensively during the periods of the year when the value of R is at a minimum.

7.8   THE EPIDEMIOLOGICAL SIGNIFICANCE OF THE BASIC REPRODUCTIVE RATE *R*

The concept of a basic reproductive rate and its measurement are of central importance to the epidemiological study and control of infectious disease agents. The magnitude of *R* determines the ability of a parasite to perpetuate itself within the host population and, in conjunction with the density-dependent processes which act to regulate the spread of infection, determines the abundance and prevalence of infection. For any given parasitic species, *R* will vary from one geographical location to the next as a consequence of climatic factors and the prevailing sociological conditions within the human population.

The value of the basic reproductive rate directly reflects the degree of difficulty that will be encountered in attempts to control the spread of infection. Other things being equal, parasites with high *R* values will be much more difficult to control than those with low values. If disease control ceases before eradication is achieved, the time taken for the infection to return to its precontrol level is inversely related to the magnitude of *R*.

The measurement of *R* and the determination of the action of control measures on reproductive success are essential for the quantitative assessment of the impact of control policies on the abundance and prevalence of infection (see equation 23). Many rate parameters, such as parasite reproduction, survival and infection rates, determine the value of *R*. The development of methods to estimate these parameters from horizontal and longitudinal studies of disease prevalence and intensity is an important research priority in the epidemiological study of infectious diseases.

REFERENCES AND FURTHER READING

Anderson R.M. (1980a) The dynamics and control of direct life cycle helminth parasites. *Lecture Notes in Biomathematics*, vol.39, pp. 278–322. Berlin: Springer-Verlag.

Anderson R.M. (1980b) The control of infectious disease agents: strategic models. In G.R. Conway (ed.) *Pest and Pathogen Control: Strategy, Tactics and Policy Models*, London, John Wiley & Sons.

Anderson R.M. (1980c) The population dynamics of indirectly transmitted diseases: the vector component. In R. Harwood and C. Koehler (eds) *Comparative Aspects of Animal and Plant Pathogen Vectors*, pp. 13–43. New York, Praeger.

Anderson R.M. & May R.M. (1978) Regulation and stability of host-parasite population interactions: I Regulatory processes. *J. Anim. Ecol.* **47**, 219–47.

Anderson R.M. & May R.M. (1979a) Population biology of infectious diseases. Part I. *Nature* **280**, 361–7.

Anderson R.M. & May R.M. (1979b) Prevalence of schistosome infections within molluscan populations: observed patterns and theoretical predictions. *Parasitology* **79**, 63–94.

Anderson R.M. & May R.M. (1982) The epidemiology of directly transmitted infectious diseases: control by vaccination. *Science* **215**, 1053–60.

Anderson R.M., Mercer J.G., Wilson R.A. & Carter N.P. (1982) Transmission of *Schistosoma mansoni* from man to snail: experimental studies of miracidial survival and infectivity in relation to larval age, water temperature, host size and host age. *Parasitology* (in press).

Anderson R.M., Whitfield P.J. & Dobson A.P. (1978) Experimental studies on infection dynamics: infection of the definitive host by the cercariae of *Transversotrema patialense*. *Parasitology* **77**, 189–200.

Arfaa F. & Ghadirian E. (1977) Epidemology and mass-treatment of ascariasis in six rural communities in Central Iran. *Am. J. trop. Med. Hyg.* **26**, 866–71.

Black F.L. (1966) Measles endemicity in insular populations: critical community size and its evolutionary implications. *J. Theor. Biol.* **11**, 207–11.

Boray J.C. (1969) Experimental fascioliasis in Australia. In B. Dawes (ed.) *Advances in parasitology*, vol.7, pp. 85–210. London, Academic Press.

Bray R.S. & Harris W.G. (1977) The epidemiology of infection with *Entamoeba histolytica* in Gambia, West Africa. *Trans. R. Soc. trop. Med. Hyg.* **71**, 401–7.

Buxton P.A. (1940) Studies on populations of head-lice (*Pediculus humanus capitis*: Anoplura). III. Material from South India. *Parasitology* **32**, 296–302.

Carter N., Anderson R.M. & Wilson R.A. (1982) Transmission of *Schistosoma mansoni* from man to snail; laboratory studies of the influence of snail and miracidial densities on transmission success. *Parasitology* (in press).

Christensen B.M. (1978) *Dirofilaria immitis*: Effects on the longevity of *Aedes trivittatus*. *Expl. Parasit.* **44**, 116–23.

Christensen B.M. & Hollander A.L. (1978) Effect of temperature on vector-parasite relationships of *Aedes trivittatus* and *Dirofilaria immitis*. *Proc. helminth Soc. Wash.* **45**, 115–19.

Chu K.Y., Massoud J. & Sabbaghian H.C. (1966) Host-parasite relationship of *Bulinus truncatus* and *Schistosoma haematobium* in Iran. 3. Effect of water temperature on the ability of miracidia to infect snails. *Bull. Wld. Hlth. Org.* **34**, 131–3.

Crofton H.D. (1971) A quantitative approach to parasitism. *Parasitology* **62**, 179–93.

Croll N.A., Anderson R.M., Gyorkos T.W. & Ghadirian E. (1982) The population biology and control of *Ascaris lumbricoides* in a rural community in Iran. *Trans. R. Soc. trop. Med. Hyg.* **76**, 187–97.

Dietz K. (1976) The incidence of infectious diseases under the influence of seasonal fluctuations. In J. Berger, W. Bühler, R. Repeges & P. Tautu, (eds.) Mathematical Models in Medicine *Lecture Notes in Biomathematics*, **11**, pp. 1–5. Berlin, Springer-Verlag.

Fleming A.F., Storey J., Molineaux L., Iroko E.A. & Attai E.D.E. (1979) Abnormal hemoglobins in the Sudan savanna of Nigeria. I. Prevalence of haemoglobins and relationships between sickle cell trait, malaria and survival. *Ann. trop. Med. Parasit.* **73**, 161–72.

Garrett-Jones C. & Shidrawi G.R. (1969) Malaria vectorial capacity of a population of *Anopheles gambiae*. *Bull. Wld Hlth Org.* **40**, 531–45.

Griffiths D.A. (1974) A catalytic model of infection for measles. *Appl. Statist.* **23**, 330–9.

Grove D.I. & Warren K.S. (1976). Relation of intensity of infection to disease in hamsters with acute schistosomiasis mansoni. *Am. J. trop. Med. Hyg.* **25**, 608–12.

Hill R.B. (1926) The estimation of the number of hookworms harboured by the use of the dilution egg count method. *Am. J. Hyg.* **6**, (Suppl.), 19–41.

Keymer A.E. & Anderson R.M. (1979) The dynamics of infection of *Tribolium confusum* by *Hymenolepis diminuta*: the influence of infective stage density and spatial distribution. *Parasitology* **79**, 195–207.

Krupp I.M. (1961) Effects of crowding and of superinfection on habitat selection and egg production in *Ancylostoma caninum*. *J. Parasit.* **47**, 957–61.

Lie K.J., Heyneman D. & Kostanian N. (1975) Failure of *Echinostoma linfoense* to reinfect snails already harbouring that species. *Int. J. Parasit.* **5**, 483–6.

Macdonald G. (1957) *The Epidemiology and Control of Malaria*, Oxford, Oxford University Press.

Macdonald G. (1965) The dynamics of helminth infections, with special reference to schistosomes. *Trans. R. Soc. trop. Med. Hyg.* **59**, 489–506.

May R.M. (1977) Togetherness among schistosomes: its effects on the dynamics of infection. *Math. Biosci.* **35**, 301–43.

May R.M. & Anderson R.M. (1979) Population biology of infectious diseases. Part II. *Nature* **280**, 455–61.

Muench H. (1959) *Catalytic Models in Epidemiology*. Harvard, Harvard University Press.

Muller R. (1977) *Worms and Disease: A Manual of Medical Helminthology*. London, Butler and Tanner.

Nawalinski T., Schad G.A. & Chowdbury A.B. (1978) Population biology of hookworms in children in rural west Bengal. I. General parasitological observations. *Am. J. trop. Med. Hyg.* **27**, 1152–61.

Ongom V.L. & Bradley D.J. (1972) The epidemiology and consequences of *Schistosoma mansoni* infection in West Nile, Uganda. I. Field studies of a community of Panyagoro. *Trans. R. Soc. trop. Med. Hyg.* **66**, 835–51.

Pan C-T. (1965) Studies on the host-parasite relationship between *Schistosoma mansoni* and the snail *Australorbis glabratus*. *Am. J. trop. Med. Hyg.* **14**, 931–76.

Pennycuik L. (1971) Frequency distributions of parasites in a population of three-spined sticklebacks, *Gasterosteus aculeatus* L. with particular reference to the negative binomial distribution. *Parasitology* **63**, 389–406.

Peters W. (1978) Medical Aspects: Comments and discussion. II. In A.E.R. Taylor & R. Muller (eds.) *The Relevance of Parasitology to Human Welfare Today* pp. 25–40. Oxford, Blackwell Scientific Publications.

Riordan K. (1977) Long-term variations in trypanosome infection rates in highly infected tsetse flies on a cattle route in south-western Nigeria. *Ann. trop. Med. Parasit.* **71**, 11–20.

Rosenfield P.L., Smith R.A. & Wolman M.G. (1977) Development and verification of a schistosomiasis transmission model. *Am. J. trop. Med. Hyg.* **26**, 505–16.

Schmid W.D. & Robinson E.J. (1972) The pattern of a host-parasite distribution. *J. Parasit.* **58**, 907–10.

Stiven A.E. (1964) Experimental studies on the epidemiology of the host-parasite system. *Hydra* and *Hydramaeba hydroxena* (Entz). II The components of a simple epidemic. *Ecol. Monogr.* **34**, 119–42.

Sturrock R.F. & Webbe G. (1971) The application of catalytic models to schistosomiasis in snails. *J. Helminth.* **45**, 189–200.

Warren K.S. (1973) Regulation of the prevalence and intensity of schistosomiasis in man: immunology or ecology? *J. Infect. Dis.* **127**, 595–609.

Watkins C.V. & Harvey L.A. (1942) On the parasites of silver foxes on some farms in the South West. *Parasitology* **34**, 155–79.

Wilkins H.A. (1977) *Schistosoma haematobium* in a Gambian community. I The intensity and prevalence of infection. *Ann. trop. Med. Parasit.* **71**, 53–8.

Williams C.B. (1944) Some applications of the logarithmic series and the index of diversity to ecological problems. *J. Ecol.* **32**, 1–44.

Yorke J.A. & London W.P. (1973) Recurrent outbreaks of measles, chickenpox and mumps. II. Systematic differences in contact rates and stochastic effects. *Am. J. Epidemiol.* **98**, 469–82.

Chapter 8
Control
G.A. Schad

8.1   INTRODUCTION

Eradication of parasites has been the goal of various local, national and international programmes which promised relief from parasitic disease for infected populations of man and/or animals. Rarely, however, was this attained; for most parasites, the goal was unrealistic. Control, as distinct from eradication, accepts certain levels of parasitism as *tolerable* and is therefore more likely to be achieved.

This chapter discusses control of parasites in populations rather than in individuals since the latter is considered in textbooks of medical and veterinary parasitology. The level of control considered satisfactory will differ according to the species of host and its value to society, the pathogenicity of the parasite, and the danger that infected carriers represent as sources for new outbreaks of disease. Control of parasites in food animals usually aims at reducing parasitism to a level having no effect on productivity, provided that this is economically feasible. In companion and sporting animals, even when such animals are reared commercially, economic factors may not be the only considerations. Rather, humanitarian and aesthetic considerations often influence the degree of control desired, driving this toward eradication. The latter becomes increasingly possible for small groups of expensive animals maintained under conditions permitting rigorous management of sanitation, food intake, interaction with other animals and other ecological factors.

For parasites of man, the degree of control desired can vary from mere reduction of parasite burden to subclinical levels in a particular population especially at risk, to complete global eradication. Thus, in Georgia, USA, hookworm disease, as distinct from mere infection, was prevalent among poor Whites in rural areas having well-drained soils. Once this population was identified, the reduction of its worm loads to subclinical levels became the state's modest, clearly defined goal. In contrast, a programme for the global eradication of malaria was initiated by the World Health Organization (WHO) in 1954. Endemic malaria was eradicated from many marginal and insular areas of its vast original range (e.g. USA, USSR, most of Europe, most Caribbean Islands) and although once under excellent control in some previously highly endemic regions (India, Sri Lanka), it has re-emerged, transforming areas which were virtually malaria-free into areas which are again highly malarious. This resurgence has forced an evaluation of goals. Consequently, WHO has defined four levels of acceptable malaria control, depending on the resources available. These are:

1   reduction/prevention of mortality due to malaria by administration of anti-malaria drugs to all those suffering from the disease;

2   reduction/prevention of specific mortality and reduction in morbidity by providing anti-malaria drugs to all those suffering from the disease and to those in highly vulnerable groups (children, workers in development schemes, etc.);

3   prevention of mortality and reduction of morbidity and prevalence by administration of antimalaria drugs (as for 2 above) and by carrying out vector control measures;

4   application of control measures on a country-wide basis with the ultimate objective of eradicating the disease (see WHO, 1978).

The failures of the malaria eradication programme, and many others in public health or agricultural pest control, demonstrate that, in insular situations and under some other special sets of circumstances, eradication of a harmful organism may be feasible, but that it is rarely possible in continental areas where large, genetically variable populations are adapted to survive periodic physicochemical and biological adversity, and where surviving, neighbouring populations of the target organism can rapidly infiltrate into areas which have been brought under control.

8.2   PARASITE LIFE HISTORIES AND CONTROL STRATEGIES

Parasites may have direct life histories in which no intermediate host occurs, and in which the free-living infective stage is directly infective for the definitive host (monoxenous species), or they may have one or more intermediate hosts (heteroxenous species).

It might seem that the former would be more easily controlled than the latter, since only the definitive host(s) and the external environment need to be considered when applying control measures. For example, safe sewage disposal will lead to the satisfactory control of faecally transmitted, monoxenous parasites of man, although this will be a slow process. Similarly, for grazing animals, anthelmintic treatment along with movement to safe pasture will limit trichostrongyle parasitism to acceptable levels.

However, although with one host there are advantages with regard to control there is the important disadvantage that it usually involves human cooperation, i.e. that of infected individuals or of owners of infected animals. Cooperation, even from those likely to benefit directly, is often capricious, and, therefore, in practice heteroxenous parasites may be those more easily controlled. The early success of the malaria eradication programme is attributable to the use of professional spray teams, who, without the direct involvement of the infected populations, treated the inside walls of houses with residual insecticides, usually DDT. This provided excellent control of the vector and interrupted malaria transmission over vast areas.

Monoxenous parasites usually lack the capacity to multiply outside their definitive hosts, hence one dispersal stage entering the external environment will yield only one infective stage. In contrast, heteroxenous parasites frequently reproduce in their intermediate hosts and the tremendous biotic potential of stages in these hosts makes control difficult. For digenean control, prevention of faecal pollution of snail habitats must approach perfection, or anthelmintic treatment of the definitive host must achieve virtually complete parasitological cure, since each successfully invaded snail will shed thousands of cercariae.

The strategy of control may also be influenced by the ability of a parasite to multiply within its definitive host. Theoretically, if multiplication can occur, infection must be prevented completely in order to prevent disease. Protozoans differ from most helminths with regard to multiplication in the definitive host; while in the former this is the rule, in the latter it occurs rarely. Thus, helminth and protozoan control programmes differ in philosophy since low grade helminthic infection or reinfection will usually be acceptable. Indeed, low level exposure to helminths may be a desirable flaw in a control programme, since regular reinfection may be the basis for the induction and maintenance of a strong protective immune response. This will prevent serious levels of infection from developing, should the programme falter.

8.3   METHODS OF CONTROL

8.3.1   Prevention of environmental contamination

(a)   Chemotherapy

Antiparasitic treatment is the most common form of parasite control. It has the important advantage that it brings prompt relief to those infected, and by reducing the number of organisms in this population, it also reduces environmental contamination.

To maximize the benefits of chemotherapy, infected populations should be treated and then protected from rapid re-infection. This can be achieved by timing treatment to coincide with a season unfavourable for parasite transmission. Alternatively, animals may be treated and moved to safe new quarters or pasture. Treatment may be followed by chemoprophylaxis if a suitable drug is available (see section 8.3.6c).

Treatment of nematode infections during seasons unfavourable for transmission does not always prevent the rapid re-establishment of patent, adult worm infections. Many gastrointestinal nematodes are adapted to seasonally varying external environmental conditions so that they spend the unfavourable season in a dormant larval state, usually in the tissues of the alimentary tract (see Michel, 1974, and Schad, 1977). The dormant larvae are more resistant to the usual anthelmintics than are normally developing or adult worms and, therefore, survive to develop when the external environment becomes suitable for transmission once again. Thus, in areas having cold winters, *Haemonchus contortus* and other gastrointestinal nematodes of sheep may survive both treatment and adverse weather conditions in a latent state within the host. In early spring, they resume development, mature and lay eggs which contaminate pastures just as a new crop of highly susceptible young lambs becomes available. Under these circumstances, successful control depends upon the careful choice of an anthelmintic effective against arrested larvae or on treatment to remove the adult worms as they develop from the reservoir of overwintered larvae. Chemotherapy *per se* is discussed in Chapter 9; a contemporary review of parasiticides for the treatment of domestic animals is provided by Theodorides (1980).

Chemotherapeutic treatment of livestock on the open range, or of valuable wild animals, presents a special problem. Parasiticides may be incorporated in salt blocks but this does not guarantee that an appropriate dose is ingested. A particularly clever solution to this problem has been devised to control lungworm (*Protostrongylus* spp.) infections in wild Rocky Mountain Bighorn Sheep in North America. Fermented applemash is placed in mountain meadows where the wild sheep learn to expect it. An anthelminthic is then combined with the mash in quantities sufficient so that the addicted, infected sheep ingest the compound in parasiticidal doses. Parasite transmission has been markedly reduced, resulting in a beneficial effect on the breeding success of the sheep under field conditions.

(b)   Sanitation

Sanitation has complemented chemotherapy in parasite control since the beginning of the great campaigns against the faecally transmitted parasites of man. By 1920 it was realized that, without adequate sanitation, the benefits of mass treatment programmes would be short-lived. Consequently, in rural tropical and subtropical areas, numerous programmes were initiated to install some form of sanitation. These often failed, and sometimes even contributed to increased parasitism. Unless the sanitary latrine's function in interrupting the transmission of faecally borne diseases is understood, it goes unused, or if used, it is abandoned when it becomes fouled or falls into disrepair. By then, members of the affected population may have been conditioned to defecate in the vicinity of the latrine, which can lead to a dense spatial aggregation of faeces and an increase in the intensity of parasite transmission.

In recent years, communal sanitary complexes have been built to combine toilet, bathing and laundry facilities and sometimes to supply piped water as well. These have been well received in several areas where schistosomiasis occurs and have contributed to a decrease in the prevalence of infection. Elaborate units of this type are more likely to be valued and maintained than simple latrines or privies, and, therefore, may have a longer useful life. On the other hand, they are expensive. However, if biogas production were an additional function they might prove economically feasible for poor rural areas.

Similar units could be of value in the densely populated, impoverished belts of squatter habitation surrounding most large cities in the developing nations. In these areas, faecally transmitted parasites are highly prevalent, since sanitary facilities are inadequate, and, in the absence of health education, promiscuous defecation is tolerated.

The sanitary disposal of animal wastes is often impractical for cultural or economic reasons. However, it is feasible for research animals, furbearers raised on wire, swine or exotic species maintained on concrete, or particularly valuable companion or sporting animals, whose excreta may be removed daily from runs, stables, or other limited areas. Indeed, it is increasingly common for urban and suburban societies to demand that faeces of dogs be removed from city streets by persons responsible for their care. The rationale for the so-called 'Scoop Laws' existing in many highly developed industrial societies is largely the prevention of nematode parasitism (toxocariasis) in children. Exposure to *Toxocara canis* is also being restricted by the establishment of specified, segregated areas in public parks where dogs may be brought for exercise.

The faeces of housed animals (e.g. cattle, horses) may be stacked or stored in an enclosed area. Dense packing can generate enough heat to kill the free living stages of parasites except in outer layers. More complete destruction can be obtained by the addition of chemical toxicants, some of which can enhance the value of the manure as fertilizer.

8.3.2   Destruction of free-living stages

When contamination of the external environment with the dispersal stages of parasites cannot be prevented, it would seem, *a priori*, that these free-living stages would be good targets for control. This could have one of the advantages usually associated with vector control (see section 8.3.3), namely the use of professionals employed by public agencies, rather than the private infected or affected individuals, to carry out control programmes.

(a)   Chemical and physical methods

Unfortunately, protozoan cysts, helminth eggs, and the infective larvae of nematodes are extremely resistant to toxic chemical agents and, hence, this approach has had little actual use. Nevertheless, on small pieces of ground, nematode larvae may be destroyed chemically if survival of vegetation is not desired. The runs of kennels may be treated with sodium borate or other nematocides to kill hookworm larvae. Generally, however, control under these situations (kennels, zoos, small paddocks) is preventative, by creation of permanently inhospitable ecological conditions, i.e. destruction of soil, application of impervious surfaces, provision of good drainage and removal of shading vegetation or structures. In small areas, these measures may be supplemented with steam treatment or flaming with a weed burner.

Digeneans also have free living larvae, but chemical control is rarely, if ever, directed specifically against these stages. Miracidia and cercariae are short-lived and new populations are constantly entering the environment either from eggs deposited by definitive hosts or from molluscan intermediate hosts. As was indicated earlier, the intermediate hosts serve as amplifiers, greatly increasing the output of infective stages for the next host over the input from the previous one. For these reasons, chemical controls are directed against snails, any larvicidal action being a useful side-effect.

(b)   Biological control

A broad spectrum of microbial agents attacks the free-living stages of parasites. Among the best known and most interesting of these are the nematode-trapping fungi, the hyphae of which produce loops or other specialized structures to capture and digest soil-dwelling nematodes (Fig. 8.1). The trapping devices of many species also produce toxins which immobilize nematodes almost immediately. These fungi have been used to limit hookworm transmission in mines in the USSR.

In nature, fungi also destroy helminth eggs in rich, biologically active soils. Some investigators emphasize the decline in the abundance of eggs with time that occurs in such soils, and refer to this process as 'the autocleansing ability of the soil'. Fig. 8.2 shows the process of egg destruction investigated with the eggs of Ascaris suum from which the external albuminoid coat has been removed.

Among higher organisms, various invertebrates ingest and destroy free-living stages of parasites in faeces or soil. These include larval and adult arthropods, micro-biverous and predaceous nematodes, annelids and molluscs. Some genera of free living nematodes (Dorylaimus, Actinolaimus, Mononchus) have buccal cavities that are highly adapted for predation (Fig. 8.3). They must play an important role in regulating the preparasitic populations of protozoa and helminths; it has been reported that one Mononchus destroyed 1332 other nematodes during a 12 week period. A useful review of the biological control of plant parasitic nematodes relevant also to animal parasites is that by Mankau, 1980.

Of these invertebrates, only dung beetles have been tested specifically for parasite control. Some dung beetles, 'tumble bugs', form faeces into small pellets

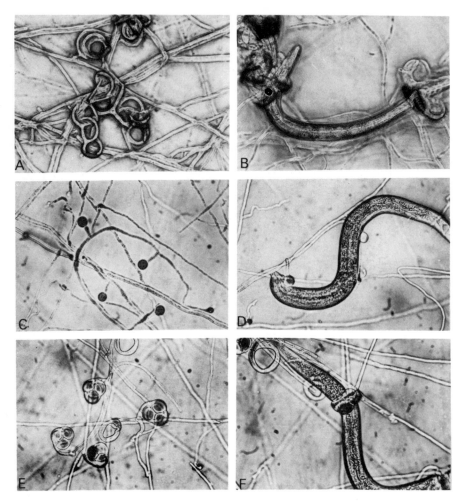

Fig. 8.1. Nematode-trapping fungi. (Top) *Arthrobotrys conoides* forms networks of loops (A) which capture nematodes (B) by adhesion. (Middle) *Dactylella drechsleri* produces stalked, adhesive knobs (C), these also trap nematodes by adhesion (D). (Bottom) Constricting rings of *A. dactyloides* are highly developed organelles composed of three cells (E). When a nematode enters, the cells swell rapidly and grip the worm (F). (After Pramer, 1964.)

which they roll away from the main faecal deposit and bury. Others bury dung directly at the site of deposition and by burying it deeply, act as useful agents for parasite control. For example, in the southern USA herbage from pasture with only normal numbers of beetles carried almost four times as many trichostrongyle larvae as did herbage from pasture whose insect population was artificially augmented with beetles. This reduction in the pasture-worm-population was reflected in a 2.5-fold reduction in mixed trichostrongyle infections in calves.

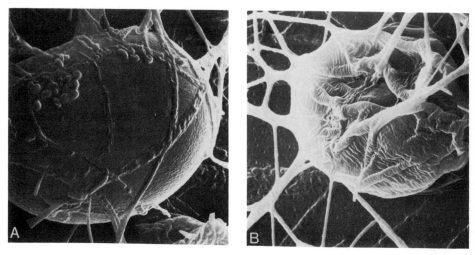

Fig. 8.2. Destruction of *Ascaris suum* eggs by *Verticillium chlamydosporium*. A: experimentally decorticated egg exposed to fungal attack; the fungus has overgrown the egg but has not yet penetrated it. B: partially collapsed egg after penetration. (After Lysek, 1979.)

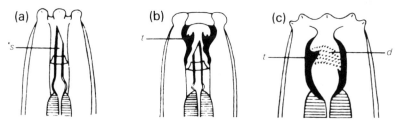

Fig. 8.3. Diagrams of the anterior ends of some predatory nematodes to show buccal armature. (a) *Dorylaimus*; (b) *Actinolaimus*; (c) *Mononchus*. *d:* denticles; *s:* stylet; *t:* tooth. (After Lee & Atkinson, 1976.)

Exotic dung beetles have been imported into Australia where the native species do not bury ruminant faeces which, therefore, accumulates on pasture. Similarly, in the southern USA where, on improved pastures, the population density of cattle may be particularly high, the indigenous beetles cannot cope with the faecal output. Consequently, species have been imported from the ruminant-rich African plains. These have been chosen for their capacity to bury large amounts of manure deeply and, although fly control has been the primary objective, additional benefits in the reduction of helminth population should accrue.

(c)   Grazing management

The population of infective larvae on pasture can also be reduced if it is grazed by hosts which do not allow the ingested worms to establish or to mature.

Cattle or horses have been grazed after sheep or older resistant animals have followed young susceptible ones on pastures. This method of parasite control, which has been known for many years, is enjoying a new popularity. Australian studies have shown that alternation of yearling cattle and sheep on a 6-month cycle, especially when combined with anthelmintic treatment given at the time of rotation, will reduce parasitism to acceptable levels. Young animals introduced to this system at weaning gained more weight, produced 23% more wool and suffered fewer deaths than did sheep that received the treatments only; indeed, the former were as productive as sheep treated monthly but maintained on permanent pasture.

8.3.3   Destruction of intermediate hosts and vectors

Most heteroxenous parasites of man or domestic animals can be grouped into two categories: (a) those that use vertebrate intermediate hosts, and (b) those that use arthropods or molluscs. Since the vertebrate intermediates are usually food-animal species, reduction in their number is rarely, if ever, a practical approach to control. Other more appropriate methods are discussed subsequently in sections 8.3.4 and 8.3.5.

In contrast, control of parasites having invertebrate intermediate hosts often rests on destruction of the latter, usually with pesticides. Since these lack specificity, and since practical application cannot always be narrowly focused in time and space, destruction of non-target organisms is an attendant, undesirable side-effect. Additionally, the accumulation of chemical residues in wild animal species has had a marked effect on their reproductive success and population density. This has aroused concern about the long-term effects of pesticides on human and domestic animal populations.

To make the use of pesticides as specific and as safe as possible, to increase the spectrum of control methods available, and to choose the most cost-effective strategy from the array of options available, requires detailed knowledge of vector biology, a good grasp of theoretical population ecology, and thorough training in applied control methodology. This has resulted in the growth of vector biology and control as a discipline in its own right, related to, but distinct from parasitology. In this chapter, the discussion of vector biology and control will emphasize widely used tactics and strategies or particularly interesting new methods of vector control. More intensive and extensive treatments of the subject are included in the list of references and readings.

(a)   Environmental control

This method attempts to alter the environment so that target species can no longer find the habitats necessary for their survival. Programmes can range in scale from the simple removal of discarded containers which serve as breeding sites for mosquitoes, to engineering projects requiring government sanction and support.

With regard to mosquitoes, environmental control is concerned almost exclusively with the elimination of breeding habitats and will differ depending on whether anopheline or culicine mosquitoes are the target organisms. Within these groups, particular species may have idiosyncratic habitat preferences, but generally anophelines deposit their eggs in relatively still areas along the shoreline of substantial bodies of fresh water (e.g. ponds, rivers and lakes). They do not breed in small, natural or artificial containers (e.g. bamboo stubs, empty cans, discarded tyres), and most species are intolerant of polluted water. Important exceptions are *Anopheles stephensi* and *A. gambiae*, major vectors of malaria in India and tropical Africa, respectively. The former will breed in small containers and the latter in pools and puddles of ground water.

The preferred breeding habitats of culicine mosquitoes are diverse. Depending on the species, mosquitoes of the genus *Aedes* deposit their eggs in temporary pools, ditches, paddy fields, small containers and a variety of other habitats. Members of the genus *Culex* are similarly catholic in their breeding requirements. Some species, including *Culex pipiens*, an important vector of *Wuchereria bancrofti*, breed in polluted water and have prospered in crowded urban, tropical areas where antiquated, overloaded sewage systems and open drains provide suitable breeding habitats. These differences influence the kinds of environmental manipulations which can be used most effectively to achieve control.

Before DDT came into general use, environmental modification was one of the major forms of mosquito control. The reduction of breeding habitats was not simply confined to draining and filling, but rather the breeding biology of particular target species was elucidated thoroughly and, on the basis of this knowledge, habitats were altered in diverse ways to render them unsuitable for breeding. Since this technique depended on the recognition of species-specific habitat characteristics, it became known as 'species sanitation'. Along with large scale environmental change, such as building dikes to lower the salinity of salt marshes for the control of halophilic species, other less dramatic changes were made. These included shading of streams to make them unsuitable for sun-loving species, or alternatively, clearing of vegetation to increase light intensity and to raise water temperature to discourage shade-loving species.

The same approach applies equally to the other vectors. Thus, tsetse fly control has involved the clearing of wooded areas and their replacement with cultivated land, or, for species which live along water courses, clearing of riverine or lakeside vegetation. This can be restricted further, so that only fords and other areas of human streamside activity are cleared.

Theoretically, at least, similar methods can be used for all intermediate host species. Many forms of habitat alteration are used in mollusc control, e.g. draining, filling, alternately raising and lowering water levels, increasing flow rates by concreting, straightening and clearing irrigation canals, removal of shade, and controlled planting of rice to permit water flow. Where fascioliasis is a major problem on valuable agricultural land, drainage systems using tile drains represent an expensive but effective form of snail control.

(b)   Chemical control

Along with 'species sanitation', the application of larvicides to breeding habitats of anophelines was once the major approach to malaria control. These methods, along with careful species-specific studies of mosquito breeding biology, became obsolete when it was realized that the weakest link in the mosquito transmission of malaria, given the availability of a cheap effective residual insecticide, was the indoor resting behaviour of adult, anthropophilic anophelines. This coincidence (availability of DDT and recognition of vector endophily) led to the WHO sponsored, global malaria eradication programme, which was based largely on the spraying of the interior walls of houses with residual insecticides. Its success was remarkable, reducing the endemic zone of malaria from one populated by 2049 million, to one populated by 1612 million people, even after the recent resurgence of the infection (see Noguer et al., 1978). The approach failed where dwellings lacked walls, were exceedingly temporary, or where a pattern of indoor biting and resting did not exist.

Valuable additional benefits with reference to the control of parasitic diseases in man sometimes resulted from the spraying of households with residual insecticides. For instance, in the Solomon Islands, where *Wuchereria bancrofti* is transmitted by endophilic, night-biting anophelines, the malaria control programme reduced the prevalence of filariasis. In some of the smaller islands, the parasite was actually eradicated. Similarly, because the sandfly vectors (*Phlebotomus* spp.) of *Leishmania donovani* were highly susceptible to DDT, the prevalence of kala azar was reduced greatly in many parts of Asia.

It must be emphasized that the use of DDT for malaria control is generally considered to have contributed insignificantly to the occurrence of environmental insecticide residues and to their incorporation into food chains. These problems arose largely through the agricultural misuse of the insecticide. For *Anopheles* control in most parts of the world, DDT was sprayed on the interior walls of the dwellings, however primitive, and provided that the pressure on the mosquitoes was not relaxed, excellent control and often eradication were achieved. Where spraying became irregular or was terminated, eradication failed, and, in some cases, insecticide resistance developed. Resistant forms are capable of metabolizing DDT and related insecticides and the use of insecticides for agricultural purposes has contributed largely to insecticide resistance among mosquitoes (see Chapin &

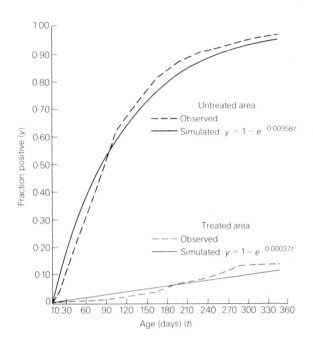

Fig. 8.4. Age-cumulated prevalence of malaria in infants as determined by microscopic examination of blood smears in insecticide-treated and untreated areas. (After Payne *et al.*, 1976.)

Wasserstrom, 1981). It has also been suggested that the spraying of household interiors has selected for outdoor resting mosquitoes, and escape from the usual spraying procedures.

In many parts of the tropical world, the control of insect-borne parasitic disease still depends heavily on DDT and other insecticides. The striking effect that the well-planned, environmentally prudent use of an insecticide can have on the incidence of malaria is illustrated in Fig. 8.4. The periodic application of feni-trothion to the inside of dwellings was the only intervention used in this investigation of the impact of control in an area of near holoendemic malaria. For some vectors the use of insecticides is the only practical method. Furthermore, satisfactory control of some parasites continues to rest solely on the reduction of vector populations. Thus, control of onchocerciasis (river blindness) in West Africa depends exclusively on the destruction of blackflies by the application of larvicides to rivers and streams. For this purpose, Abate, a biodegradable carbamate with low toxicity for nontarget species, has been used extensively. Unfortunately, foci of resistance to this insecti-cide have begun to appear in the Volta River Basin. The control of trypanosomiasis is also mainly a matter of vector (tsetse) control by use of insecticides. This can be highly specific, as when a residual insecticide is applied only to shoreline vegetation within 5 feet of the ground during the dry seasons of the year, or when it is used to impregnate simple cloth and netting traps suspended along water courses. Alterna-tively, it can be totally lacking in specificity as when ultra-low-volume (ULV) spraying of non-residual insecticides is conducted with fixed wing aircraft. Aircraft, particularly helicopters, are used to apply residual insecticides to dense thickets and linear habitats, including woodland borders. The downwash of the helicopter rotor increases penetration of the insecticide into the canopy of vegetation.

Chemical control remains the sole practical way to reduce tick infestations on livestock. This is particularly important in Australia, sub-Saharan Africa and South America, where tick populations may build up to enormous densities. Furthermore, ticks are vectors of serious parasitic diseases of cattle (babesiosis and theileriosis). *Theileria* spp., the causative agents of East Coast Fever, are particularly important in East Africa, where 40% of the calf crop may be lost to this disease. Depending on whether 2- and 3-host ticks or 1-host ticks are the predominant species, successful control may depend on treatment at 20 day, or even 7 day intervals. Although chutes (crushes) are used with elaborate spray races or dips, the treatment of large herds is time-consuming, expensive, and may cause injury due to handling.

The number of pesticides available for use in the control of parasites has decreased as arthropods have become resistant and as insecticide research and development have declined. Furthermore, the cost of insecticides has increased sharply, particularly that of the most recent products (hormone-like substances and synthetic pyrethrums).

Molluscicides continue to play an important part in the control of snail-borne diseases. They are applied to streams and irrigation canals by a variety of self-feed devices; small habitats, pools, back waters, seepages and the like may be treated manually or sprayed. Aerial spraying has also been used to treat extensive, irrigated areas, but generally large bodies of water have been considered unsuitable for molluscicide treatment. However, recent investigations on Lake Volta, the largest artificial lake in the world, suggest that excellent control of rampant urinary bilharziasis can be achieved with molluscicides. This depends on the fact that most human contact with the water occurs in relatively small, discrete foci near lakeside villages. By temporarily isolating these foci with plastic barriers, molluscicidal concentrations of Niclosamide can be delivered. Although the treated areas are re-invaded by snails relatively rapidly, periodic molluscicide application planned on the basis of the prepatent period of *Schistosoma haematobium* in the snail will probably interrupt transmission significantly.

To increase the efficiency of molluscicide application, a new slow-release technology has developed. Sophisticated behavioural investigations are contributing to the improvement of these techniques so that molluscicidal baits will combine a slow-release snail attractant with an arrestant, phagostimulant and a bound molluscicide.

Although molluscicides have not had the unfortunate biocidal effects of insecticides, this may be because they have not had the same degree of use. There is considerable evidence that a great variety of aquatic organisms feeds on the larval stages of digeneans, and if populations of the former were to be decimated, the intensity of parasite transmission would increase. For instance, guppies *(Poecilia reticulata)* are voracious larvivores, eating as many as 1000 cercariae per hour. Indeed, in both laboratory and field investigations these fish were shown to protect mice from the acquisition of heavy burdens of *Schistosoma mansoni*.

Chaetogaster limnaei, an ectocommensal oligochaete on snails (Fig. 8.5), is also an important predator of free-swimming digenean larvae and there is good evidence that *C. limnaei* is an important regulator of digenean abundance under field conditions. When *C. limnaei* is abundant, invasion of snails by free swimming, actively penetrating larvae is markedly reduced, whereas there is no reduction in the invasive success of miricidia that remain within the egg shell and are ingested passively as the snail feeds.

Many invertebrates (planaria, leeches, and insusceptible species of snails) can act as lethal decoys for the miracidia of *Schistosoma mansoni*; attempts to penetrate such organisms are fatal. When susceptible snails are confined to one end of an experimental channel and miracidia are introduced at the other, the snails can be protected from infection by the interposition of decoy species; in experimental channels the infection rate among target snails can be reduced from over 90% to zero by introducing appropriate decoys. In natural habitats, where transmission of *S. mansoni* was known to occur, drainage ditches were emptied, cleared, refilled, and stocked with

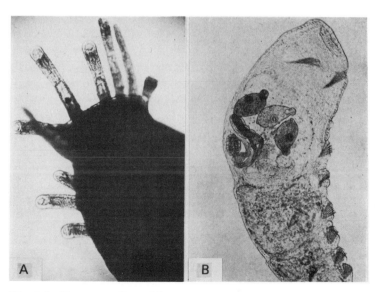

Fig. 8.5. *Chaetogaster limnaei limnaei*, an ectocommensal annelid of snails and a predator on free swimming larval trematodes. A: The anterior end of the snail, *Physa gyrina*, showing eight projecting *C.l.limnaei* and two tentacles. B: *C.l.limnaei* containing three ingested cercariae. (After Sankurathri & Holmes, 1976.)

presumptive decoys: snails, guppies, shrimps, tadpoles or all of these insusceptible species. Each of the decoy species reduced the infection rate of *Biomphalaria glabrata*, the target organism. Protection varied directly with the logarithm of the surface area of the decoys and inversely with the logarithm of the density of the miracidia. The snail, *P. marmorata*, was the best decoy.

Decoy animals rarely attain the high densities used in experiments, and miracidial concentrations are probably very high near stools deposited in stationary water so infection may not be suppressed by decoys. However, since these other species must limit the intensity of transmission under field conditions, the possible side-effects of molluscicides require careful consideration to minimize the accidental destruction of natural agents of biological control.

(c)   Genetic control

Genetic control of insects, particularly through the release of irradiated sterile males, has been widely publicized, and has caught the imagination of both the scientific and lay public. Other less widely discussed methods of genetic control include: (i) the introduction of translocation chromosomes into target populations; (ii) the use of incompatible males to render females sterile through cytoplasmic incompatibility between sperm and ova; and (iii) the release of males of a closely related species to produce sterile mating or sterile hybrids. These techniques are discussed in detail by Davidson (1974) and by Pal and La Chance (1974).

The release of irradiated sterile males was a spectacular success in the south-eastern USA, where, during winter, the range of the screw worm fly contracted to the southern warm parts of the Florida peninsular. Unfortunately, similar success has not been attained in northern Mexico nor the south-western USA, where dispersal of new flies from deeper in Mexico has made control difficult.

A massive attempt by WHO to control *Culex fatigans* in a continental situation failed, even though the daily release of 100 000 chemosterilized males reduced the number of viable eggs to 13% in the test area near New Delhi. Unfortunately, a reduction in adult population density could not be demonstrated, probably due to immigration of mosquitoes from neighbouring areas. This project was terminated prematurely for political reasons.

In contrast, the experimental release of chemosterilized males of *Anopheles albimanus* at Lake Apastepeque in El Salvador (see also section 8.3.3d) markedly depressed the abundance of this species, particularly during the season when the mosquito normally reaches peak density. The mosquito population gradually regained normal levels of abundance over a 4-month period after the releases were terminated. The spectacular success of this experiment resulted from the choice of species and isolated locale as the effects of sterile male release were not negated by the immigration of mosquitoes from neighbouring areas.

Low initial population densities and slow recovery from a significant numerical decline make tsetse flies suitable candidates for genetic control. This seems to be borne out by field trials in Upper Volta, where release of irradiated males (7–10 sterile males: 1 wild male for a 3 year period), eradicated tsetse flies from two small areas (5 km²) isolated by barriers of cleared land sprayed with insecticides to prevent immigration. This method can be improved by reduction of the fly population in the area to be treated before sterile males are released. Indeed, some authorities feel that in tsetse control, sterile male release will find its greatest applicability in the elimination of residual populations after other control programmes have been carried to the point of diminishing returns.

(d)   Biological control

This is an area of active research, but few methods have been developed for practical use in the field. With regard to ticks and tsetse flies, the recognition and cataloguing of diseases, parasites and predators still represent a research frontier, and so little has been done to test biological agents for the control of these arthropods.

The biological control of mosquitoes has experienced greater progress, and larvivorous fish (particularly the top minnow, *Gambusia*), have been employed in malaria control for many years. More recently the guppy, *Poecilia*, has come into prominence since it flourishes in polluted waters and can be released in open sewers, faecally contaminated pools under stilt houses and numerous other small stagnant habitats. These characteristics are compatible with the use of this fish in both rural and urban areas where culicine mosquitoes are important vectors of human filariasis.

Other organisms have been considered for mosquito control, including viruses, bacteria, fungi, protozoa, nematodes and predatory insects. Among the more promising microbial agents are toxic strains of *Bacillus thuringiensis* and *B. sphaericus*. Some strains kill larvae upon ingestion of a single spore, its toxin being released by digestion in the mosquito gut (Fig. 8.6).

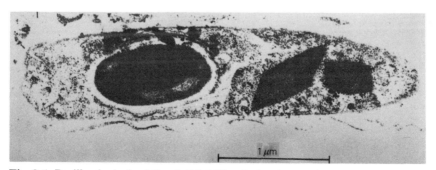

1 μm

Fig. 8.6. *Bacillus thuringiensis* (strain BA-068), a fatal pathogen of mosquito larvae, containing a developing spore and two crystals of toxin. (After Reeves, 1973.)

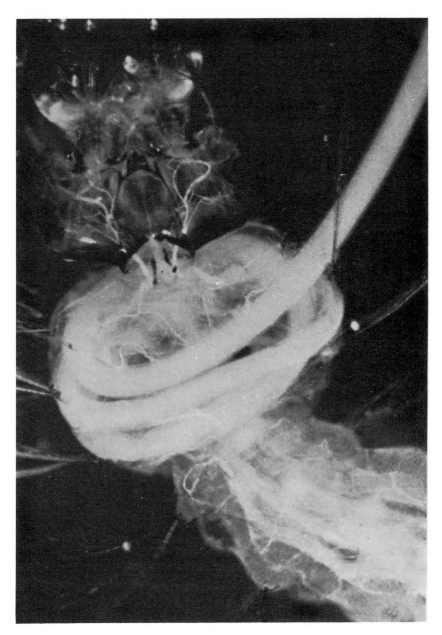

Fig. 8.7. A mermithid nematode (*Romanomermis culicivorax*: a biological agent for the control of mosquitoes. (After Petersen, 1973.)

Nematodes, particularly mermithids (Fig. 8.7), have become candidates for use in insect control programmes, since the prevalence of mermithid infection can be high, exceeding 80%, and since parasitism is usually fatal. The adult female worm emerges from its host for a period of maturation as a free-living organism; its exit punctures the exoskeleton with an attendant fatal loss of body fluids. The infective larvae of one particularly promising species, *Romanomermis culicivorax*, can be mass reared with simple equipment at minimal cost (10 cents (5p)/million) and can be applied inundatively to breeding habits with conventional sprayers. It has been used in large scale field tests against *Anopheles albimanus*, which is the principal vector of malaria in Central America and is resistant to chlorinated hydrocarbons as well as other insecticides. At an isolated lake in El Salvador, population reductions ranging up to 74% were achieved (see Petersen *et al.*, 1978).

The use of mermithids for the long-term control of vector species depends on a concordance with regard to the suitability of habitats for their larvae and for those of their hosts. This is true also when the predatory mosquito larvae of the genus *Toxorhyncites* are to be used to control other species. For this reason, *T. brevipalpis* has been proposed for the control of *Aedes polynesiensis*, both being container-breeding species. Release of artificially reared adults at the end of the dry season should result in high densities of toxorhynchid larvae in containers just when the rains begin, and they would be expected, therefore, to inhibit the normal wet season increase of *Aedes polynesiensis* populations. In laboratory tests, individual *T. brevipalpis* destroyed from 154–358 other mosquito larvae, depending on temperature, which controlled the length of the larval life of the predator.

Biological control of molluscs has been used in the field for 20 years or more. In 1956, the large freshwater snail, *Marisa cornuarietis*, a competitor of *Biomphalaria glabrata*, was introduced into the headwaters of a series of creeks of a watershed near San Juan, Puerto Rico. This initial introduction was a spectacular success, the introduced snail having reduced the target species to small residual populations throughout the area. *Marisa* has subsequently played a considerable role in schistosome control in Puerto Rico, where, ultimately it was used to control *B. glabrata* in ponds and lakes throughout the island, but it was not as effective in streams as it initially seemed. In Puerto Rico, the snail has had no adverse effects on desirable plant or animal species. However, concern about damage to valuable aquatic plants, particularly rice, has delayed its introduction elsewhere despite field trials in Egypt which were entirely favourable.

The list of other organisms known to affect snails adversely includes bacteria, protozoa, helminths, annelids, arthropods, molluscs and various snail-eating vertebrates. Of these, several have been investigated in the laboratory, but few field trials have been implemented. The reviews by Berg (1973) and Jordan *et al.* (1980) provide an entry into the literature. Since field studies have been limited, only a few organisms which, by laboratory evaluation or restricted field trials, have appeared to be specific efficient agents of snail control, will be discussed.

A large Belostomatid bug, *Limnogeton fieberi*, is a voracious snail eater which does not attack arthropods, amphibia or fish under laboratory or field conditions. If mass rearing could be accomplished, this insect could play a valuable role in an integrated control programme, particularly in Egypt, where it is already considered an important factor in the natural regulation of Bulinid snail populations. Alternatively, after careful testing for adverse side-effects, *Limnogeton fieberi* could be introduced into other areas where it might become a self-perpetuating limiting agent.

Larvae of marsh flies (Sciomyzid Diptera) are highly specialized predators of gastropods. Some species attack terrestrial and amphibious snails; after the female fly has laid an egg on a snail's shell, the larva invades the soft tissues of the gastropod and when these have been consumed, it pupates within the empty shell. Other species attack aquatic snails. These lay their eggs on emergent vegetation; the larvae hatch from the eggs and find their own snail hosts. Unfortunately, most species that attack aquatic snails are only efficient in locating prey near the surface of the water.

Marsh flies are of interest as biological control agents because they are closely associated with snails in all stages, and, therefore, are unlikely to become pests if introduced into new areas. Furthermore, the active searching ability of the female fly is an important attribute for a biological control agent.

In the only introduction attempted to date, a Nicaraguan sciomyzid, *Sepedon macropus*, was released in the Hawaiian Islands. The fly has become established on four of the islands, and its larvae are killing the molluscan intermediate host of the liver fluke, *Fasciola gigantica*, without apparent undesirable environmental effects. Unfortunately, no attempt was made to determine whether there has been a significant effect on either the parasite or the snail population.

Various vertebrate predators of snails have been suggested for use in the control of schistosomiasis and fascioliasis. Fish ponds are potential sites for schistosome transmission, and limited investigations have shown that edible fish (*Serranochromis* spp.) can prevent colonization of ponds by schistosome-bearing molluscs. In small, wet pasture habitats, domestic ducks can affect lymnaeid snail populations significantly and in the protein deficient areas of the world, where snail-borne parasitism is particularly important, food–animal species which are also molluscivorous could be an important element in any integrated control programme.

8.3.4   Destruction of parasites within intermediate hosts

(a)   Competitive interactions between digenean larvae in gastropods

Although snails may shed two or even three species of cercariae, multiple infections frequently occur much less often than would be expected if chance alone governed co-occurrence, suggesting that in certain combinations digenean larvae are antagonistic, and that one species may exclude another. Considering the great demands that digenean larvae make on the resources provided by their molluscan hosts, it is not surprising that strong interspecific, competitive, interactions occur (see the review by Lim & Heyneman, 1972).

Investigations have generally involved an echinostome as one interactant, since the rediae of this group are motile, facultative predators with powerful sucking pharynges. One species, *Paryphostomum segregatum*, can detect other digeneans in distant parts of a snail, and will leave its normal habitat deep in the snail's visceral mass to seek out and destroy entering larvae in superficial sites, including the tentacles. Rediae usually destroy other larvae by ingesting all or part of the competing organism. However, exclusion of one species by another does not necessarily depend on the highly specialized predatory attributes of *P. segregatum* and other echinostomes. The brood sacs of some digeneans are sedentary sporocysts that lack a mouth with which to attack other organisms. Nevertheless, they too can inhibit the development of other trematodes, presumably through the release of a chemoantagonist, having an antibiotic-like function.

In experimental field trials conducted in South East Asia, either *Schistosoma spindale*, a parasite of bovines, or *Trichobilharzia brevis*, a schistosome of waterfowl, was eliminated from small ponds by inundatively seeding them with the eggs of an echinostome. Eradication occurred when the echinostome infected 60–70% of the snails.

For inundative seeding, echinostome eggs are harvested from rats infected specifically for this purpose; since sufficient eggs for practical field use cannot be obtained in this way, intramolluscan competitive exclusion has yet to be included in actual trematode control programmes.

Alternatively, the competing parasite could be introduced with the hope that it would become established, propagate naturally and eventually contribute to the control of a target species. Some anomalies in the distribution of *Fasciola hepatica* suggest that this might be possible. Sometimes *Fasciola hepatica* is absent from sheep in suitable areas densely populated with appropriate snail hosts. Apparently the snails are pre-empted as hosts for *F. hepatica* by echinostome infections maintained in large flocks of resident waterfowl. This suggests that stocking ponds, low wet areas of pasture and other small, discrete, snail habitats with appropriately parasitized vertebrates could eventually bring about a useful reduction in a target species. That a new parasite might prosper in introduced hosts of small economic value (e.g. ducks, fish) may not be an important objection in practice. Indeed, if the vertebrate host for the control agent was an acceptable food species, and if its parasites were not excessively pathogenic, control by the introduction of parasitized vertebrates might have a fringe benefit in contributing to the amelioration of protein malnutrition which is so prevalent in much of the tropical world.

(b)   *Destruction of parasites within vertebrate intermediate hosts*

This technique applies mainly to food animal species intended for human consumption and the destruction of the parasite usually occurs after slaughter. Thus, this subject is included under meat processing (section 8.3.5b).

Chemotherapeutic destruction of the muscle larvae of *Trichinella spiralis* several weeks prior to the slaughter of pigs has been suggested, but since this raises the question of possible chemical and biological residues in human food, it is not likely to come into use very rapidly. With the advent of taeniaicides active against metacestodes, chemotherapy is theoretically feasible with regard to the control of human taeniases, but the same objections hold.

8.3.5   Prevention of exposure to infection

Since parasite control will rarely be complete, the occurrence of infective stages either in intermediate hosts or free in the environment is to be expected. Thus, prevention of invasion represents one important tactic for control. Possible approaches include provision of safe drinking water, meat inspection and processing, mechanical barriers to invasion by skin-penetrating larvae or to biting arthropod vectors, repellent chemicals and avoidance by appropriate behaviour.

(a)   *Safe drinking water*

The infective stages of a number of parasites of man (e.g. *Giardia, Dracunculus, Spirometra*) gain entry to the body in contaminated water. Giardiasis is a particularly interesting example of a water-borne parasitic infection in that it has come into prominence recently as an infection of the wealthy. Drinking water taken directly from pristine streams in several North American mountain resorts was shown to contain cysts of the *Giardia* of beavers. This is transmissable to man and can cause epidemic giardiasis in areas where supposedly pure, untreated water is used for drinking..

The period 1981–90 has been designated *International Drinking Water Supply and Sanitation Decade* by the United Nations. One of the official goals for the decade is the elimination of the guinea worm, *Dracunculus medinensis*, from the list of important parasites of man. A high degree of control, if not eradication, should be possible for this heteroxenous parasite, since its intermediate host (*Cyclops*) can be easily removed from drinking water by simple filtration.

(b)   *Meat inspection and processing*

The detection of tapeworm larvae in meat intended for human consumption, along with legislation making the sale of infected carcasses a punishable offence, are among the oldest public health measures. In 1434 in Regensburg, a medieval German city, a butcher was imprisoned for attempting to sell 'measly' pigs, i.e. pigs infected with the bladderworms (cysticerci) of *Taenia solium*. To make the cysticerci inconspicuous to his customers he had punctured the individual bladders.

Present day meat inspection endeavours to identify carcasses infected with the metacestodes of *Taenia solium*, *T. saginata*, *T. ovis* and *Echinococcus granulosus*. Success depends largely on the abundance of cysts and their location in sites where visualization is possible. *Trichinella spiralis* is not sought at meat inspection in North America and elsewhere, since its muscle-inhabiting larvae are microscopic; in Europe, however, muscle samples are taken for trichinoscopy. This technique involves the use of a microscope which projects an image of the material under examination on a screen for efficient, continuous surveillance of samples. Meat-borne protozoa (e.g. *Toxoplasma*, *Sarcocystis*) are not specifically sought at meat inspection.

The fate of parasitized carcasses varies nationally, but whether they are merely identified to warn the consumer or condemned for human consumption, meat inspection has contributed notably to the decline of meat-borne helminthiases.

Freezing, cooking and other forms of meat processing contribute to the destruction of food-borne parasites generally. The widespread use of home freezers in affluent societies has contributed importantly to the control of these parasitisms. More comprehensive discussions of meat hygiene are available in a recent textbook (Libby, 1975).

(c)   *Mechanical methods*

To prevent human infections with skin-penetrating parasites (e.g. hookworms, schistosomes), shoes, boots, or gloves have been worn, largely as a matter of individual initiative. Rarely has the provision of footwear been an integral part of a parasite control programme, although in Puerto Rico charitable and governmental organizations did provide the rural poor with shoes for protection against hookworms. In most of the rural tropics where footwear would be most useful, comfort and cost make its widespread use unlikely. Indeed, in places where it would be most protective, it is least likely to be worn, since mud can be washed more readily from feet than from expensive shoes.

Controlled groups (e.g. military personnel) can be persuaded to wear boots, head nets and clothing providing extensive covering. This affords a degree of protection against skin-penetrating and vector-borne parasites; the effectiveness of apparel can be enhanced by impregnation with repellent and larvicidal agents.

Bed nets have had relatively wide acceptance in urban tropical areas and in rural areas where custom, furnishings and residental construction permit their use.

Window screening, although widely used to provide comfort to people in affluent societies, has had relatively little use in the control of vector-borne parasites of man. Provision of piped water and bathing and laundry facilities serves a similar function in the control of human schistosomiasis as it limits contact with natural, contaminated waters.

Like screening, topical insect repellents have been used most extensively to provide relief from blood sucking insects *per se* rather than from the parasites they transmit. Ointments with repellent or larvicidal properties have been developed for protection against ancylostomiasis and schistosomiasis, but only with respect to the former has there been extensive, practical, use in the field. For example, ointments have been used to protect Japanese farmers from invasion by hookworms.

(d)   Animal husbandry

Excellent control, and indeed exclusion of parasites, is possible when domestic and laboratory animals (poultry, swine, cats) are raised indoors in total confinement. In these systems, isolation prevents the introduction of pathogens including parasites. While this highly sophisticated form of animal husbandry presently applies to few species in few countries only, it will spread throughout the industrialized world when it becomes economically feasible. An intermediate degree of isolation can be obtained by holding livestock in open barns or dry lots to eliminate the risk of pasture-induced infection. Exclusion of livestock from low lying, wet pasture by fencing is standard practice in fluke control.

Pasture rotation has failed as a practical method for preventing parasitic disease in grazing animals. Although cattle and sheep can easily be moved to fresh pasture before nematode eggs are translated into infective larvae, the latter are too long-lived to permit return to previously stocked pasture within an economically feasible time frame. Attempts to speed rotation by treatment of pasture with soil sterilants, nematocidal fertilizers or by burning have yet to succeed (see section 8.3).

(e)   Behaviour modification

Little is known about animal behaviour which might help to minimize exposure to parasitism. Avoidance of areas immediately surrounding faecal deposits is a well known characteristic of the grazing behaviour of domestic herbivores. Indeed, the predatory behaviour of carnivores appears to predispose them to infection. Parasitized prey often display morphological or behavioural changes which act as signals releasing a predatory response on the part of the carnivores. Recent work in Canada suggests that even when modern man is the predator, this system functions; moose killed early in the hunting season have heavier *Echinococcus* infections than those killed later.

In the case of man, adaptive behaviour with regard to avoiding infection is well known. Some customs are based on naïve and, in fact, useless attempts to avoid infection. Penis shields, for example, probably developed from the desire to avoid urinary bilharziasis. In this instance, the association between the disease and water was correctly made, although the route of parasite entry proved to be other than that supposed. On the other hand, laws and taboos concerning the eating of pork have limited infection with *Taenia solium* and *Trichinella spiralis* in Jews, Muslims and others.

Human behaviour, which leads to avoidance of faecally polluted ground, has been described in detail with regard to transmission of hookworms in South Asia. There is a gradient in the degree of avoidance from the east, where climate favours intense transmission and simple latrines are constructed, to the west, where a long dry season interrupts transmission and stools are deposited on the ground with little effort to avoid contact with the adjacent soil. In Burma, small platforms are constructed to extend over water or low ground providing a simple latrine; in Assam and parts of Bangladesh, horizontal tree trunks, dikes and banks provide for the separation of people and excrement-laden soil. Still further west along the climatic gradient, bamboo stubs or bricks are used as simple pedestals to elevate the feet above surrounding faecal pollution. Finally, in relatively dry areas of Bengal and much of the remainder of India, little effort is made to avoid contact with the soil during defecation. Kochar *et al.* (1976) emphasize that protective human behaviour needs to be identified and that these existing, normal protective practices should form the basis of elementary health education.

8.3.6   Prevention of successful maturation and disease

(a)   *Protection by naturally acquired infections*

The resistance that mature animals manifest to many parasitic infections is due in part to aging *per se* and in part to acquired immunity (see Chapter 6). Indeed, if exposure to parasitism is probable, frequent low-grade natural immunizing exposure can be desirable. That such exposure does protect against subsequent heavy infection has been demonstrated for various parasites (e.g. *Nematodirus spathiger* in sheep, *Ancylostoma caninum* in dogs). The classical long-standing high prevalence/low density relationship in human hookworm infection as it occurs in eastern India is explicable on this basis.

Acquired resistance may develop also when animals are exposed to abnormal strains or species of parasites. In the western USA the domestic sheep and each of the species of wild sheep has its own strain of *Haemonchus*. These hosts tolerate heterologous infections and previous exposure to them confers some resistance to homologous strains.

For a similar phenomenon in man, Nelson (1974) coined the term 'zooprophylaxis' and described a number of enigmatic situations where serious human schistosomiasis would be expected but did not occur or was only a minor problem. Zoophilic bilharzia are particularly abundant in these areas and he suggested that, in the course of penetrating and undergoing partial devlopment in man, they provoke a strong cross-protection. Studies using laboratory animal models support this suggestion.

(b)   Vaccination

If naturally acquired infection can induce protection, then vaccination should provide this benefit with the additional advantage that the host will not be subjected to the vagaries of exposure under field conditions. Unfortunately, immunoprophylaxis has not progressed as rapidly as had been hoped, but the intense present day activity in parasite immunology appears ready to yield an array of potential vaccines (see section 6.9).

(c)   Chemoprophylaxis

If exposure to infection is inevitable, killing of the infective stage during entry or soon after invasion of its host represents a useful approach to control (see Chapter 9).

In many parts of the world malaria prophylaxis has become an expected part of life for many residents and virtually all visitors. With regard to the helminth parasites of man, diethylcarbamazine (DEC) can be used to prevent eyeworm (*Loa loa*) infection, and metrifonate—an inexpensive, well-tolerated anti-schistosome drug—to protect against urinary bilharziasis.

Unfortunately, the long-term use of a drug may have unpredicted adverse side-effects and prophylaxis has the disadvantage that, in the absence of symptoms, members of a population at risk fail to take the necessary quantities of medication. This undermines control and accelerates the development of drug resistance. Furthermore, long-term prophylactic treatment of large populations is expensive, and often beyond the means of nations where parasitic disease is particularly prevalent.

In veterinary parasitology, a number of chemoprophylactic agents are in widespread use. These are especially valuable when infection with the mature parasites is difficult to treat, or if the parasite has a significant zoonotic potential. For example, the heartworm (*Dirofilaria immitis*) lives in the right ventricle and pulmonary artery of dogs, and the presently available adulticidal drugs are relatively toxic arsenicals. Furthermore, when the adult worms are killed, they may embolize to the lungs, causing life-threatening obstructions. For these reasons, prophylactic treatment with a larvicide, diethylcarbamazine (DEC), is strongly recommended. This drug kills the developing larvae while they are still small and before they migrate to the heart.

Styrylpyridinium is often combined with DEC, so that dogs are also protected from hookworms and ascarids, particularly *Toxocara canis*. The latter is the major causative agent of visceral larva migrans in children and occasionally wanders to the eye where it causes serious visual impairment. The ocular lesion resembles a malignant growth on the retina, and therefore, has led to the unnecessary surgical removal of parasitized eyes. For these reasons, toxocariasis is one of the few remaining zoonoses of public health importance in highly developed, affluent societies.

8.3.7   Destruction of vertebrate alternative or reservoir hosts

Most leishmaniases of man are zoonoses. One approach to the control of some of these infections is the destruction of mammalian reservoir hosts. Thus, in the USSR, large scale destruction of gerbils (*Meriones* sp. and *Rhombomys* spp.) by poisoning their burrows and by ploughing their colonies has succeeded in providing control near human habitations. Reinvasion has been prevented by ecological change, i.e. converting land to agricultural use, thereby rendering it unsuitable for gerbils.

Destruction of excess or free ranging dogs has played a part in the control of visceral leishmaniasis, particularly in China, and has contributed importantly to the eradication of hydatidosis in Iceland and its control in South America.

At one time, attempts were made to control African trypanosomiasis in livestock by the systematic slaughter of wildlife, particularly antelope. This failed and the technique has been abandoned.

8.3.8   Integrated control

Integrated control is an overall approach to limiting populations of pests, pathogens or vectors which employs a number of different tactics, strategically, on the basis of thorough knowledge gained through holistic ecological and/or epidemiological investigations. It avoids overdependence on a single method—a lesson learned largely from the history of abuses of DDT for the control of plant pests. A multifaceted approach to parasite control has been considered ideal since the early days of parasite control programmes, when it was realized that mass treatment alone rarely brought effective long-term relief to parasitized populations. However, while integrated control should prove particularly effective against some parasites, a single tactic could be equally effective when directed against other species.

With the advent of chemotherapeutic agents having very low toxicities and high efficacies against the parasites of man, periodic treatment may prove to be a useful alternative to a multitactical approach for societies wealthy enough to provide regular mass treatment. However, frequent chemotherapy invites drug resistance, an increasingly serious problem, as the costs of pharmaceutical research and development increase sharply and fewer new compounds become available for the control of tropical diseases. Thus, the hope for control based on a single tactic may again prove illusory.

(a)   Integrated control of monoxenous parasites

Since there is no scope for anti-vector measures, monoxenous parasites are less suited to an integrated programme than are heteroxenous ones. Integrated control, therefore, usually involves a combination of treatment and/or sanitation to reduce environmental contamination, manipulation of the external environment to make it less hospitable for the growth and survival of infective stages, and protection of hosts from invasion or maturation of pathogenic levels of the infectious agent.

The importance of sheep to the Australian economy has led to particularly comprehensive epidemiological investigations of ovine, parasitic gastroenteritis in different climatic zones of the continent. On the basis of these investigations, recommendations for parasite control have been formulated for farms on which only treatment is practical, and for others where treatment can be integrated with grazing management to minimize reinfection and to optimize control. Only the combined programme as recommended for summer rainfall areas will be used as an example.

The epidemiological investigations upon which control is based are summarized in Fig. 8.8. In the summer rainfall areas, the parasites of particular importance are the trichostrongyle nematodes: *Haemonchus contortus*, *Ostertagia circumcincta* and *Trichostrongylus colubriformis*. The abundance of free-living infective larvae of each of the parasites varies seasonally; this may or may not be reflected in an attendant seasonal variation in parasitic worm burden. During some seasons, new infection is not reflected promptly by an increased adult worm density, because invading larvae become latent (e.g. *Haemonchus* in autumn–winter); these larvae do not mature for several months. The variation in adult worm burden may or may not have a prompt effect on the available pasture populations of infective larvae, since in cool weather the larval development is slow, and in dry weather the migration of larvae onto vegetation is inhibited.

When all three genera are considered together, it is apparent that the pasture populations of infective larvae decline to an annual nadir in late spring or early summer (Fig. 8.8). This presents an opportunity to treat the flock when reinfection will be minimal, thus extending the time until treatment will be required again. The effectiveness of the anthelmintic treatment is enhanced by using a pasture for lambing which was grazed during the preceding fall and winter by adult sheep or cattle. These animals ingest and destroy infective larvae on pasture, either because they are naturally resistant to the spectrum of parasites present (cattle) or because they have acquired resistance (mature sheep). Thus, appropriate grazing management permits full pasture utilization without contributing importantly to its contamination with respect to subsequent lambing.

To minimize the contamination of pasture in autumn, sheep are treated with an anthelmintic active against both adult worms and arrested larvae. This treatment

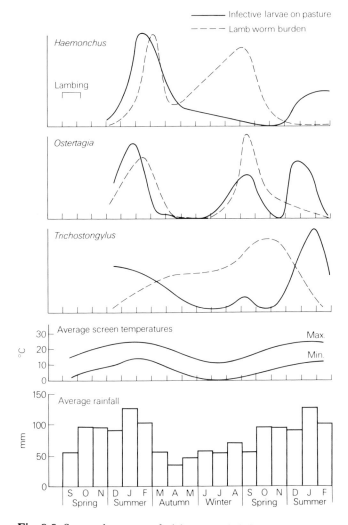

Fig. 8.8. Seasonal patterns of trichostrongyle infection in spring-born lambs grazing contaminated pasture from birth to 18 months and meteorological data for the comparable period at Armidale, Australia. (After Anderson *et al.*, 1978.)

removes arrested larvae of *O. circumcincta* before they are able to resume development. To obtain the greatest benefit from this treatment, the sheep are moved to pasture which has been grazed by cattle in the previous 3-month period.

Before lambing, i.e. in the late winter or early spring, when the sheep are gathered for shearing, another treatment is scheduled and the pregnant ewes are moved to safe pasture as described previously. Treatment removes any adult worms which would contribute to spring pasture contamination as well as arrested larvae of *H. contortus*, which would otherwise contribute to a periparturient rise in egg output in pregnant ewes.

(b)   *Integrated control of heteroxenous parasites*

With regard to the control of insect-borne parasites, the integrated programmes directed against the human filariases (*Wuchereria bancrofti* and *Brugia malayi*) in Sri Lanka have been remarkably successful. In an endemic coastal strip of the island, where coconut groves are the predominant feature, routine control of *Wuchereria bancrofti* depends on identification of infected individuals (case-finding), chemotherapy and particularly on weekly larvicidal treatment of mosquito breeding pools. These include pits for soaking coconut husks used in making rope. Unfortunately, the pits cannot be sprayed when in use, and, furthermore, there is no organized programme for removal of discarded coconut shells and other small containers which serve as breeding sites for mosquitoes.

Nevertheless, over a period of several years, the infection rate was reduced markedly to about 1%. It has been suggested that, if the existing programme could be supplemented further to control the breeding of mosquitoes in the husk pits all year round and in small containers, the vector population could be reduced by 90% and transmission would cease. These additional needs for interrupting transmission suggest the use of biological control agents for the husk pits when in use (see section 8.3.3d), and community self-help for the disposal of small breeding containers. In public health, self-help is enjoying renewed interest on the basis of the innumerable reports of its success in the control of vector-borne diseases in China. Whether a substantial degree of community cooperation would be forthcoming where little compulsion can be brought to bear is problematical.

The control of *Brugia malayi* has been even more spectacular. Indeed, eradication has been reported. The parasite is transmitted by mosquitoes of the genus *Mansonia*. These are dependent on certain plants (*Pistia, Eichornia*) for their survival; the larvae remain submerged throughout development, puncturing plants with a special tube to obtain air.

Before the control programme was initiated, the parasite occurred in isolated foci throughout the island wherever appropriate mosquitoes were abundant. In these areas, case-finding and chemotherapy were again part of the programme, but the destruction of the plants necessary for the larval life of the mosquito vector played a crucial role.

With regard to snail-borne diseases such as schistosomiasis, a modern integrated programme for control would choose from among tactics such as chemotherapy, snail control and provision of a safe water supply. Jordan (1977) has provided data from a series of carefully conducted studies designed to evaluate each of these separately. Fig. 8.9 shows a map of the Caribbean Island, St. Lucia, where each method was evaluated in a different isolated valley, and the results of several years of

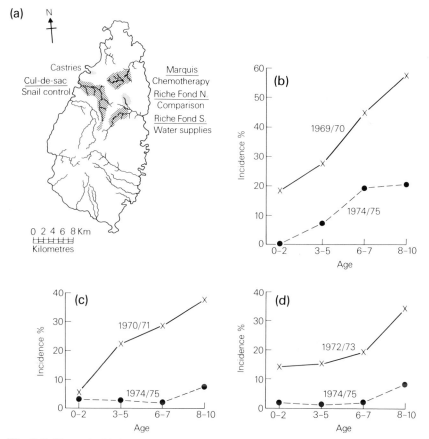

Fig. 8.9. Control of *Schistosoma mansoni* on St. Lucia, West Indies. (a) Map showing location of each of 3 control areas (isolated valleys) and an untreated area reserved for comparison. (b) Incidence of new infections in Cul de Sac Valley before (1969–70) and after (1974–75) four years of snail control. (c) Incidence of new infections before (1970–71) and after (1974–75) installation of water supplies to reduce human contact with schistosome-infested streams in Riche Fond South. (The first village was supplied in 1970, the last in 1972.) (d) Incidence of new infections before (1972–73) and after (1974–75) two chemotherapy campaigns in Marquis Valley. (After Jordan, 1977.)

intensive, superbly managed control; this was based on thorough preliminary investigations of the local ecology and epidemiology of schistosomiasis. The success of each programme is evident.

Jordan sums up the advantages of the individual forms of control, showing that the use of molluscicides does not require the cooperation of the community, and is effective even if significant numbers of infected individuals migrate into the area under treatment. Unfortunately, it is of little help to those with existing disease.

Like snail control, safe water supply can reduce transmission effectively, but it brings little relief to heavily infected people. Convenient, safe, water supplies are, however, generally desired and provide additional social and medical benefits.

Chemotherapy reduces transmission rapidly, and, under conditions prevailing in St. Lucia, it was inexpensive. Furthermore, it brought quick relief to those suffering disease. It has the disadvantage that it may not interrupt transmission effectively if a significant number of infected individuals avoid treatment, or if immigration of infected individuals is a significant factor. Under continental conditions, where important alternative definitive hosts exist, treatment of man alone may be inadequate. Thus, for long-term control the combination, chemotherapy and interruption of transmission with molluscicides or installation of water supplies, remains the ideal for which to strive.

An evolving programme using all the major components of schistosome control has been in effect in Puerto Rico since 1954. This programme began with mass chemotherapy, but after drug-related deaths occurred, treatment of infected individuals was left to individual initiative. The lack of safe anthelmintics for mass treatment led to a concentration on snail control. In Puerto Rico this was approached by the full spectrum of chemical, biological and environmental methods. A series of

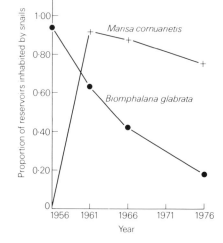

Fig. 8.10. Displacement of *Biomphalaria glabrata* by *Marisa cornuarietis* in major reservoirs of Puerto Rico between 1956 and 1976. (After Jobin *et al.*, 1977.)

engineering projects (swamp drainage, channelization of streams, etc.) altered major snail habitats and various molluscicides were applied depending upon the state of the art. The most remarkable aspect of this programme was the heavy reliance placed on *Marisa cornuarietis*, the molluscan competitor of *Biomphalaria glabrata*, the snail host of *Schistosoma mansoni* in Puerto Rico. Throughout the island, *Marisa* was introduced into standing water habitats: farm ponds, irrigation reservoirs and large lakes. The success of this is shown in Fig. 8.10. An independent programme brought sanitary improvements and safe water supplies to many parts of the island throughout the period of control. Health education probably made a considerable impact on behavioural aspects of transmission.

The results of this diversified effort, which shifted in emphasis with the availability of new tactics, was evaluated by a shifting series of techniques. Initially, an annual snail census along with faecal examination of first-grade school children was used to evaluate progress, but, in 1966, when the prevalence of infection in first-graders approached zero, skin-testing of 5th grade children, which had begun in 1963, became the criterion for evaluating progress. Fig. 8.11 shows that there was a striking decline in the prevalence of infection as judged by skin tests between 1963 and 1976. Indeed Negron–Aponte and Jobin (1979) suggest that now that safe,

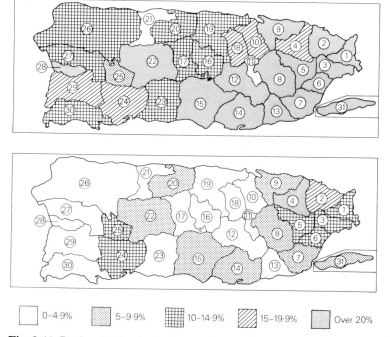

| | 0–4·9% | | 5–9·9% | | 10–14·9% | | 15–19·9% | | Over 20% |

Fig. 8.11. Regional reduction in the prevalence of *Schistosoma mansoni* infection in Puerto Rico as judged by skin test surveys conducted in 1963 (top) and 1976 (bottom). (After Negron-Aponte & Jobin, 1979.)

relatively inexpensive anti-schistosome drugs are available, eradication by mass chemotherapy will prove less expensive than control through the continual maintenance of a programme designed to manage snail populations. Their optimism may well be justified, considering the advantages of an insular situation for any control or eradication programme.

REFERENCES AND FURTHER READING

Anderson N., Dash K.M., Donald W.D., Southcott W.H. & Waller P.J. (1978) Epidemiology and control of nematode infections. In A.D. Donald, W.H. Southcott & J.K. Dineen (eds.) *The Epidemiology and Control of Gastrointestinal Parasites of Sheep in Australia*, pp. 23–52. East Melbourne, Commonwealth Scientific and Industrial Research Organization.

Ansari N. (1973) *Epidemiology and Control of Schistosomiasis (Bilharziasis)*. Baltimore, University Park Press.

Armour J. (1975) The epidemiology and control of bovine fascioliasis. *Vet. Rec.* **96**, 198–201.

Beard T.C. (1973) The elimination of echinococcus from Iceland. *Bull. Wld. Hlth. Org.* **48**, 655–60.

Beesley W.N. (1973) Control of arthropods of medical and veterinary importance. In B. Dawes (ed.) *Advances in Parasitology*, vol. 11, pp. 115–83. London, Academic Press.

Berg C.O. (1973) Biological control of snail-borne diseases: a review. *Expl. Parasit.* **38**, 318–30.

Chapin G. & Wasserstrom R. (1981) Agricultural production and malaria resurgence in Central America and India. *Nature* **293**, 181–5.

Chu K.Y. (1978) Trials of ecological and chemical measures for the control of *Schistosoma haematobium* transmission in a Volta Lake village. *Bull. Wld. Hlth. Org.* **56**, 313–22.

Davidson G. (1974) *Genetic Control of Insect Pests*. New York, Academic Press.

Gemmell M.A. (1979) Hydatidosis control—a global view. *Aust. vet. J.* **55**, 118–25.

Holmes J.C. & Bethel W.M. (1972) Modification of intermediate host behaviour by parasites. In E.U. Canning & C.A. Wright (eds.) *Behavioural Aspects of Parasite Transmisson*, pp. 123–50. London, Academic Press.

Jobin W.R., Brown R.A., Velez S.P. & Ferguson R.F. (1977) Biological control of *Biomphalaria glabrata* in major reservoirs of Puerto Rico. *Am. J. trop. Med. Hyg.* **26**, 1018–23.

Jordan P. (1977) Schistosomiasis—research to control. *Am. J. trop. Med. Hyg.* **26**, 877–86.

Jordan P., Christie J.D. & Unrau G.O. (1980) Schistosomiasis transmission with particular reference of possible ecological and biological control. *Acta tropica* **37**, 95–135.

Kochar V.K., Schad G.A., Chowdhury A.B., Dean C.G. & Nawalinski T.A. (1976) Human factors in the regulation of parasitic infections. In F.X. Grollig & H.B. Haley (eds.) *Medical Anthropology*, pp. 287–313. Amsterdam, Mouton Publishers.

Laird M (1977) *Tsetse: The Future for Biological Methods in its Integrated Control*. Ottawa, International Development Research Centre.

Laird M. (1980) Biocontrol in veterinary entomology. *Adv. vet. Sci. Comp. Med.* **24**, 145–77.

Lee D.L. & Atkinson H.J. (1976) *Physiology of Nematodes*. 2nd ed. London, Macmillan.

Libby J.A. (1975) *Meat Hygiene*. Philadelphia, Lea & Febiger.

Lim H.K. & Heyneman D. (1972) Intramolluscan inter-trematode antagonism: a review of factors influencing the host–parasite system and its possible role in biological control. In B. Dawes (ed.) *Advances in Parasitology*, vol. 10, pp. 191–268. London, Academic Press.

Lofgren C.S., Dame D.A., Breeland S.G., Weidhaus D.E., Jeffrey G., Kaiser R., Ford H.R., Boston M.D. & Baldwin K.F. (1974) Release of chemosterilized males for the control of *Anopheles albimanus* in El Salvador. III. Field methods and population control. *Am. J. trop. Med. Hyg.* **23**, 288–97.

Lysek H.L. (1979) Possible biological control of geohelminths. *Helminthologia* **16**, 107–13.

Mankau R. (1980) Biological control of nematode pests by natural enemies. *Ann. Rev. Phytopathol.* **18**, 415–50.

Marinkelle C.J. (1980) The control of leishmaniases. *Bull. Wld. Hlth. Org.* **58**, 807–18.

Matthewson M.D. (1976) *Cattle Tick Control.* Berkhamsted, Wellcome Research Laboratories.

Michel J.F. (1974) Arrested development of nematodes and some related phenomena. In B. Dawes (ed.) *Advances in Parasitology*, vol. 12, pp. 279–366. London, Academic Press.

Miller T.A. (1978) Vaccines against parasites, fact or fiction. In A.M. Fallis (ed.) *Parasites, Their World and Ours*, pp. 89–98. Ottawa, Royal Society of Canada.

Negron-Aponte H. & Jobin W.R. (1979) Schistosomiasis control in Puerto Rico. Twenty-five years of operational experience. *Am. J. trop. Med. Hyg.* **28**, 515–25.

Nelson G.S. (1974) Zooprophylaxis with special reference to schistosomiasis and filariasis. In E.J.L. Soulsby (ed.) *Parasitic Zoonoses, Clinical and Experimental Studies*, pp. 273–85. New York, Academic Press.

Noguer A., Wernsdorfer W., Kouznetsov R.K. & Hempel J. (1978) The malaria situation in 1976. *WHO Chronicle* **32**, 9–17.

Pal R. & LaChance L.E. (1974) The operational feasibiity of genetic methods for control of insects of medical and veterinary importance. *A. Rev. Ent.* **19**, 269–92.

Payne D., Grab B., Fontaine R.E. & Hempel J.H.G. (1976) Impact of control measures on malaria transmission and general mortality. *Bull. Wld. Hlth. Org.* **54**, 369–77.

Petersen J.J. (1973) Role of mermithid nematodes in biological control of mosquitoes. *Expl. Parasit.* **33**, 229–47.

Petersen J.J., Chapman H.C., Willis O.R. & Fukuda T. (1978) Release of *Romanomermis culicivorax* for the control of *Anopheles albimanus* in El Salvador. *Am. J. trop. Med. Hyg.* **27**, 1268–73.

Pramer D. (1964) Nematode-trapping fungi. *Science* **144**, 382–88.

Reeves E. (1973) *Mosquito Control: Some Perspectives for Developing Countries.* Washington DC, National Academy of Sciences.

Sankurathri C.S. & Holmes J.C. (1976) Effects of thermal effluents on parasites and commensals of *Physa gyrina* Say (Mollusca: Gastropoda) and their interactions at Lake Wabaman, Alberta. *Can. J. Zool.* **54**, 1742–53.

Schad G.A. (1977) The role of arrested development in the regulation of nematode populations. In G.S. Esch (ed.) *Regulation of Parasite Populations*, pp. 111–67. New York, Academic Press.

Schad G.A. & Rozeboom L.E. (1976) Integrated control of helminths in human populations. *A. rev. Ecol. Syst.* **7**, 393–420.

Schad G.A., Soulsby E.J.L., Chowdhury A.B. & Gilles H. (1975) Epidemiological and serological studies of hookworm infection in endemic areas in India and West Africa. In *Nuclear Techniques in Helminthology Research*, pp. 41–54. Vienna, International Atomic Energy Agency.

Southwood T.R.E. (1977) Entomology and mankind. *Am. Scient.* **65,** 30–9.

Theodorides V.J. (1980) In J. Georgi (ed.) *Parasitology for Veterinarians.* Philadelphia, Saunders.

Thomas J.D. & Assefa B. (1978) Behavioural responses to exogenous chemicals by the snail hosts of schistosomiasis. In F.E. Brinckman & J.E. Montemarano (eds.) *5th International Symposium on the Controlled Release of Bioactive Materials,* pp. 4.1–4.18. Washington, United States Bureau of Standards.

Upatham E.S. & Sturrock R.F. (1973) Field investigations on the effect of other aquatic animals on the infection of *Biomphalaria glabrata* by *Schistosoma mansoni* miricidia. *J. Parasit.* **59,** 448–53.

WHO (1978) Malaria Control—a reoriented strategy. *WHO Chronicle* **32,** 226–30.

Chapter 9
Chemotherapy
W.E. Gutteridge

9.1   INTRODUCTION

Chemotherapy as a means of controlling infectious diseases was developed by Ehrlich and his colleagues in Germany towards the end of the last century. Ehrlich at that time was studying the staining properties of a number of dyes for protozoa such as trypanosomes and malaria parasites. He conceived the idea that it ought to be possible to find dyes (i.e. drugs) which would selectively destroy pathogens but leave host cells undamaged. His approach was most successful initially with diseases caused by parasites. By 1930, as a result of careful selection and chemical modification, first of dyes and later of other chemical structures, to improve their activity against parasites and reduce their toxicity to hosts, a number of drugs were developed which were useful in the control of parasitic diseases (e.g. organic arsenicals and suramin for trypanosomiasis; plasmoquine for malaria; organic antimonials for schistosomiasis).

It is not always appreciated that Ehrlich's approach was far less successful with antibacterial drugs. It needed the discovery first of antimetabolites such as the sulphonamides and later antibiotics such as penicillin to open up this area of chemotherapy.

Today, lead compounds from which it might be possible to develop new drugs are sought by screening both compounds which have been chemically synthesized (the Ehrlich approach) and those which have been isolated from the fermentation products of microorganisms (the antibiotic approach). Once a lead compound has been detected, however, the original Ehrlich principles are followed in both cases. The chemical structure of the compound is modified, and the member of the series thus synthesized which is most active against the pathogen and least toxic to the host, is selected. It is a curious and so far unexplained fact that with the exception of the anticoccidial drug monensin, the antitrichomonad drug metronidazole, and the anthelmintic avermectins, all the currently used antiparasitic drugs were originally chemically synthesized *de novo*. Thus the story of the development of today's antiparasitic drugs goes right back to the beginnings of chemotherapy itself.

9.2   CURRENTLY USED DRUGS

All the common parasitic diseases of man and domestic animals can be controlled, at least in part, by drugs. For some of them, chemoprophylactic agents are also available. Basic information on those in most common use is given in Tables 9.1–9.3, columns I–III (see pp. 294–318 for all tables in this chapter). The limitations on their use are discussed in sections 9.6 and 9.7.

Note that, particularly for coccidiosis (Table 9.1), combinations of drugs are used. These have proved advantageous in reducing the rate of development of drug resistant strains of *Eimeria* (see section 9.6). Only the 2,4-diaminopyrimidine/ sulphonamide (or sulphone) combinations, however, have been shown to be synergistic (the activity of the combination is greater than the sum of the individual activities).

9.3   CHEMISTRY

The chemical structures of the most commonly used antiparasitic drugs are given in Tables 9.1–9.3 (column IV). A number of general points can be made about these structures.

They contain a very restricted range of elements: C, H, O and N are the only almost universal elements. Sulphur occurs in some, often as part of a ring structure (e.g. nifurtimox, niridazole, levamisole). Fluorine, chlorine, iodine and phosphorus also occur occasionally (commonly in the anthelmintic phenols and organo-phosphorus compounds), but not with the overall frequency seen in herbicides and insecticides. Inorganic elements are rare, the only ones in the table being arsenic and antimony, in two of the most toxic groups of drugs on the list.

Ring structures are very common: for example, the benzene ring itself is present in more than half of the drugs under consideration. Many of the others are nitrogen-containing rings (e.g. pyrimidine, imidazole, quinoline, piperazine), often with the nitrogen in the quaternary configuration such that the drugs have a net positive charge at physiological pH (e.g. antrycide, bephenium). Common substituents on the rings are methyl, methoxy, hydroxymethyl, hydroxy and amino groups, though more bulky substituents do occur. Nitro groups are also quite common, though they are now viewed with suspicion since many nitrocompounds have been found to be mutagenic and carcinogenic. Free sulphydryl groups are not found. These are probably too biologically active to be selectively toxic.

Thus it is clear that drugs with a high degree of selective toxicity are not exotic chemical structures made up of unusual elements and chemical groups. Rather, they are made of the same elements and chemical groups which are found naturally among the chemicals of the cell. What makes them toxic to the parasite is the fact that the elements and chemical groups are combined to produce unusual configurations.

9.4   MECHANISMS OF ACTION

The proper establishment of the primary mode of action of a drug requires a systematic study of its effects on the various metabolic processes of a parasite at the lowest concentrations that stop its growth, kill it, or lead to its expulsion from the host. Only when such a survey is complete can it be concluded confidently that a particular pathway or reaction is most sensitive to inhibition by a drug and is therefore the primary target of that drug. Systematic studies of this type have been carried out with a number of antibacterial drugs but only rarely with those active against parasites. Thus in most cases, it has only been possible to indicate in Tables 9.1–9.3 (column V) what is the *most likely* mechanism of action of a particular drug.

Extensive study of the biochemical modes of action of antimicrobial drugs over many years has led to the identification of six key areas of metabolism as targets for drug action: energy metabolism; membrane function; cofactor synthesis; nucleic acid synthesis; protein synthesis; wall synthesis. Note the absence of lipid metabolism and carbohydrate synthesis from this list. Presumably, these processes are too similar in bacteria and mammalian cells for *selective* inhibition to be possible. Bacteria have the prokaryotic type of cell organization; all parasites are eukaryotes. Not surprisingly, therefore, studies on the mode of action of antiparasitic drugs have produced a different list of vulnerable areas of metabolism. In particular, there is no real equivalent of the bacterial cell wall in parasites, but they do contain important structural proteins—microtubules—which are not present in bacteria, and in addition helminths have a neuromuscular system which is not found at all in unicellular microorganisms. A list of the main target areas of antiparasitic drugs is given in Table 9.4.

Table 9.4 also summarizes the mechanisms of action of each class of antiparasitic drug. Note that the majority of the antiprotozoal drugs affect biosynthetic metabolism. Of those that affect energy metabolism, most are either still in human use, though rather toxic because of the absence of a satisfactory alternative (arsenicals, antimonials, suramin), or are veterinary drugs where the degree of selectivity toxicity required is less than for human drugs (robenidine, quinolones). This suggests that there are rather more differences in biosynthetic metabolism between protozoa and vertebrates than there are in energy metabolism.

In contrast to antiprotozoal drugs, most of the anthelmintic drugs affect energy metabolism or the neuromuscular system. This should not be taken as an indication that helminth metabolism in these areas is much more distinct than that seen in vertebrates. It is much more likely to be a reflection of the lack of vulnerability of non-growing mature worms (except for egg production) to inhibitors of biosynthetic processes, and the vulnerability of the neuromuscular system of gut-dwelling parasites to orally administered drugs which are not well absorbed by the host.

9.5   MECHANISMS OF SELECTIVITY TOXICITY

Investigations of antimicrobial drugs have shown that the establishment of the biochemical mode of action of a drug often also provides an explanation of why only the pathogen is killed. This has in many cases also proved to be true with antiparasitic drugs. The five basic mechanisms found to underly the selective action of antimicrobial drugs are given in Table 9.5. Most of the antiprotozoal drugs are selective either because they are taken up preferentially by the parasite or because they can discriminate between isofunctional targets in the host and parasite (Tables 9.1–9.3, column VI and Table 9.5). There is little information available on this subject for the anthelmintic drugs but it is likely that most of them fall into the same two categories.

There are only three sites of action of antiparasitic drugs so far detected which have no equivalent in vertebrate cells: L-α-glycerphosphate oxidase in African trypanosomes; dihydropteroate synthetase in sporozoans; fumarate reductase in helminths. These are exploited respectively by suramin, sulphonamides and sulphones and possibly levamisole. In addition, 5-nitroimidazoles such as metronidazole are selective because they are activated in the parasite by a system which has no equivalent in vertebrate cells. This relatively short list is undoubtedly a reflection both of the similarity of the biochemistry of parasites and vertebrate cells and also of our present poor knowledge of the mechanisms of action of many antiparasitic drugs.

9.6   DRUG RESISTANCE

As has been indicated previously, all the common parasitic diseases of man and domestic animals can be controlled, at least in part, by drugs. How long this situation will last, however, is a matter for conjecture since drug resistance is becoming an increasing problem. This has long been a difficulty in the control of coccidiosis since chickens are normally given continuous prophylactic treatment by mixing a drug or a combination of drugs with the diet. For example, the average life of an anticoccidial drug in continuous usage is probably no more than 2 years, though it begins to look as if monensin will be an important exception. There are now, however, also problems of resistance with antitrypanosomal drugs such as ethidium and antrycide and antimalarial drugs such as chloroquine and pyrimethamine. Because of this, ethidium and antrycide are now little used for the control of animal trypanosomiasis in Africa and much of the malaria in Far East Asia no longer responds to chloroquine. It is hoped that the development of mefloquine will ease the problem of chloroquine resistance and pyrimethamine has been given a new lease of life by being administered in combination with dapsone. Even so, it is clear that drug resistance will be a continuing problem in parasite chemotherapy.

Studies, particularly with antibacterial drugs, have led to the recognition of five basic mechanisms by which microorganisms can become resistant to drugs:

1   metabolism of the drug to an inactive form;
2   alteration in permeability so that the drug no longer enters the pathogen;

3   metabolic lesion bypassed by alternative metabolic pathway;

4   target altered so that its sensitivity to inhibition is decreased;

5   target enzyme increased in quantity so that the pathogen can survive high percentage inhibitions of activity.

Little experimental work has been done on mechanisms of resistance of antiparasitic drugs though examples are known of resistance in categories 2, 4 and 5.

A very common mechanism of resistance, seen particularly in drugs with a mechanism of selective toxicity involving differential permeability, is reduction in permeability to the drug. There is at least some evidence that resistance to diamidines, phenanthridines, aminoquinaldines and 4-aminoquinolines falls into this category. Only resistance to the 4-aminoquinoline chloroquine, and the diamidine pentamidine, have been studied in detail. Resistance to chloroquine involves loss of the high affinity chloroquine-binding site and thus failure to concentrate drug from the medium. It appears to be a stable character which is inherited in a simple Mendelian fashion, undergoes genetic recombination with other markers and probably arises by mutation and selection in the presence of the drug. Resistance to pentamidine appears to involve alterations in the transport system such that it has either lower V_{max} or higher K_m or a combination of the two (see Chapter 5).

Strains of malaria resistant to pyrimethamine have been shown to contain increased quantities of an altered dihydrofolate reductase which no longer binds the drug as well as the parent enzyme. Resistance arises by mutation and the genetic factors involved can undergo recombination with other markers in crosses between resistant and sensitive parasite lines.

9.7   FUTURE DEVELOPMENTS

Although there are a large number of drugs that can be used for the control of parasitic diseases, there are problems associated with the use of many of them. Some, such as suramin, which have been in use for a long period of time and are now patent-free, are not always freely available. Others, such as pentamidine and the antischistosomal antimonials, cannot be given orally; this makes them relatively expensive to administer on a large scale. Some must be given for long periods (120 days for nifurtimox); this compounds the problems of side-effects. Many do not work against all stages of the disease. For example, suramin, because it does not cross the blood–brain barrier, is ineffective in the late stage of human trypanosomiasis; diethylcarbamazine is inactive against adult filarial worms and is therefore of limited value in the treatment of onchocerciasis. Some, such as Mel B and the antimonials, are highly toxin and only retained because there is, or has been until recently, no alternative. Attempts are being made, in leishmaniasis especially, to overcome this problem by using liposome encapsulated drugs, but this technique is still at the experimental stage. With others, such as chloroquine, the spread of drug resistance is causing concern (see section 9.6).

It is clear, therefore, that there is the need for a new generation of antiparasitic drugs. Programmes of research, screening and development are in operation in some pharmaceutical companies. Most of these, however, are orientated towards the parasites of veterinary importance (especially coccidia, liver flukes, tapeworms and intestinal nematodes) since there is a reasonable chance here, because of the size of the market, of recouping the high research and development costs of modern drugs. Few companies are, however, actively seeking drugs for human parasitic diseases since the majority of these afflict the poor of the developing countries of the world. The World Health Organization, in collaboration with the World Bank and the United Nations Development Programme, has, however, recently taken the initiative here with the launching of an ambitious Programme for Research and Training in Tropical Diseases. Five of the six diseases included in this programme concern parasites (trypanosomiasis, leishmaniasis, malaria, schistosomiasis, filariasis). One of the objectives of the programme is the development and distribution of effective chemotherapeutic agents for these diseases. There are signs already that this programme is not only stimulating basic research on these diseases in academic institutions but is also reawakening the interest of the pharmaceutical industry in them. The number of research papers appearing in the literature on these parasites is increasing rapidly and a number of joint WHO/pharmaceutical industry development programmes are under way (e.g. mefloquine with Roche for malaria and praziquantel with Bayer for schistosomiasis). It will be surprising if there are not some useful new developments in this field over the next decade.

FURTHER READING

Alving C.R., Steck E.A., Hanson W.L., Loizeaux P.S., Chapman W.L. & Waits V.B. (1978) Improved therapy of experimental leishmaniasis by use of a liposome encapsulated antimonial drug. *Life Sciences* 22, 1021–6.

Barrett J. (1981) *Biochemistry of Parasitic Helminths*. London, Macmillan.

Cohen S.S. (1979) Comparative biochemistry and drug design for infectious diseases. *Science* 205, 964–71.

Foster R. & Richards H.C. (1970) Recent advances towards the chemotherapeutic control of schistosomiasis. *Bull. chem. Ther.* 4, 293–7.

Franklin T.J. & Snow G.A. (1981) *Biochemistry of Antimicrobial Action*, 3rd ed. London, Science Paperbacks, Chapman and Hall.

Gale E.F. (1966) The object of the exercise. In B.A. Newton & P.E. Reynolds (eds.) *Biochemical Studies of Antimicrobial Drugs*, pp. 1–21. Cambridge, Cambridge University Press.

Gale E.F., Cundliffe E., Reynolds P.E., Richmond M.H. & Waring M. (1981) *The Molecular Basis of Antibiotic Action*, 2nd ed. London, John Wiley.

Gutteridge W.E. (1976) Chemotherapy of Chagas' disease: the present situation. *Trop. Dis. Bull.* **73**, 699–705.

Gutteridge W.E. & Coombs G.H. (1977) *Biochemistry of Parasitic Protozoa.* London, Macmillan.

Joyner L.P. (1981) The chemotherapy of protozoal infections of veterinary importance. *J. Protozool.* **28**, 17–19.

Mansour T.E. (1979) Chemotherapy of parasitic worms: new biochemical strategies. *Science* **205**, 462–9.

Peters W. (1980) Chemotherapy of malaria. In J.P. Kreier (ed.) *Malaria, Vol. I. Epidemiology, Chemotherapy, Morphology and Metabolism*, pp. 145–283. New York, Academic Press.

Pinder R.M. (1971) Recent advances in the chemotherapy of malaria. *Prog. med. Chem.* **8**, 231–316.

Richards H.C. & Foster R. (1969) Chemotherapy of tropical diseases. *Rep. Prog. appl. Chem.* **54**, 200–19.

Ryley J.F. & Betts M.J. (1973) Chemotherapy of chicken coccidiosis. *Adv. pharmac. Chemother.* **11**, 221–93.

Sanderson B.E. (1973) Anthelmintics in the study of helminth metabolism. In A.E.R. Taylor & R. Muller (eds.) *Chemotherapeutic Agents in the Study of Parasites*, pp. 53–82. Oxford, Blackwell Scientific Publications.

Schnitzer R.J. & Hawking F. (eds.) (1963) *Experimental Chemotherapy*, vol. 1. New York, Academic Press.

Schonfeld H. (ed.) (1981) *Antiparasitic Chemotherapy. Antibiotics and Chemotherapy*, vol. 30. Basel, S. Karger.

Steck E.A. (1981) The chemotherapy of protozoal infections of man. *J. Protozool.* **28**, 10–16.

Van den Bossche H. (ed.) (1972) *Comparative Biochemistry of Parasites.* New York, Academic Press.

Van den Bossche H. (ed.) (1976) *Biochemistry of Parasites and Host–Parasite Relationships.* Amsterdam, Elsevier/North Holland.

Van den Bossche H. (1976) The molecular basis of anthelminthic action. In H. Van den Bossche (ed.) *Biochemistry of Parasites and Host–Parasite Relationships*, pp. 553–72. Amsterdam, Elsevier/North Holland.

Van den Bossche H. (1978) Chemotherapy of parasitic infections. *Nature* **273**, 626–30.

Van den Bossche H. (ed.) (1980) *The Host Invader Interplay.* Amsterdam, Elsevier/North Holland.

WHO (1981) *Chemotherapy of Malaria*, 2nd ed. WHO Monograph Series No. 27. Geneva, WHO.

Williamson J. (1976) Chemotherapy of African Trypanosomiasis. *Trop. Dis. Bull.* **73**, 531–42.

Table 9.1. Drugs active against protozoa.

I Disease/drug	II Use	III Class	IV Chemical structure	V Target and mode of action	VI Mechanism of selective toxicity
TRYPANOSOMIASIS					
Tryparsamide	Late treatment in man—*T. gambiense* only	Arsenicals		*Energy metabolism* Blocks glycolysis by inhibition of the ATP-yielding reaction pyruvate kinase	Combination of differential permeability, target discrimination and greater importance of target in parasite energy metabolism
Mel B (Melarsoprol)	Late treatment in man; toxic; patients need to be hospitalized	Arsenicals			
Suramin (Antrypol) (Bayer 205)	Early treatment in man—does not cross blood–brain barrier	Sulphated naphthylamine		*Energy metabolism* Blocks NADH oxidation by inhibition of α-glycero-phosphate oxidase and dehydrogenase	Enzyme system unique to parasite
Antrycide (Quina-pyramine)	Treatment in cattle; resistance now a problem	Aminoquinaldine		*Protein synthesis* Displaces poly-amines and Mg^{2+} from ribosomes and causes their aggregation	Differential permeability

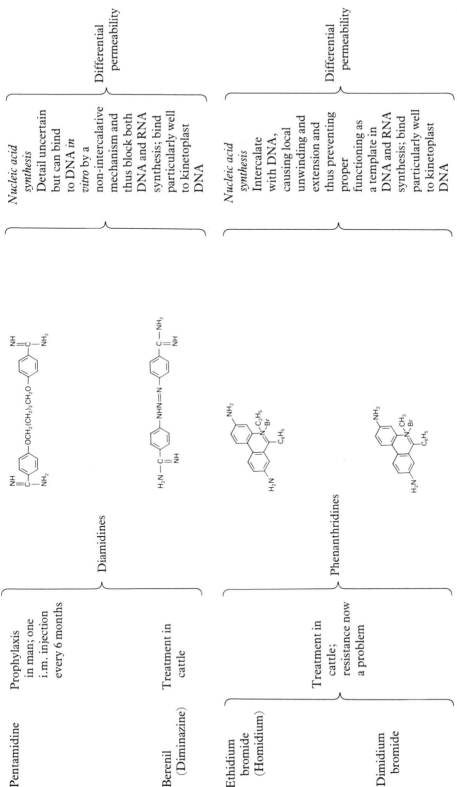

		Mode of action	
Pentamidine	Prophylaxis in man; one i.m. injection every 6 months	*Nucleic acid synthesis* Detail uncertain but can bind to DNA *in vitro* by a non-intercalative mechanism and thus block both DNA and RNA synthesis; bind particularly well to kinetoplast DNA	Differential permeability
Berenil (Diminazine)	Treatment in cattle		
Diamidines			
Ethidium bromide (Homidium)	Treatment in cattle; resistance now a problem	*Nucleic acid synthesis* Intercalate with DNA, causing local unwinding and extension and thus preventing proper functioning as a template in DNA and RNA synthesis; bind particularly well to kinetoplast DNA	Differential permeability
Dimidium bromide			
Phenanthridines			

continues

Table 9.1. *continued*

I Disease/drug	II Use	III Class	IV Chemical structure	V Target and mode of action	VI Mechanism of selective toxicity
CHAGAS' DISEASE					
Nifurtimox (Lampit) (Bayer 2502)	Treatment but not prophylaxis; side-effects	5-Nitrofuran		*Nucleic acid synthesis* Drug activated by partial reduction of the nitro-group.	Uncertain but probably higher rate of activation in parasite
Benznidazole (Radanil) (Ro 7.1051)	Treatment but not prophylaxis; side-effects	2-Nitroimidazole		Active metabolite probably alkylates DNA and thus blocks nucleic acid synthesis. Parasite may also be damaged by H_2O_2 accumulation as a result of drug activation since it does not contain catalase	

Pentostam	Treatment of cutaneous infections in man	Antimonial		*Energy metabolism* Detail uncertain; may be as antimony potassium tartrate (Table 9.2) or as arsenicals (see Trypanosomiasis)	Combination of differential permeability, target discrimination and greater importance of target in parasite energy metabolism
Amphotericin B	Treatment of cutaneous infections in man	Polyene		*Membrane function* In fungi, action involves binding to membrane sterol and thus allowing leakage out of K^+ and other materials; some evidence for this in *Leishmania*	Uncertain; in fungi, relates in part to differences in sterol content between host and parasite
Pentamidine	Treatment of visceral infections in man	Diamidine		*Nucleic acid synthesis* Uncertain in *Leishmania*. See action on trypanosomes	

continues

Table 9.1 *continued*

I Disease/drug	II Use	III Class	IV Chemical structure	V Target and mode of action	VI Mechanism of selective toxicity
TRICHOMONIASIS AND AMOEBIASIS					
Metronidazole (Flagyl)	Treatment in man; in trichomoniasis, both sexual partners should be treated	5-Nitromidazole		*Nucleic acid synthesis* Activated by partial reduction of the nitro-group by the pyruvate–ferrodoxin oxidoreductase complex and then alkylates DNA, blocking nucleic acid synthesis	Drug activation occurs only in the parasite
COCCIDIOSIS					
Amprolium plus	Prophylaxis in chickens by continuous administration in diet	Thiamine analogue		*Co-factor synthesis* Blocks thiamine uptake and hence interferes with decarboxylations reaction	Host transport less sensitive to inhibition
Ethopabate		Para aminobenzoic acid		Blocks dihydropteroate synthetase and so FH$_4$ synthesis	Enzyme unique to parasite

Drug	Use	Group	Mode of action	Basis of selectivity
Amprolium plus	Prophylaxis in chickens by continuous administration in diet	See above	*Co-factor synthesis* See above	See above
Ethopabate plus			See above	See above
Sulpha-quinoxaline			Blocks dihydropteroate synthetase and so FH_4 synthesis	Enzyme unique to parasite
Buquinolate	Prophylaxis in chickens by continuous administration in diet; resistance developed very quickly to this series	Quinolones	*Energy metabolism* Analogue of ubiquinone, which forms part of the coccidial electron transport chain; blocks electron transport and hence NADH oxidation and ATP synthesis	Uncertain but probably parasite and host ubiquinones differ
Decoquinate				
Methyl benzoquate (Nequinate)				
Monensin	Prophylaxis in chickens by continuous administration in diet; little sign of resistance so far	Antibiotic	*Membrane function* Ionophore and so causes cell to lose its cations	Unknown

Amprolium plus — Unknown

Ethopabate plus — Unknown

continues

Table 9.1. *continued*

I Disease/drug	II Use	III Class	IV Chemical structure	V Target and mode of action	VI Mechanism of selective toxicity
Clopidol	Prophylaxis in chickens by continuous administration in diet	Pyridone		Unknown	Unknown
Robenidine		Robenidine		*Energy metabolism* Uncertain but may inhibit the respiratory chain	
Nicarbazin		Complex of carbanilide and a pyrimidine		Unknown	
Zoalene (Dinitolmide)		Nitrobenzamide			
Arprinocid		Purine analogue		*Nucleic acid synthesis* Interferes with the inter-conversion of purines and so blocks nucleic acid synthesis	Uncertain but probably discrimination at the enzyme level

Drug	Use	Class	Structure	Mode of action
Diaveridine plus Sulpha-quinoxaline	Prophylaxis in chicken by continuous administration in diet; combinations are synergistic and resistance develops less readily	2,4-Diamino-pyrimidines and sulphonamides	CH$_3$O, CH$_3$O—, CH$_2$, N N NH$_2$ NH$_2$ N N—NHSb$_2$, NH$_2$	*Co-factor synthesis* 2,4-Diamino-pyrimidines are competitive inhibitors of dihydrofolate reductase. Sulphonamides block dihydropteroate synthetase. Thus both block the synthesis of FH$_4$ from GTP and so interfere with the action of FH$_4$ in active one carbon transfer reactions	2,4--Diamino-pyrimidines discriminate between host and parasite dihydrofolate reductases. Sulphonamides are selective because dihydropteroate synthetase occurs only in the parasite. Vertebrates require preformed FH$_4$
Ormetoprim plus Sulpha-dimethoxine			CH$_3$O, CH$_3$O, CH$_3$, CH$_2$, N N NH$_2$ NH$_2$ H$_2$N— —SO$_2$NH— N OCH$_3$ N OCH$_3$		

TOXOPLASMOSIS

Drug	Use	Class	Structure	Mode of action
Pyrimethamine plus Dapsone	Treatment in man	2,4-Diamino-pyrimidine and sulphone	CH$_3$CH$_2$, N N NH$_2$ NH$_2$, Cl— H$_2$N— —SO$_2$— —NH$_2$	See diaveridine and sylpha-quinoxaline above	See diaveridine and sulpha-quinoxaline above

continues

Table 9.1. *continued*

I Disease/drug	II Use	III Class	IV Chemical structure	V Target and mode of action	VI Mechanism of selective toxicity
MALARIA					
Quinine	Mainly restricted to treatment of chloroquine-resistant cases	Natural product		*Nucleic acid synthesis* Probably as chloroquine below	Probably as chloroquine below
Primaquine	To clear liver of exoerythrocytic stages and thus to prevent relapse	8-Amino-quinoline		*Energy metabolism* Probably metabolized to a quinoline diquinone structure which blocks electron transport at the ubiquinone level	Mammalian and malaria ubiquinones differ
Chloroquine	Prophylaxis (daily) and treatment	4-Amino-quinoline		*Nucleic acid synthesis* Binds to DNA by intercalation and so blocks nucleic acid synthesis; or may block haemoglobin digestion and cause amino acid starvation	Differential permeability: the drug is concentrated 100–600 fold by infected erythrocytes

Drug	Use	Chemical class	Structure	Mode of action	
Pyrimethamine	Prophylaxis (weekly)	2,4-Diaminopyrimidine		*Cofactor synthesis* See diaveridine	See diaveridine
Pyrimethamine plus Dapsone (Maloprim)	Prophylaxis (weekly)	2,4-Diaminopyrimidine and sulphone	See above	*Cofactor synthesis* See diaveridine and sulpha-quinoxaline	See diaveridine and sulpha-quinoxaline
Minocycline	Treatment of drug-resistant cases	Tetracycline		*Protein synthesis* Unknown in malaria but antibacterial tetracyclines block protein synthesis at chain elongation	Unknown in malaria; in bacteria, differential permeability
Clindamycin	Treatment of drug-resistant cases	Chlorinated lincomycin		*Protein synthesis* As tetracycline above	Unknown in malaria; in bacteria, drug discriminates between bacterial and mammalian ribosomes

continues

Table 9.1. *continued*

I Disease/drug	II Use	III Class	IV Chemical structure	V Target and mode of action	VI Mechanism of selective toxicity
Mefloquine (WR 142,490)	In clinical trials for use in cases of drug resistance	Quinoline methanol		*Nucleic acid synthesis* Probably as chloroquine but it has been reported *not* to intercalate with DNA *in vitro*	Uncertain but probably as chloroquine
BABESIOSIS					
Berenil (Diminazine)	Treatment in cattle	Diamidine		*Nucleic acid synthesis* Uncertain but see berenil in trypanosomiasis	Uncertain but see berenil in trypanosomiasis
Imidocarb	Treatment in cattle; also active against *Anaplasma*	Imidazoline		*Nucleic acid synthesis* Uncertain but see berenil in trypanosomiasis	Uncertain

THEILEROSIS

Parvaquone	Naphthoquinone	Energy *metabolism*
Trials for East Coast Fever, *T. parva*. Also active against *T. annulata*. Will be released on to the market in the near future.		Ubiquinone analogue. Uncertain but in malaria, blocks electron transport at the ubiquinone level
		Uncertain but probably parasite and mammalian ubiquinones differ

Table 9.2. Drugs active against platyhelminths.

I Disease/drug	II Use	III Class	IV Chemical structure	V Target and mode of action	VI Mechanism of Selective toxicity
SCHISTOSOMIASIS					
Antimony potassium tartrate			O=C—O HC—O—Sb, ½ H₂O HC—O O=C—O—OK	*Energy metabolism* Inhibitors of phosphofructokinase, the rate-limiting reaction of schistosome glycolysis; thus block glycolysis and so lactate production and ATP synthesis	Combination of differential permeability, greater importance of glycolysis in schistosome and, most important, drug discrimination between host and parasite enzymes
Antimony dimercapto-succinate	*S. haematobium*	Antimonials	KOOC H C—S Sb—S H C—S CH—CH KOOC KOOC		
Stibophen					
Niridazole (Ambilhar)	*S. haematobium* only	5-Nitrothiazole		*Energy metabolism* Uncertain but causes reduction of glycogen levels due to inhibition of glycogen phosphorylase phosphatase	Uncertain but may discriminate between host and parasite enzymes

Name	Specificity	Chemical class	Structure	Site and mode of action	
Metrifonate	S. haematobium only	Organophosphorous	CH_3O—$P(=O)$—$CHC(OH)$<Cl_2 ... $(CH_3O)_2P(=O)CHC(OH)Cl·CCl$	*Neuromuscular system* See antinematode action (Table 9.3)	See antinematode action (Table 9.3)
Lucanthone (Miracil D)	S. haematobium infestations only	Xanthone	$NHCH_2CH_2N(C_2H_5)_2$; thioxanthone with CH_3	*Neuromuscular system* Can intercalate with DNA *in vitro* but probably interfere *in vivo* with neuromuscular system by binding to acetylcholine binding sites	Unknown
Hycanthone (metabolite of above)	S. haematobium and S. mansoni infestations	Xanthone	$NHCH_2CH_2N(C_2H_5)_2$; thioxanthone with CH_2OH		
Oxamniquine	Only S. mansoni infestations; single dose active; widely used in Brazil	Tetrahydroquinoline	$HOCH_2$, NO_2, tetrahydroquinoline with $CH_2NHCH<\!^{CH_3}_{CH_3}$	*Neuromuscular system* Uncertain but some evidence for this	Unknown
Praziquantel	S. haematobium, S. mansoni and S. japonicum infestations; clinical trials completed, now on the market	Pyrozinoisoquinolinone	cyclohexyl—CO—pyrazinoisoquinolinone	*Neuromuscular system* Causes spastic paralysis in worms, maybe by effects on membrane potential of muscle cells. Also said to inhibit fumarate reductase	Unknown

continues

Table 9.2. *continued*

I Disease/drug	II Use	III Class	IV Chemical structure	V Target and mode of action	VI Mechanism of selective toxicity
FASCIOLIASIS					
Hexachloro-phene			*(chemical structure)*	*Energy metabolism* Stimulate oxygen uptake by intact flukes *in vitro* and uncouple oxidative phosphorylation by mammalian mitochondria. It is likely that this uncoupling is also occurring in the flukes. In addition it appears that the fumarate reductase system is also uncoupled by these drugs. Thus, overall, the worms are deprived of ATP	Uncertain; will uncouple mammalian mitochondria so presumably these drugs are concentrated by the worms. Apparently not well absorbed by the mammalian gut; appear to reach the flukes via the bile
Bithionol	Treatment of cattle and sheep	Phenol derivatives	*(chemical structure)*		
Oxyclozanide			*(chemical structure)*		
Nitroxynil			*(chemical structure)*		
Disophenol			*(chemical structure)*		

CESTODIASIS

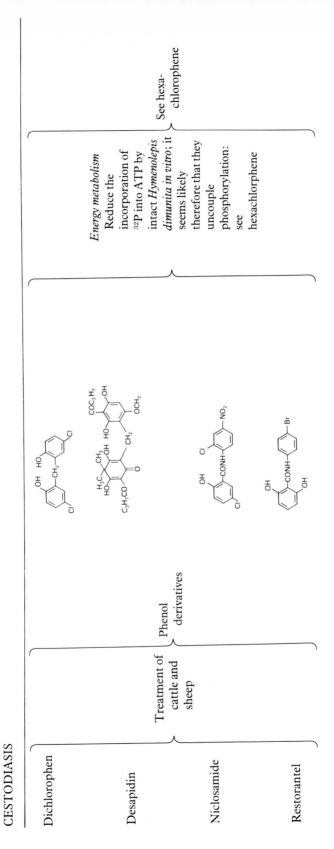

Dichlorophen

Desapidin

Treatment of cattle and sheep

Phenol derivatives

Niclosamide

Restorantel

Energy metabolism
Reduce the incorporation of ³²P into ATP by intact *Hymenolepis dimunita in vitro*; it seems likely therefore that they uncouple phosphorylation: see hexachlorphene

See hexa-chlorophene

continues

Table 9.2. *continued*

I Disease/drug	II Use	III Class	IV Chemical structure	V Target and mode of action	VI Mechanism of selective toxicity
Mepacrine (Quinacrine) (Atabrine)	Treatment in man	Acridine		*Neuromuscular system* As an antimalarial, intercalates with DNA and blocks nucleic acid synthesis; this effect unlikely to be significant here	Unknown
Mebendazole	Treatment in man, especially of *Echinococcus* infestations	Benzimidazole carbamate		*Microtubular function* See anti-nematode benzimidazole carbamates (Table 9.3)	Uncertain. See anti-nematode benzimidazole carbamates (Table 9.3)
Praziquantel	Treatment of man and domestic animals, especially of mature stages; trials in progress	Pyrizonoiso-quinolinone		*Neuromuscular system* See its action in schistosomiasis	Unknown

Table 9.3. Drugs active against nematodes.

I Disease/drug	II Use	III Class	IV Chemical structure	V Target and mode of action	VI Mechanism of selective toxicity
INTESTINAL NEMATODE INFECTIONS					
Dithiazanine iodide	*Trichuris, Enterobius, Strongyloides, Ascaris*, in man and animals	Cyanine dye		*Energy metabolism* Low levels block glucose uptake and O_2 utilization; exact action uncertain	Unknown
Piperazine	*Trichinella, Ascaris, Enterobius*, in man and animals	Piperazine		*Neuromuscular system* Paralyses nematode muscle, probably by a (reversible) curare-like effect on neuromuscular junctions	Uncertain but paralytic effect less on mammalian muscle so probably target discrimination
Bephenium	*Ancylostoma, Ascaris, Nematodirus* in man and animals	—		*Neuromuscular system* Analogue of acetylcholine. Blocks acetylcholine esterase and thus neuromuscular transmission	Appears to differentiate between parasite and mammalian acetylcholine esterases

continues

Table 9.3. *continued*

I Disease/drug	II Use	III Class	IV Chemical structure	V Target and mode of action	VI Mechanism of selective toxicity
Haloxon				*Neuromuscular system* Potent inhibitors of nematode acetylcholine esterase and therefore block neuromuscular transmission; act by phosphorylation of the esteratic site. IC_{50} (concentrations for 50% inhibiton) range from 10^{-5}–10^{-12} M; good correlation between these values and their anthelmintic activities	
Crufomate	Infestations of *Strongyloides* and other gut nematodes in domestic animals	Organo-phosphorous			Appear to discriminate between nematode and mammalian acetylcholine esterases, e.g. 1000-fold difference between IC_{50} of naphtahlophos for *Nippostrongylus* enzyme and that from mouse erythrocytes
Trichlorfon (Metrifonate)					
Dichlorvos					
Naphthalophos					

	Broad spectrum of activity	Structure	Microtubule function	Uncertain
Albendazole	Broad spectrum of activity including *Trichuris*, *Ascaris*, *Trichinella*, *Enterobius*, *Ancylostoma* and *Capillaria*. Use restricted initially to domestic animals but now under trial for use in man	Benzimidazole carbamate (NHCOOCH₃); substituent $CH_3CH_2CH_2S$–	*Microtubule function* Bind *in vitro* to tubulin and thus block its assembly into microtubular proteins. Electron microscope studies on worms from treated animals show gradual loss of cytoplasmic microtubules suggesting that binding occurs also *in vivo*; this agrees with biochemical studies since glucose uptake appears impaired, leading to loss of glycogen and acetylcholine esterase accumulates. Glucose uptake and acetylcholine esterase export would require intact cytoplasmic microtubules	Uncertain. It has always been considered that tubulin is a conserved protein and that therefore it was unlikely that drugs could discriminate between parasite and host tubulin. Some (but not all) recent binding studies and analysis of mammalian and nematode tubulins during electrophoresis in gels, suggest there are some differences; thus target discrimination may be involved
Mebendazole		Benzimidazole carbamate (NHCOOCH₃); substituent phenyl–CO		
Oxfendazole		Benzimidazole carbamate (NHCOOCH₃); substituent phenyl–S→O		
Oxibendazole		Benzimidazole carbamate (NHCOOCH₃); substituent $CH_3CH_2CH_2CH_2O$–		
Parbendazole		Benzimidazole carbamate (NHCOOCH₃); substituent C_4H_9		

continues

Table 9.3. *continued*

I Disease/drug	II Use	III Class	IV Chemical structure	V Target and mode of action	VI Mechanism of selective toxicity
Morantel	Nematode infestations in animals	Substituted tetrahydro-pyrimidines	*(chemical structure)*	*Neuromuscular system* Uncertain. Inhibit fumarate reductase *in vitro* but most significant effects are on the neuromuscular system	Unknown
Pyrantel			*(chemical structure)*		
Levamisole (*laevo* isomer of tetramisole)	*Strongyloides, Ancylostoma, Ascaris* etc. in animals		*(chemical structure)*	*Energy metabolism* Inhibits fumarate reductase but it is not certain this is the primary action. Also affects neuromuscular system	Fumarate reductase unique to parasite

Ivermectin (Ivermec)	Avermectins	Very broad spectrum of activity against nematode infestations. Recently released on to the market		*Neuromuscular system* Causes cessation of movement in treated worms, apparently by blocking nerve-to-nerve transmissions in systems using γ-aminobutyric acid (GABA) as neurotransmitter. Works by potentiating GABA action	Peripheral mammalian nervous system uses acetylcholine as neurotransmitter GABA functions in mammalian brain as well as generally in nematodes but the drug does not cross the mammalian blood–brain barrier.

OTHER NEMATODE INFECTIONS

Diethyl-carbamazine (Hetrazan)	Piperazine	Lymphatic filariasis, Onchocerciasis (microfilaria only), *Loa loa* infestations in man		*Neuromuscular system* Uncertain but probably as piperazine itself	Probably target discrimination

continues

Table 9.3. *continued*

I Disease/drug	II Use	III Class	IV Chemical structure	V Target and mode of action	VI Mechanism of selective toxicity
Suramin (Bayer 205) (Antrypol)	Onchocerciasis in man; active against micro- and macrofilaria	Sulphated naphthylamine		Unknown. Must be different to action on trypanosomes (Table 9.1) as α-glycerophosphate oxidase not present. Blocks dihydrofolate reductase and other enzymes *in vitro*; not certain if this is significant *in vivo*	Unknown
Niridazole (Ambilhar)	Trials for Draconculosis in man	5-Nitrothiazole		*Energy metabolism* Unknown here but see its action in schistosomiasis (Table 9.2)	Unknown
Mebendazole	Trials for Onchocerciasis and Dracunculosis in man	Benzimidazole carbamate		*Microtubule function* See albendazole	Uncertain See albendazole

Table 9.4. Summary of possible modes of action of antiparasitic drugs.

Cofactor synthesis	Nucleic acid synthesis	Protein synthesis	Membrane function	Microtubule function	Energy metabolism	Neuromuscular system
ANTIPROTOZOAL						
Amprolium	Diamidines	Antrycide	Monensin	—	Arsenicals	—
Sulphonamides	Phenanthridines	Minocycline	Amphotericin B		Suramin	
Sulphones	Nifurtimox	Clindamycin			Antimonials	
2,4-Diamino-	Benznidazole				Robenidine	
pyrimidines	5-Nitroimidazoles				Quinolones	
	Arprinocid				Menoctone	
	Quinine				Primaquine	
	Chloroquine					
	Mefloquine					
ANTHELMINTIC						
	—	—	Avermectins	Benzimidazoles	Dithiazanine	Organophosphorous
					Antimonials	Xanthones
					Niridazole	Piperazines
					Levamisole	Bephenium
					Phenols	Praziquantel
						Mepacrine
						Oxamniquine
						Tetrahydropyrimidines
						Avermectins

Unknown: Clopidol, Nicarbazin, Zoalene (antiprotozoal); Bunamidine, Suramin (anthelmintic).

Table 9.5. Summary of likely mechanisms of selective toxicity of antiparasitic drugs.

Differential uptake	Drug activation in parasite	Unique target in parasite	Drug discriminates between isofunctional targets in host & parasite	Pathway blocked more important in parasite than host
ANTIPROTOZOAL				
Arsenicals	Nifurtimox	Suramin	Arsenicals	Arsenicals
Diamidines	Benznidazole	Sulphonamides	Antimonials	Antimonials
Phenanthridines	5-Nitroimidazoles	Sulphones	Amprolium	
Antrycide			Amphotericin B	
Antimonials			Quinolones	
Quinine			2,4-Diaminopyrimidines	
Chloroquine			Primaquine	
Mefloquine			Clindamycin	
Minocycline			Menoctone	
ANTHELMINTIC				
Antimonials	—	Levamisole	Antimonials	Antimonials
Phenols		Avermectins	Bephenium	
			Organophosphorous	
			Piperazines	
			Niridazole	

Unknown: Clopidol, Robenidine, Nicarbazin, Zoalene, Monensin, Arprinocid (antiprotozoal); Benzimidazoles, Dithiazanine, Xanthones, Oxamniquine, Praziquantel, Bunamidine, Mepacrine, Suramin, substituted tetra-hydropyrimidines (anthelmintic).

Chapter 10
Further reading
F.E.G. Cox

10.1 INTRODUCTION

The literature of parasitology is enormous and is growing rapidly. The rate at which papers are being published can be seen from an examination of the two major abstracting journals *Helminthological Abstracts* and *Protozoological Abstracts* which published 6579 and 4826 abstracts respectively during 1981. Papers on different aspects of parasitology are published in virtually every journal devoted to animal biology or human or veterinary medicine and there are over twenty journals that are essentially parasitological ones. It is obviously impossible for anyone to keep up with all this information and this short chapter is merely intended to introduce the reader to the specialist literature of the subject so that particular topics that have been mentioned in this book can be followed up.

10.2 TEXTBOOKS

Despite the importance of parasitology, there are relatively few textbooks available at the present time. Specialist books have already been listed at the end of appropriate chapters and the main textbooks of protozoology and helminthology are cited in the suggested reading for Chapters 1 and 2. The general textbooks that are currently available are listed in Appendix A at the end of this chapter. All of them cover the more important parasites in some detail and are useful books that complement this one. Also listed are Chandler and Read (1960) and Cheng (1964). These books are out of print and out of date, but they contain so much basic factual information that they ought to be owned by anyone who is or wishes to be a parasitologist. Among the other books, the emphasis in Cheng (1973), Noble and Noble (1976), and Smyth (1976) is essentially zoological and that of the others is largely medical.

10.3 JOURNALS

There are many journals devoted to parasitology, and the 'top twenty' are listed in Appendix B. The title of each indicates the emphasis but most of them contain papers on virtually any aspect of parasitology, for example those that appear to cater for tropical medicine frequently have papers on parasites of laboratory animals widely used as models for human disease. Three recent journals, *Molecular and Biochemical Parasitology*, *Parasite Immunology* and *Systematic Parasitology*, specifically cater for specialist interests. A word of warning is necessary here because many parasitologists prefer to publish in non-parasitological journals and similar papers may be published in, for example, *Parasite Immunology*, *Clinical and Experimental Immunology* or *Infection and Immunity*. For this reason, it is necessary not only to be aware of what is being published in the parasitological journals but also in others. The simplest way to do this is to use specialist abstracting journals.

10.4   ABSTRACTING JOURNALS

The three main parasitological abstracting journals are *Helminthological Abstracts* (*A, Animal Helminthology*) and *Protozoological Abstracts*, both published by the Commonwealth Agricultural Bureaux from the Commonwealth Institute of Helminthology, St. Albans, U.K., and *Tropical Diseases Bulletin* published by the Bureau of Hygiene and Tropical Diseases, London School of Hygiene and Tropical Medicine (see Appendix C for addresses). All these are published monthly and contain not only the titles of papers but also brief summaries of their contents. These abstracts are prepared by parasitologists (who are identified at the end of each abstract) and are therefore authoritative, sometimes critical and always informative. Each issue is well indexed and cross-indexed and for each journal there is also an annual index. Anyone seeking information can easily find it and the abstract is usually sufficient to indicate whether or not it is worth while seeking out the original paper. Brief mention must also be made of *Biological Abstracts* and *Index Medicus* but, because of their wide coverage, parasitological information tends to be submerged and they are not as useful as the parasitological abstracting journals.

10.5   ANNUAL AND OCCASIONAL PUBLICATIONS

The best known and most widely read annual publications are *Advances in Parasitology* (Academic Press), which contains fairly long review articles covering virtually all aspects of parasitology, and the *Symposia of the British Society for Parasitology* which contain the papers given at the autumn meetings of this society. '*Advances*' have been published annually since 1962 and each volume has been widely acclaimed by reviewers and much used by professional parasitologists and students alike. *The Symposia of the British Society for Parasitology* have been published annually from 1962–80 by *Blackwell Scientific Publications* and each contains a number of review papers related to a particular theme. From 1982, the symposia are being published as a volume of *Parasitology* (see Appendix B). *Parasitology* also publishes reviews called *Trends and Perspectives* which are aimed largely at teachers and students and are also published separately.

10.6   OTHER SOURCES OF INFORMATION

There are now many ways of obtaining the title of a paper from a key word and these range from reading *Current Contents*, of which the *Life Sciences* section is the most useful, to sophisticated computerized retrieval systems. The use of these systems is beyond the scope of this book but their role and importance should be obvious. The *Index Catalogue of Medical and Veterinary Zoology*, formerly distributed by the U.S. Department of Agriculture and which will in future be published by the Oryx Press, in particular contains a wealth of valuable information.

10.7   TEACHING AIDS

Excellent parasitological material can be obtained from many of the major biological supply houses. Transparencies can also be obtained from some of these but the best sources of such materials are the Meddia slide series published by the Royal Tropical Institute Amsterdam, in collaboration with the World Health Organization, whose classifications include, *malaria, schistosomiasis, trypanosomiasis, leishmaniasis, filariasis, amoebiasis, geohelminth infections, other helminth infections* and *other protozoal infections*, and the Foundation for Teaching Aids at Low Cost (TALC) London, whose classifications include *Protozoa* (mainly South American) and *the microscopical diagnosis of tropical diseases* (see Appendix C for addresses). These transparencies are inexpensive and excellent. They include photographs of parasites, clinical cases and field conditions and are accompanied by brief but informative booklets and, in the case of TALC, optional cassette commentaries.

APPENDIX A: Some general textbooks of parasitology

Beck J.W. & Davies J.E. (1981) *Medical Parasitology*, 3rd ed. St. Louis and London, C.V. Mosby.
Blecka L.J. (1980) *Concise Medical Parasitology*, London, Addison-Wesley.
Chandler A.C. & Read C.P. (1961) *Introduction of Parasitology*, 10th ed. London, J. Wiley and Son.
Cheng T.C. (1964) *The Biology of Animal Parasites*, Philadelphia, W.B. Saunders.
Cheng T.C. (1973) *General Parasitology*, New York, Academic Press.
Markell E.K. & Voge M. (1981) *Medical Parasitology*, 5th ed. Philadelphia, W.B. Saunders.
Noble E.R. & Noble G.A. (1976) *Parasitology, The Biology of Animal Parasites*, 4th ed. Philadelphia, Lea and Febiger.
Peters W. & Gillies H.M. (1981) *A Colour Atlas of Tropical Medicine and Parasitology*, 2nd ed. London, Wolfe Medical Publications.
Schmidt G.D. & Roberts L.S. (1977) *Foundations of Parasitology*, St. Louis, C.V. Mosby.
Smyth J.D. (1976) *Introduction to Animal Parasitology*, 2nd ed. London, Hodder and Stoughton.
World Health Organization (1979) *Parasitic Zoonoses*, WHO Technical Report No. 637. Geneva, WHO.
Zaman V. (1979) *Atlas of Medical Parasitology*, Lancaster, MTP Press.

APPENDIX B: Twenty of the most useful parasitological journals

Acta Tropica, Basel, Schwabe.
American Journal of Tropical Medicine and Hygiene, Lawrence, Kansas, Allen Press.
Annales de Parasitologie Humaine et Comparée, Paris, Masson.
Annales de la Société Belge de Medécine Tropicale, Antwerp, Institute of Tropical Medicine.
Annals of Tropical Medicine and Parasitology, London, Academic Press.
Bulletin of the World Health Organization, Geneva, WHO.
Experimental Parasitology, New York, Academic Press.
International Journal for Parasitology, Oxford, Pergamon Press.
Journal of Helminthology, London, London School of Hygiene and Tropical Medicine.
Journal of Parasitology, Lawrence, Kansas, Allen Press.
Journal of Tropical Medicine, Oxford, Blackwell Scientific Publications.
Molecular and Biochemical Parasitology, Amsterdam, Elsevier/North Holland.
Parasite Immunology, Oxford, Blackwell Scientific Publications.
Parasitology, Cambridge, Cambridge University Press.
Proceedings of the Helminthological Society of Washington, Lawrence, Kansas, Allen Press.
Systematic Parasitology, The Hague, W. Junk.
Transactions of the Royal Society of Tropical Medicine and Hygiene, London, Royal Society of Tropical Medicine and Hygiene.
Tropenmedizin und Parasitologie, Stuttgart, Georg Thieme.
Veterinary Parasitology, Amsterdam, Elsevier/North Holland.
Zeitschrift fur Parasitologie–Parasitology Research, Berlin, Springer Verlag.

APPENDIX C: Useful addresses

Bureau of Hygiene and Tropical Diseases, London School of Hygiene and Tropical Medicine, Keppel Street, London WC1E 7HT, UK.
Commonwealth Agricultural Bureaux, Farnham House, Farnham Royal, Slough SL3 3BN, UK.
Foundation for Teaching Aids at Low Cost, Institute of Child Health, 30 Guildford Street, London WC1N 1EH, UK.
Royal Tropical Institute, Department of Tropical Hygiene, Section of Medical Education and Training, Mauritskade 63, 1092 AD Amsterdam, The Netherlands.

Index

Reference should also be made to the detailed contents list on pages v–ix.